creative writing & rewriting

John Kuehl
NEW YORK UNIVERSITY

creative writing & rewriting

contemporary American novelists at work

APPLETON-CENTURY-CROFTS / New York
DIVISION OF MEREDITH PUBLISHING COMPANY

667–1

Library of Congress Catalog Card Number: 67–18495

Also published by Meredith Press under the title, WRITE AND REWRITE

PRINTED IN THE UNITED STATES OF AMERICA

E 52852

acknowledgments

"Where Is the Voice Coming From?" by Eudora Welty, copyright © 1963 by the New Yorker Magazine, Inc.

"The Ballet of Central Park" by Kay Boyle, copyright © 1964 by Kay Boyle.

First chapter of *The Great Gatsby* by F. Scott Fitzgerald and second chapter of *The Pistol* by James Jones reprinted with the permission of Charles Scribner's Sons from *The Great Gatsby*, pp. 1–26, by F. Scott Fitzgerald (Copyright 1925 Charles Scribner's Sons; renewal copyright 1953 Frances Scott Fitzgerald Lanahan) and from *The Pistol*, pp. 24–35, by James Jones (Copyright © 1958 James Jones).

"Idiots First" by Bernard Malamud reprinted from *Idiots First* by Bernard Malamud by permission of Farrar, Straus & Giroux, Inc. Copyright © 1961 by Bernard Malamud.

From *One Day* by Wright Morris. Copyright © by Wright Morris. Reprinted by permission of Atheneum Publishers.

From *All the King's Men*, copyright 1946 by Robert Penn Warren. Reprinted by permission of Harcourt, Brace & World, Inc.

From *Letting Go*, by Philip Roth. © copyright 1961, 1962 by Philip Roth. Reprinted by permission of Random House, Inc.

From *Second Skin* by John Hawkes, copyright © 1963 and 1964 by John Hawkes. Reprinted with permission of the publisher, New Directions.

Excerpts from *Proud Flesh* by Robert Penn Warren. © copyright 1967 by Robert Penn Warren. Reprinted by permission of Random House, Inc. *Caution:* Warning is hereby given that *Proud Flesh*, being fully protected under the Copyright Law of the United States of America, the British Commonwealth, including the Dominion of Canada, and all other countries of the Berne and Universal Copyright Conventions, is subject to royalty. All performance rights, including professional, amateur, motion picture, recitation, lecturing, public reading, radio and television broadcasting, and the rights of publication and of translation into foreign languages, are strictly reserved. Inquiries should be addressed to Permissions Department, Random House, Inc., 501 Madison Avenue, New York, N.Y. 10022.

Chapter One of *The Long March* by William Styron copyright © 1952 by William Styron; by permission of Harold Matson Co. Inc.

preface

This book came into being as a direct result of my experience as a creative writing teacher at Princeton University. There the course was divided between private conferences and a weekly seminar. While the private conferences—which treated each individual's own work-in-progress—seemed successful enough, I soon became dissatisfied with the conventional methods of presenting the subject to a group. These consisted of requiring the class to analyze anthologized fiction on the one hand, and on the other to discuss stories submitted by classmates. Both the student-critic and the student-author learned something, but unfortunately the wrong sort of thing. The student-critic learned to use more skillfully the new-critical tools already acquired through previous English courses; the student-author learned how a few sympathetic peers reacted to his efforts. Neither learned very much about writing, however, as the emphasis was on product rather than process.

At this time I was also doing research among the F. Scott Fitzgerald Papers in the Princeton University Library. Here I found the holograph or pencil version of The Great Gatsby, which solved the problem I have just described by providing a fresh exercise for my seminar members. After receiving photocopies of the initial chapter of the holograph, they first proceeded to consider the changes Fitzgerald had made on the document itself and then those he had made between the composition of the holograph and the publication of the novel. The students debated these changes enthusiastically. That the new exercise proved rewarding may be ascribed to two factors: First, they were experiencing as a group the writing process over the written product orientation each was obtaining in conferences. Second, since the author had been a professional—an artist—they were witnessing the resolution of difficulties not merely similar to their own but also of a more sophisticated nature.

Discovering no significant drawbacks to this approach except the lack of readily accessible materials, I decided to expand it into a full-scale book containing sufficient manuscripts to serve the typical class at least one semester. Letters went out to several distinguished contemporary American authors whose craft reflected the conceptual as well as the formal interests of young writers here and now. A few responded negatively, contending that art should remain a private matter, but most responded affirmatively—in part, I suppose, because many of them were teachers. Even the authors who possessed no early drafts sent encouragement. For instance, Mr. James Gould Cozzens said: "I think your idea's a good one and might indeed do something to make 'creative writing' a little less unteachable."

In another context, unteachable has always been the principal charge leveled against creative writing courses. And to a certain extent this charge is understandable. No one can wholly explain—let alone inculcate—those qualities that establish author X as great and author Y as mediocre. But then, no competent instructor would attempt to do so, for the competent instructor realizes his work commences with the student's work, not before or after it. He knows that he is teaching creative re-writing and that while none of the pupils may become great they should all become better.

The charge of unteachable probably originates in romantic notions concerning "genius." Many people still attribute exceptional talent to supernatural powers. For them, analyses of artistic processes are as impious as psychoanalyses of mental processes. For them, unusual ability, like human character, is inborn, omnipresent, static. Nothing could be less true, as this book demonstrates—at least with regard to the creation of fiction. Good writing, even great writing, results largely from conscious, painstaking labor.

preface

Students schooled in the genius tradition react ambivalently toward the fact that fashioning stories and novels, like any difficult craft, requires effort. On the one hand, they feel relieved. Seeing how crude the preliminary drafts of even the finest authors are tends to make them less disconsolate about their own early performances. On the other hand, they feel burdened. Few have exerted the patience these authors display over and over as passage after passage emerges from a long sequence of versions. While it is encouraging to discover that ultimate capability cannot be revealed at a sitting, it is discouraging to discover that such capability will never be attained without constant application.

This book, however, is not designed exclusively for students of creative writing. Anyone who simply likes to read contemporary American fiction—represented here by Eudora Welty, Kay Boyle, James Jones, Bernard Malamud, Wright Morris, F. Scott Fitzgerald, Philip Roth, Robert Penn Warren, John Hawkes and William Styron—should find the book enjoyable. But those with a critical bent will experience deeper pleasure, since the commentaries appended at the end of the units are frequently interpretative. Moreover, these commentaries exploit an analytical tool seldom employed in the discussion of stories and novels: a comparison of drafts that derives meaning by uncovering some of the author's intentions.

Each commentary concentrates on what I have taken to be the single most pressing problem of its unit. Although other problems are not similarly examined and isolated, many are pointed out.

With very few exceptions, the drafts and the authors' statements have been transcribed as they were written, including typographical errors. Drafts incorporating revisions were printed instead of drafts exhibiting revisions for several reasons. Authorial changes often involve great mechanical difficulties in attempting to transcribe and reproduce them. Indeed in a number of cases obliteration was so efficient that any earlier state or states were undecipherable. Besides, the writing problems treated here frequently transcend simple word or phrase changes. To give the reader an approximate idea of the appearance of a draft exhibiting revisions, however, the previously unpublished first chapter of the holograph version of The Long March is reproduced in the Appendix. As for the Glossary, responsibility for its definitions of literary terms is solely my own.

preface *I wish to thank the Princeton University Research Fund and the staffs of the Princeton University Library, the Yale University, and the Library of Congress. Without the generosity of the contributing authors, whose dedication to craft is expressed in their willingness to be seen in a "state of undress," this book could never have been completed.*

John Kuehl

contents

preface v

I

language		Eudora Welty	
draft		*published version*	
FROM THE UNKNOWN	4	Where Is the Voice Coming From?	5

commentary 16

II

language & characterization		Kay Boyle	
THE BALLET OF CENTRAL PARK		The Ballet of Central Park	
Passage I			
draft #1, draft #3	22	*published version*	23
Passage II			
notes, draft #6	24	*published version*	25

Passage III

draft #1, draft #2 26 — *published version* 27

Passage IV

draft #2 28 — *published version* 29

Passage V

draft #8, draft #10 30 — *published version* 31

published version

The Ballet of Central Park 32

commentary 45

III

characterization — *James Jones*

draft

THE PISTOL

Chapter Two 52

published version

The Pistol

CHAPTER TWO 53

commentary 66

IV

characterization & structure — *Bernard Malamud*

draft material

A LONG TICKET FOR ISAAC 70

published version

Idiots First 71

commentary 94

V

characterization, structure, & setting — *Wright Morris*

second draft of matamoros episode up to ending (abridged)

ONE DAY 100

first ending
MATAMOROS EPISODE 108

second ending
MATAMOROS EPISODE 109

ending of the matamoros episode
published version 120

commentary 126

VI

characterization, structure, & symbolism

F. Scott Fitzgerald

pencil draft
THE GREAT GATSBY
Chapter I 132

published version
The Great Gatsby
CHAPTER ONE 133

commentary 163

VII

narrative focus

Philip Roth

draft
LETTING GO
Chapter I 170

published version
Letting Go
CHAPTER ONE 171

commentary 230

VIII

verse-drama into novel

Robert Penn Warren

unpublished play (excerpt)
PROUD FLESH
Act III, Scene iii 236
Act III, Scene iv 242
Act I, Scene ii 248

published novel (excerpt)
All the King's Men
CHAPTER NINE 237
CHAPTER TEN 243
CHAPTER SIX 249

commentary 260

IX

story into novel — *John Hawkes*

published story

The Nearest Cemetery 266

published novel (excerpt)

Second Skin

excerpt #1

"THE GENTLE ISLAND" 273

excerpt #2

"DRAG RACE ON THE BEACH" 277

commentary 284

afterword 289

glossary 291

appendix

facsimile of a draft — *The Long March: William Styron*

facsimile of a draft 295

published version 305

creative writing
& rewriting

I

language

Eudora Welty

Eudora Welty, who was born in 1909 in Mississippi where she now lives, holds a B.A. degree from the University of Wisconsin and an Litt.D. from the Western College for Women. Among her many honors are a Guggenheim fellowship, 1942; O. Henry Memorial Prize for the short story, 1942 and 1943; National Institute of Arts and Letters grant in literature, 1944. In 1955 the American Academy of Arts and Letters awarded Miss Welty the Howells Medal, presented every five years in recognition of the most distinguished work of American fiction published during that period, for The Ponder Heart *(novel, 1954). Her books include* A Curtain of Green *(stories, 1941),* The Robber Bridegroom *(novella, 1942),* The Wide Net and Other Stories *(1943),* Delta Wedding *(novel, 1946),* The Golden Apples *(connected stories, 1949),* The Bride of the Innisfallen and Other Stories *(1955), and* The Shoe Bird *(juvenile, 1964).*

*Miss Welty has described her problem in "Where Is the Voice Coming From?" (*The New Yorker, *July 6, 1963) as "one of compactness." But her revisions were aimed at another stylistic consideration too. A comparison of the published story with a preliminary draft entitled "From the Unknown" shows how the author made her language more vivid.*

FROM THE UNKNOWN

I says to my wife, "Just reach and turn it off. And be quiet. You don't need to set and look at a black nigger face no longer than you want to or listen to what you don't want to hear. It's a free country."

That's how I give myself the idea.

I says, I could find where that nigger lives without a bit of trouble.

And I ain't saying it might not be pretty close to where I live. The other hand, there could be other reasons for knowing a place in the dark. It's where you all go for the thing you want most when you want it. Ain't that right?

The First National Branch Bank sign tells you in lights all night long, even, what time it is, and how hot. When it was midnight, and 92, that was me going by.

So leave Five Points at the Rotisserie ("Come As You Are," ha ha), and ride out Delta Drive, past Jackson Surplus & Salvage, not much beyond the Yum Yum Steak House and the Trailer Camp, not as far as where the signs commence to say Live Bait, Used Parts, Fireworks, Peaches, and Sister Roberts Reader & Advisor, stop before you hit the city limits, and duck back sharp towards the railroad. And his street's paved.

I knowed I could find it without no trouble. And there was his light on, waiting for me. In his car port, if you please. His car's gone. He's out planning some further mischief, like I thought he'd be. All I had to do was pick my tree and get behind it. I don't suppose I even had unduly long to wait.

Now it wasn't no bargain I'd struck, it wasn't no deal.

Where Is the Voice Coming From?

I says to my wife, "You can reach and turn it off. You don't have to set and look at a black nigger face no longer than you want to, or listen to what you don't want to hear. It's still a free country."

I reckon that's how I give myself the idea.

I says, I could find right exactly where in Thermopylae that nigger's living that's asking for equal time. And without a bit of trouble to me.

And I ain't saying it might not be because that's pretty close to where I live. The other hand, there could be reasons you might have yourself for knowing how to get there in the dark. It's where you all go for the thing you want when you want it the most. Ain't that right?

The Branch Bank sign tells you in lights, all night long even, what time it is and how hot. When it was quarter to four, and 92, that was me going by in my brother-in-law's truck. He don't deliver nothing at that hour of the morning.

So you leave Four Corners and head west on Nathan B. Forrest Road, past the Surplus & Salvage, not much beyond the Kum Back Drive-In and Trailer Camp, not as far as where the signs start saying "Live Bait," "Used Parts," "Fireworks," "Peaches," and "Sister Peebles Reader and Adviser." Turn before you hit the city limits and duck back towards the I. C. tracks. And his street's been paved.

And there was his light on, waiting for me. In his garage, if you please. His car's gone. He's out planning still some other ways to do what we tell 'em they can't. I thought I'd beat him home. All I had to do was pick my tree and walk in close behind it.

I didn't come expecting not to wait. But it was so hot, all I did was hope and pray one or the other of us wouldn't melt before it was over.

Now, it wasn't no bargain I'd struck.

language

I heard what you heard about Big Red Hydrick. Sure everybody knows about Big Red Hydrick. Big Red he got word to the Governor's Mansion he'd go up yonder for him and shoot that nigger Meredith clean out of school, if he's let out of the pen to do it. Old Ross turned <u>that</u> over a time or two in his mind before saying him no, it stands to reason.

I ain't no Big Red Hydrick, I ain't in no Pen, and I ain't ask Governor Barnett to give me one thing. Unless he wants to give me a pat on the back for the trouble I took this morning. But he don't have to if he don't want to. I done what I done for my own pure-D satisfaction.

As soon as I heard the wheels, I knowed it wouldn't be no different from what it turned out. That was him and bound to be him. The right nigger heading in a new white car up his concrete driveway to his carport with the carport light on, shining. I knowed it when he got out to go in the house. I'd have knowed him even without the car and the light and the house waiting for him. I knowed him like I know this is me now. I knowed him even by his listening back.

Never seen him before, never seen him since, never seen anything but his picture, never seen his face any time at all and didn't have to, want to, need to, not even yet, never hope to and never will and never can! I didn't see Evers ever. But there was no question in my mind.

He was the one.

His back was fixed, fixed on me like a preacher's eyeballs when he's yelling "Are you saved?"

He's the one: I'd already brought up my gun, I'd already aimed it. And I'd already got him--too late for him or me to turn by an inch.

Something dark like the wings of a bird spread on his back and pulled him down. He climbed up once, like a man under a sheet. And I mean it was a sheet of blood, and like blood could weigh a ton he walked with it on his back. Didn't get no further than his door. And fell to stay.

He was down. He was down, and a ton load of bricks on his back wouldn't have laid any heavier. There on his paved driveway of poured concrete, yes sir.

And it wasn't till that minute that a mockingbird quit singing. He didn't hush till I let go of my load. He'd been sitting there singing up my sweetgum tree. Either he was up early, or he hadn't never gone to bed--he was like me. I was on top of the world myself. For once.

Eudora Welty

I've heard what you've heard about Goat Dykeman, in Mississippi. Sure, everybody knows about Goat Dykeman. Goat he got word to the Governor's Mansion he'd go up yonder and shoot that nigger Meredith clean out of school, if he's let out of the pen to do it. Old Ross turned that over in his mind before saying him nay, it stands to reason.

I ain't no Goat Dykeman, I ain't in no pen, and I ain't ask no Governor Barnett to give me one thing. Unless he wants to give me a pat on the back for the trouble I took this morning. But he don't have to if he don't want to. I done what I done for my own pure-D satisfaction.

As soon as I heard wheels, I knowed who was coming. That was him and bound to be him. It was the right nigger heading in a new white car up his driveway towards his garage with the light shining, but stopping before he got there, maybe not to wake 'em. That was him. I knowed it when he cut off the car lights and put his foot out and I knowed him standing dark against the light. I knowed him then like I know me now. I knowed him even by his still, listening back.

Never seen him before, never seen him since, never seen anything of his black face but his picture, never seen his face alive, any time at all, or anywheres, and didn't want to, need to, never hope to see that face and never will. As long as there was no question in my mind.

He had to be the one. He stood right still and waited against the light, his back was fixed, fixed on me like a preacher's eyeballs when he's yelling "Are you saved?" He's the one.

I'd already brought up my rifle, I'd already taken my sights. And I'd already got him, because it was too late then for him or me to turn by one hair.

Something darker than him, like the wings of a bird, spread on his back and pulled him down. He climbed up once, like a man under bad claws, and like just blood could weigh a ton he walked with it on his back to better light. Didn't get no further than his door. And fell to stay.

He was down. He was down, and a ton load of bricks on his back wouldn't have laid any heavier. There on his paved driveway, yes sir.

And it wasn't till the minute before, that the mockingbird had quit singing. He'd been singing up my sassafras tree. Either he was up early, or he hadn't never gone to bed, he was like me. And the mocker he'd stayed right with me, filling the air till come the crack, till I turned loose of my load. I was like him. I was on top of the world myself. For once.

I says, "Medgar? There was one way left, for me to be ahead of you, and stay ahead of you, by Christ, and I just taken it. Now I'm alive and you ain't. What about that, Medgar?" I said, "You seen to it, didn't you?"

It was mighty green where I stepped to the edge of where he's laying in his ring of light. That nigger wife of his, she wanted nice grass! I bet my wife would hate to pay her water bill. And her light bill. I believe the woman was in there all along, keeping awake.

There wasn't a thing I been able to think of since, that would have made it to go no better. Except a cheer to my back while I was putting in my waiting. Going home, I seen what little time it takes to get a thing done like you really want it. It was 12:34, and while I looked it changed to 35. And the temperature stuck right there. All that night it stood without dropping, 92.

When my wife's been on the job, she's looked a little too long at the newspaper.

Now she says, "They been asking that. Why somebody didn't load 'em a rifle and get some of these agitators out of the way. Didn't the fella already say it'd be a good idea? The one that writes a column ever' day?"

I says to my wife, "Find *some* way where I don't get the credit."

"Well," my wife says, "didn't the skeeters bite you? Yes," she says, "he said do it for Jackson."

I says "Jackson never done nothing for me. And I don't owe nothing to Jackson. I didn't do it for Jackson. Didn't do it for Mississippi. Didn't do it for you. Hell, any more'n I'd do something-or-other for them Kennedys! I done it for my own pure-D satisfaction."

"It's going to get him right back on TV," says my wife. "You watch for the funeral."

I says, "You didn't even leave the door-light on. So how was I even supposed to get home or drive up in the front yard?"

"Well, here's another good joke on you," says my wife next. "The N. double-A.C.P. was already fixing to fire that nigger. Says he was too easy on the white people. Why couldn't you waited? You could of got you somebody better. That's what they'll say."

I ain't but one. I reckon you have to tell *somebody.*

I stepped to the edge of his light there, where he's laying flat. I says, "Roland? There was one way left, for me to be ahead of you and stay ahead of you, by Dad, and I just taken it. Now I'm alive and you ain't. We ain't never now, never going to be equals and you know why? One of us is dead. What about that Roland?" I said. "Well, you seen to it, didn't you?"

I stood a minute—just to see would somebody inside come out long enough to pick him up. And there she comes, the woman. I doubt she'd been to sleep. Because it seemed to me she'd been in there keeping awake all along.

It was mighty green where I skint over the yard getting back. That nigger wife of his, she wanted nice grass! I bet my wife would hate to pay her water bill. And for burning her electricity. And there's my brother-in-law's truck, still waiting with the door open. "No Riders"—that didn't mean me.

There wasn't a thing I been able to think of since would have made it to go any nicer. Except a chair to my back while I was putting in my waiting. But going home, I seen what little time it takes after all to get a thing done like you really want it. It was 4:34, and while I was looking it moved to 35. And the temperature stuck where it was. All that night I guarantee you it had stood without dropping, a good 92.

My wife says, "What? Didn't the skeeters bite you?" She said, "Well, they been asking that—why somebody didn't trouble to load a rifle and get some of these agitators out of Thermopylae. Didn't the fella keep drumming it in, what a good idea? The one that writes a column ever' day?"

I says to my wife, "Find *some* way I don't get the credit."

"He says do it for Thermopylae," she says. "Don't you ever skim the paper?"

I says, "Thermopylae never done nothing for me. And I don't owe nothing to Thermopylae. Didn't do it for you. Hell, any more'n I'd do something or other for them Kennedys! I done it for my own pure-D satisfaction."

"It's going to get him right back on TV," says my wife. "You watch for the funeral."

I says, "You didn't even leave a light burning when you went to bed. So how was I supposed to even get me home or pull Buddy's truck up safe in our front yard?"

"Well, hear another good joke on you," my wife says next. "Didn't you hear the news? The N. double A. C. P. is fixing to send somebody to Thermopylae. Why couldn't you waited? You might could have got you somebody better. Listen and hear 'em say so."

I ain't but one. I reckon you have to tell *somebody*.

language

Finally, "Where's the gun then, what did you do with our main protection?" my wife says.

I tells her, "It was scorching! It was scorching hot! I wish *you'd* laid *your* finger to that gun!" I said, "It's laying on the ground in rank weeds, cooling itself off now."

"You dropped it," she says.

And I told her, "Because I'm so tired of ever'thing in the world being so hot to the touch! The doorknob, the keys to the car, the bed sheet, ever'thing, it's all like a stove lid. There just ain't much that's *worth* holding onto no more," I says, "when it's a hundred degrees in the shade by day and by night not a whole lot of difference. Unless it *is* a gun."

"Then trust you to drop it," my wife says.

"Is that how no-count I am?" she makes me say.

"Cheer up, here's one more joke before I go," says my wife. "Heard what *Caroline* said? Caroline said, 'Daddy, I just can't wait to grow up, so I can marry *James Meredith*.' I heard that in the place I work, one richbitch making another one laugh."

"At least I kept some dern teen-ager from North Jackson from getting there and doing it first," I says. "Driving his own car."

On TV and in the paper,they just know the half of it. They know who Medgar was without knowing who I am. His face was in front of the public before I shot him, then after I shot him there it was again--the same picture. And none of me. I ain't never had one made. The best that newspaper could do for me was offer a $ reward for finding out who I am. Whoever shot Medgar is worth a good deal more than Medgar is, right now.

But by the time I was moving around uptown, listening to what they had to say (that pavement in the middle of Capitol Street was as hot to my foot as the barrel of my gun!), the first thing I heard was the N. double-A. C.P. done it themselves, killed Medgar, their own man. And they proved it by saying the shooting was done by a expert (I should hope to tell you it was!) and at just the right time, to get the whites in trouble.

"They'll never find him," a man trying to sell me roasted peanuts tells me to my face.

You can't win.

"Where's the gun, then?" my wife says. "What did you do with our protection?"

I says, "It was scorching! It was scorching!" I told her, "It's laying out on the ground in rank weeds, trying to cool off, that's what it's doing now."

"You dropped it," she says. "Back there."

And I told her, "Because I'm so tired of ever'thing in the world being just that hot to touch! The keys to the truck, the doorknob, the bedsheet, ever'thing, it's all like a stove lid. There just ain't much going that's worth holding onto it no more," I says, "when it's a hundred and two in the shade by day and by night not too much difference. I wish *you'd* laid *your* finger to that gun."

"Trust you to come off and leave it," my wife says.

"Is that how no-'count I am?" she makes me ask. "*You* want to go back and get it?"

"You're the one they'll catch. I say it's so hot that even if you get to sleep you wake up feeling like you cried all night!" says my wife. "Cheer up, here's one more joke before time to get up. Heard what *Caroline* said? Caroline said, 'Daddy, I just can't wait to grow up big, so I can marry *James Meredith*.' I heard that where I work. One rich-bitch to another one, to make her cackle."

"At least I kept some dern teen-ager from North Thermopylae getting there and doing it first," I says. "Driving his own car."

On TV and in the paper, they don't know but half of it. They know who Roland Summers was without knowing who I am. His face was in front of the public before I got rid of him, and after I got rid of him there it is again—the same picture. And none of me. I ain't never had one made. Not ever! The best that newspaper could do for me was a five-hundred-dollar reward for finding out who I am. For as long as they don't know who that is, whoever shot Roland is worth a good deal more right now than Roland is.

But by the time I was moving around uptown, it was hotter still. That pavement in the middle of Main Street was so hot to my feet I might've been walking the barrel of my gun. If the whole world could've just felt Main Street this morning through the soles of my shoes, maybe it would've helped some.

Then the first thing I heard 'em say was the N. double A. C. P. done it themselves, killed Roland Summers, and proved it by saying the shooting was done by a expert (I hope to tell you it was!) and at just the right hour and minute to get the whites in trouble.

You can't win.

"They'll never find him," the old man trying to sell roasted peanuts tells me to my face.

And it's hot.

It looks like the town's on fire already, wherever you go, on every street, with crape myrtle trees and mimosa trees blooming their heads off. And a thousand cops everywhere you go, almost too young to start shaving, but streaming sweat. I'm tired of cops.

I was already tired of seeing a hundred cops getting us white folks nowheres. I stood on the corner and I watched them babyface cops loading nothing but nigger children into the paddy wagon, and they come right out of a parade and into the paddy wagon singing. And they got inside without providing a speck of trouble, and their hands held little new American flags, and all the cops could do was knock them flags a-loose from their hands, that was all, and give 'em a free ride. And children can just get 'em more flags.

Everybody: it don't get you nowhere to take nothing from nobody unless you make sure to take it for keeps, for good, for ever and ever amen.

I'll be glad to see them brickbats for a change, time they come flying. Pop bottles too, they can come flying if they want to. Hundreds, all to smash. I'm waiting on 'em to bring out them switchblade knives, like in Harlem and Chicago. Watch T.V. long enough and you'll see it to happen on Farish Street. Here it'll come pouring, because it's _in_ 'em.

I'm ready myself for that funeral.

Oh, they may find me. May catch me one day in spite of 'emselves. (But I grew up in the country.) May try to give me the electric chair, and what that amounts to is something hotter than yesterday and today put together.

But they better be getting careful. Ain't it about time us taxpayers starts to telling the teachers and the preachers and the judges of our courts how far they can go? I'd like some of those to really hear my wife.

I might even sneak old Ross in to be my lawyer, if ever should come a little trouble. How about that, Ross? I sure as hell voted for you.

I ain't going to shy if they do come after me. I ain't going to help 'em none, either.

It's too hot.

And anyways, I seen him fall. I was the one.

And it's so hot.

It looks like the town's on fire already, whichever ways you turn, ever' street you strike, because there's those trees hanging them pones of bloom like split watermelon. And a thousand cops crowding ever'where you go, half of 'em too young to start shaving, but all streaming sweat alike. I'm getting tired of 'em.

I was already tired of seeing a hundred cops getting us white people nowheres. Back at the beginning, I stood on the corner and I watched them new babyface cops loading nothing but nigger children into the paddy wagon and they come marching out of a little parade and into the paddy wagon singing. And they got in and sat down without providing a speck of trouble, and their hands held little new American flags, and all the cops could do was knock them flagsticks a-loose from their hands, and not let 'em pick 'em up, that was all, and give 'em a free ride. And children can just get 'em more flags.

Everybody: It don't get you nowhere to take nothing from nobody unless you make sure it's for keeps, for good and all, for ever and amen.

I won't be sorry to see them brickbats hail down on us for a change. Pop bottles too, they can come flying whenever they want to. Hundreds, all to smash, like Birmingham. I'm waiting on 'em to bring out them switchblade knives, like Harlem and Chicago. Watch TV long enough and you'll see it all to happen on Deacon Street in Thermopylae. What's holding it back, that's all?—Because it's *in* 'em.

I'm ready myself for that funeral.

Oh, they may find me. May catch me one day in spite of 'emselves. (But I grew up in the country.) May try to railroad me into the electric chair, and what that amounts to is something hotter than yesterday and today put together.

But I advise 'em to go careful. Ain't it about time us taxpayers starts to calling the moves? Starts to telling the teachers *and* the preachers *and* the judges of our so-called courts how far they can go?

Even the President so far, he can't walk in my house without being invited, like he's my daddy, just to say whoa. Not yet!

Once, I run away from my home. And there was a ad for me, come to be printed in our county weekly. My mother paid for it. It was from her. It says: "SON: You are not being hunted for anything but to find you." That time, I come on back home.

But people are dead now.

And it's so hot. Without it even being August yet.

Anyways, I seen him fall. I was evermore the one.

So I reach me down my guitar off the nail. 'Cause I've got me a guitar, what I've always kept, and I'll never drop that, and I set in my cheer, with nobody home but me, and I start to play, and sing a-Down. And sing a-down, down, down, down. Sing a-down, down, down, down. Down.

So I reach me down my old guitar off the nail in the wall. 'Cause I've got my guitar, what I've held onto from way back when, and I never dropped that, never lost or forgot it, never hocked it but to get it again, never give it away, and I set in my chair, with nobody home but me, and I start to play, and sing a-Down. And sing a-down, down, down, down. Sing a-down, down, down, down. Down.

According to Eudora Welty, "Where Is the Voice Coming From?" "was written in a day" and its inspiration was "the murder here in Jackson of Medgar Evers." The story is interesting on many counts, not the least of which are the transmutation of an actual event into an imagined one and the presentation of the action from the perspective and in the voice of the murderer. Much may be learned about the craft of fiction by observing how the author has rendered a real assassination as a sort of ballad, with its tone of remoteness and final emphasis on "down," and how dialogue and narration have been juxtaposed within the framework of an interior monologue to achieve maximum effectiveness. Regarding these matters, Miss Welty has said: "So in order not to have anything prejudicial in it, some changes were made in the story. Nothing essential—for this was really an 'interior' story, I was trying to show what I felt was in the mind of such people because of long familiarity with the scene, etc."

For a story of about twenty-five hundred words which was composed "overnight," the preliminary work on "Where Is the Voice Coming From?" is quite extensive. There are forty-five typescript pages, comprising early versions of the whole piece and of individual parts. With respect to sequence and length, these impress the reader by their similarities. Thus when Miss Welty speaks of her problem as being "one of compactness," she does not mean that she carved the finished story out of a much larger, radically different original. Rather, she felt the necessity of making more concise what had been given an essential shape at the very outset.

A comparison of "Where Is the Voice Coming From?" with "From the Unknown" illustrates this. In regard to sequence and length, the two bear striking resemblances. Their action may be summarized as follows: The murderer recounts some past remarks to his wife; he gives directions on how to get to the victim's house; he speaks of arriving there and of a convict; he describes the murder with its attendant circumstances; he tells about returning home and transcribes the subsequent dialogue between himself and his wife; he mentions the public reaction, the police, the possibility of rioting; he refers to being captured and decides to play the guitar.

But "From the Unknown" is less succinct than "Where Is the Voice Coming From?" for only during the course of rewriting did Miss

Welty come to solve the problem of compactness. Excepting the "Ross" passage near the end and a few scattered sentences, most of the verbiage eventually cut from the earlier version consists of single words and short groups of words. These deletions—whether substantial or not—are aimed at eliminating such superfluous phenomena as redundancies.

Important though they are, however, Miss Welty's revisions in the direction of compactness are less consequential than those aimed at increasing the story's vividness. This was achieved by transposition, substitution, and addition.

As might be expected, the few transpositions that were executed during the genesis of "Where Is the Voice Coming From?" contributed more effective arrangements of words, ideas, and events. For instance, whereas the expression "until I let go of my load" comes near the top of the paragraph beginning "And it wasn't until that minute" in the preliminary draft under consideration, its counterpart "till I turned loose my load" comes near the bottom of the same paragraph in the published version. This transposition puts things in dramatic as well as chronological order and so remedies what was formerly anticlimactic. Only being "on top of the world ... For once" now carries greater power than "till I turned loose my load," whose imagery conveys the violence of the situation through sexual slang.

The most frequent changes made between "From the Unknown" and "Where Is the Voice Coming From?" are substitutions. Aside from those supplied at The New Yorker "to prevent prejudicial references after the arrest of a man for murder," these include the replacing of less specific words by more specific ones, of less pertinent thoughts or actions by more pertinent ones, of formal speech by informal speech, of noncolloquial speech by colloquial speech, and of dull diction by lively diction. Substitutions give Miss Welty's language greater connotative power and thus broaden her meaning. For example, Delta Drive in "From the Unknown" becomes Nathan B. Forrest Road in "Where Is the Voice Coming From?" The latter's Ku Klux Klan associations provide an element of irony completely absent from the original reference. This sort of alteration—essential to the creation of good fiction—seems difficult for apprentice authors to grasp.

Additions also contribute to the increase in vividness between "From the Unknown" and "Where Is the Voice Coming From?"

language A case in point is Miss Welty's conscious reiteration in "Where Is the Voice Coming From?" of the "heat" and "light" imagery first appearing near the beginning of "From the Unknown" and whose subliminal effect helps to set the story's mood, just as her repeated new references to the brother-in-law's truck help to establish its air of reality.

The biggest single change from the preliminary draft being considered here and the published version occurs at the end where the "Ross" material has been deleted and the "President" material has been added. Miss Welty has given a practical explanation for this: ". . . the paragraph 'I might even sneak old Ross in to be my lawyer, etc.' on page 7 was deleted because of the fact that when the Beckwith man was caught & charged with the murder of Medgar Evers (which happened after I mailed the story & before publication), Barnett's firm was his legal counsel. We moved the story clear out of the state, of course, to be clear of prejudicial dangers, so some of the changes are to remove any coincidences—there were several—between my story and what later developed." In any event, the "President" material contributes more to the story's meaning than the "Ross" material. It climaxes the narrator's resentment toward the federal government, which had been hinted at earlier, and it suggested the additional information about the narrator's childhood, "my house" and "my daddy" leading toward "my home" and "my mother." Now we know that he comes from a particular county with a weekly, that his mother was permissive, that he ran away and returned. Now we may suspect his crime to have been motivated by his own private background and the discrepancies he sees between time-past and time-present.

Through skillful language revisions—cutting excess verbiage and employing transpositions, substitutions, and additions—Miss Welty converted "From the Unknown" into the more compact, more vivid "Where Is the Voice Coming From?"

II

language & characterization

Kay Boyle

Kay Boyle was born in St. Paul, Minnesota, in 1903. She has twice won a Guggenheim fellowship (1934, 1961) and the O. Henry Memorial Prize for the Best Short Story of the Year (1936, 1941). Among her many books are A Frenchman Must Die *(1946),* Thirty Stories *(1946),* 1939 *(1948),* His Human Majesty *(1949),* The Smoking Mountain *(1951),* The Seagull on the Step *(1955),* Three Short Novels *(1958),* The Youngest Camel *(1959),* Generation Without Farewell *(1960), and* Collected Poems *(1962). Miss Boyle, who has taught creative writing at several universities, is a member of the National Institute of Arts and Letters.*

On November 28, 1964, The Saturday Evening Post *published her story, "The Ballet of Central Park." Because the eleven-odd earlier drafts are sometimes incoherent and unnumbered, it is impossible to reconstruct a single reliable preliminary version. However, close analysis of selected passages reveals much about the art of revision in general and the use of language to create progressively more individual, elaborate, and complex characters in particular.*

draft #1

THE BALLET OF CENTRAL PARK

Passage I

Over her leotard, she wore a short blue dress, and her ballet slippers, their pink cotton laces knotted together, were carried across her shoulder. Her hair was wrenched back into a glossy pony-tail, and her brow was round and smooth as a doll's. But it was her eyebrows that startled one in disbelief. They were as delicate and jet black as the markings on a butterfly's wing, and seemingly as perishable . But they were an ancient and indestructible hieroglyphic, saying: "Generations of wisdom, poetry, and perception have inscribed us on this brow"

draft #3

Over her black leotard, she wore a short dress of gentiane blue, and her ballet slippers were strung across her shoulder by their knotted strings. Her hair, as light as cornsilk, was wrenched back from her brow into a glossy pony-tail, and her eyebrows were jet-black in contrast, and seemingly as perishable as the markings on the wing of a butterfly. But this was deceptive, for they were not to be effaced. They were actually an ancient hieroglyphic which, deciphered, read: "Generations of wisdom, of perception, of finesse and tact have inscribed us on this forehead." Her eyebrows were a grave and enduring statement made to the world.

She wore a short blue dress over the black legs of her leotard, and her pink satin toe shoes were slung across her shoulder by their knotted strings. Her light hair was wrenched away from her scalp into a glossy ponytail, and her eyebrows were jet black and seemingly as perishable as the markings on a night-flying moth.

notes

Passage II

This story will make it clear that I am no relation to the girl, except inasmuch as each of us is related to all children. I am just one passerby in Central Park, leading a strident, evil-faced poodle on a string, or I am the lady with dyed hair who taught Leonora ballet, or thought she did, for Leonora had no need to learn anything at all. I am also the police officer who apprehended Leonora, except that Leonora could never, in any sense, be apprehended. She was beyond seizure or arrest, for the walls of any prison would disappear once she placed the palm of her hand against the stone.

draft #6

I should state here that I am no relation to Hilary, except inasmuch as every adult is related to all children. I am as much, and as little, a stranger to her as any passerby in Central Park, where she ate her lunch, sitting on a bench, two days a week that summer. If I am not relative, I am possibly that elderly lady, twisted out of shape by the belted garment she has chosen, and the platform sandals that have seized her toes like a handful of cocktail sausages, who passes down the lanes and alley-ways of Central Park, avoiding the sight and smell of children, leading an evil-faced poodle, grey as a wasp's nest, on a string. Or I am the lady with bright orange hair, and muscles knotted high in the calves of her fine legs, who taught Hilary ballet the summer she was fourteen; or thought she taught her, for actually Hilary needed to be taught nothing. I am also the police officer who apprehended Hilary and the others, except Hilary could never, in any sense, be apprehended. She was beyond arrest or incarceration, for the walls of any prison would disappear if she laid the palm of her hand against its stone.

It should be stated here that I am no relation to Hilary, except inasmuch as every adult is related to all children. I am as casual and, at the same time, as committed, a stranger to her as any passerby in Central Park, where Hilary ate her lunch between classes, sitting on a bench, two days a week that summer. I am perhaps that idle lady, twisted out of shape by the foundation undergarment she has chosen to trap the look of youth for a little longer, her feet crippled by the high-heeled sandals that grip her toes like a handful of cocktail sausages, who has strayed over from Fifth Avenue, leading an evil-faced poodle, gray as a wasp's nest and as nervous, on an expensive string. And I am equally the lady with bright orange hair and muscles knotted high in the calves of her shapely, still agile legs, who taught Hilary ballet that summer she was fourteen, or thought she taught her, for actually Hilary needed to be taught nothing, having learned it all sometime, somewhere, before. I am also, being adult, the police officer who apprehended Hilary, except Hilary could never be apprehended. She was beyond arrest or incarceration, for the walls of any prison would disappear if she laid the palm of her hand against the stone.

draft #1

Passage III

They set off, two by two, past the fox and the coyote cages, saying nothing, but when they came to the peanut and popcorn stand, the two who had not spoken yet abruptly took on identity.

"This here's Guiseppe!" the smallest one cried out, dancing up and down. "He wants peanuts, nothing but peanuts!" He was pushing the other one straight into Hilary's arms. "He's got a big hole inside of him, and all the peanuts in the world can't fill it!" he said.

"Two bags would fill it!" Guiseppe said. When he laughed, his teeth, the only clean and unmarred substance in his make-up. "This here's Jorge from the Bronx! He lives on popcorn."

draft #2

They set off together, two by two, walking past the fox and the coyote cages, and when they came to the peanut and popcorn stand, the two who had not yet spoken abruptly took on their identities.

"This here's Guiseppe!" the smallest and sharpest one cried out, dancing up and down. "He wants peanuts, nothing but peanuts!" He was pushing the other one straight into Hilary's arms. "He's got a big hole inside of him, and all the peanuts in the world can't fill it up!"

"Maybe two bags would!" Guiseppe said. He was shaped like a wasp, with narrow shoulders hunched around his ears, and swollen eyes set far to each side of his skull.

They set off together, two by two, passing the fox and the coyote cages, and when they came to the peanut and popcorn vendor, the two who had not yet spoken abruptly took on their separate identities.

"This here's Guiseppe!" cried the quick and beautiful boy, showing his small white teeth as he danced up and down. "He wants peanuts, nothing but peanuts!" He was pushing the other one straight into Hilary's arms. "He's got a big hole inside him and all the peanuts in the world can't fill it up!"

"Maybe two bags would, just maybe!" Guiseppe said. He was as fragile as a wasp, with dark, narrow shoulders hunched around his ears, and a swollen, golden grieving eyes set on each side of his skull. When he smiled, his teeth were long and venomous. "Jorge, he likes popcorn. He steals it from the pigeons! I seen him stealing it!" he said.

published version

They set off together, two by two, passing the fox and the coyote cages, and when they came to the peanut and popcorn stand, the two who had not yet spoken abruptly took on their separate identities.

"This here's Giuseppe!" cried the delicate-boned and beautiful boy, pushing the other one into Hilary's arms as he danced up and down. "He wants peanuts, nothing but peanuts!" His teeth were white in the ivory mask of his face, and his eyes were thickly lashed. "He's got a big hole inside him and all the peanuts in the world can't fill it up!"

"Maybe two bags would, just maybe!" Giuseppe said. He had swollen, golden eyes set far to the sides of his skull, and his voice was high and wasplike when he spoke. "Jorge, he likes popcorn. He steals it from the pigeons! I seen him stealing it yesterday!" he said, his teeth grown long and venomous.

Passage IV

"We're none of us brothers," said the shoe-shine boy while the others ate. "Jorge here, he's from Puerto-Rico. Guiseppe's from Italy. My mother and father, they were born in Spain." Whatever he said, it was as if music had started playing, as if he carried within him a small harp on which the sun, and the breeze, and his own sorrow played. "My name's Federico," he went on saying. "I was named after a Spanish poet the cops killed back in Spain."

"Would you like some popcorn?" Hilary said quickly, and she held the waxed bag out to him. In fifteen minutes the ballet would begin.

"I only eat reptiles and carrion," he said.

There was no time to stop even for the camels Last summer, Jorge's brother had drowned up in the Bronx, he told her as they walked, with the others following close behind. It was a reservoir place where he'd fallen in, and there was a big high fence around it, like for a zoo, and nobody could get over the fence in time to get to him. "There was a cop there, and he couldn't get off his horse and get over the fence. People just stand around and don't do anything," he said.

"We're none of us brothers," he said. They could smell the camels, like bad butter, on the air ahead. "Jorge there, he's from Puerto Rico. Giuseppe's people, they're from Italy. My father and mother, they were born in Spain." Whatever he said, it was as if he carried within him a small harp on which the sun, and the breeze, and his own sorrow played. "My name's Federico. They named me after a Spanish poet the cops killed back in Spain," he said.

"If you'd like some popcorn," Hilary said, holding the waxed bag out to him, "I haven't touched it yet." But he shook his head.

"I only eat reptiles and carrion," he said.

There was no time left even for the camels, for in twenty minutes the ballet would begin again. The smell of them, and the sound of the seals' voices, grew fainter and fainter as Hilary and Federico climbed the steps toward the traffic of the avenue. Federico shifted the strap of his bootblack box higher on his shoulder, and he might have been speaking of something as casual as the way the grass grew between the trees, or of the tunnel of sidewalk shade that was waiting at the top. But what he was saying was that Giuseppe's brother had drowned in the Bronx two weeks ago. It was a kind of reservoir that he'd fallen into, he said, with a big fence around it, and nobody could get over the fence in time.

"There was a cop there, and even the cop couldn't get off his horse quick enough and get over the fence," Federico said, his voice low, the words he spoke playing like music in the beginning of the leafy shade.

draft #8

Passage V

"Do you prefer elephants to zebras or zebras to elephants?" Hilary asked them, and the bootblack boy looked up at her with deep and sorrowing eyes. His chest was rising and falling with the quickness of his breath as he said he preferred hooded cobras, and there was an accent to the words he spoke. The other two looked in silence at the swaying elephant. "I like armadillos," Hilary said. "I saw a lot in Mexico last summer."

"I don't know what it is," the bootblack said.

"It's a mail-clad mammal. It has like a coat of armor all over it," Hilary said quickly, shaping the ges

"I wouldn't mind being mail-clad," the bootblack said.

draft #10

"Do you prefer elephants to zebras or zebras to elephants?" Hilary asked them when she could. In the meantime, she saw that the three of them were as thin as deer, and that the backs of their necks were dark from the sun, or from the country their people had come from. The tallest one carried a shoe-shine box, but the other two were empty-handed. It was only the tallest one who dared look up at her, his chest rising and falling, rising and falling, with the labor of his breathing. He said that he liked hooded cobras, and there was an accent to these words he spoke. The other two had locked the doors of themselves and bolted the windows of their eyes. They stood looking at the swaying elephant. "I like armadillos best," Hilary went on saying. "I saw a lot in Mexico last summer."

"I don't know what that animal is," said the shoeshine boy, and the others listened but gave no sign.

"It's a mail-clad mammal. It has a coat of armor all over it," Hilary said quickly, molding the look of it with her curved hands.

"That would be good," said the shoeshine boy, and something flickered a moment in him, and then died.

"Do you prefer elephants to zebras or zebras to elephants?" Hilary asked the three of them when her heart had quieted. But it was only the tallest boy who turned his head to look at her, his chest rising and falling, rising and falling, with the laboring of his breath. He said hooded cobras were better than zebras or elephants, and his accent turned to music these words he spoke. The other two had cautiously locked the doors of themselves and drawn the blinds down as they stood looking through the bars. "I like armadillos best," Hilary went on saying. "I saw a lot in Mexico last summer."

"I don't know what that animal is," said the tallest boy; and the middle-sized boy, fragile as a wasp, with dark, narrow shoulders hunched up around his ears, gave Hilary a quick, sly glance.

"It's a mail-clad mammal. It has a coat of armor all over it," she was explaining, her curved hands shaping the way the armor fitted on.

"That would be good," the tallest boy said. He shifted the strap of the bootblack box on his shoulder. "It would be good to be like that," he said.

The Ballet of Central Park

This is a story about children, and about what happened to two or three of them in New York one summer. It is a story that has to be written quickly before it is too late. "Too late for what?" may be asked at once, and to that there is no answer. It would be dramatic, but scarcely true to say: "Before something happens to all the children in the world." But if you think back far enough, you will remember Dostoevski saying that whatever pain or martyrdom adults endure is of negligible importance because they have already been granted a certain expanse of life. They have had the time to accumulate courage and wisdom, if those were the qualities they put value on, while children have not yet had their chance. Children are still trying to feel their way, Dostoevski said (or else are shouldering or elbowing their way, or perhaps shouting or stamping or weeping their way), toward what they want to be if everything turns out right in the end. And there is another writer, the gentlest and most misconstrued of men, a man called Freud, who said that psychoanalysis could be at its best a hand reaching out to children in the dark rooms of their confusion, as a hand had never reached out to them before. To those children who carry themselves blind because they cannot bear the vision of the adult world, it could give their childhood the clarity of mountain water, he said.

The story that must be told as quickly as possible is about a little girl who was baptized Hilary by a mother and father who had no other children. They treated this isolate one as though she were a poet of distinction, an actress of international renown, and a musician as gifted and precocious as Mozart. This kind of acknowledgement had been given her since the day of her birth, and in appreciation of it, she had never ceased trying to become these things. Since the time she was six she wrote ballets and danced them out, and she put on puppet shows of her own invention, in which she spoke in four different voices. At twelve, she composed a number of small and agreeable concertos for strings and winds that the school orchestra played. At her home, somewhere in the far reaches of suburbia, she had ridden for years standing upright on a horse's back, around and around in a grassy paddock, her light hair open like a silk fan on the air behind her, her bare feet holding flexibly to the horse's rippling hide.

It should be stated here that I am no relation to Hilary, except inasmuch as every adult is related to all children. I am as casual and, at the same time, as committed, a stranger to her as any passerby in Central Park, where Hilary ate her lunch between classes, sitting on a bench, two days a week that summer. I am perhaps that idle lady, twisted out of shape by the foundation undergarment she has chosen to trap the look of youth for a little longer, her feet crippled by the high-heeled sandals that grip her toes like a handful of cocktail sausages, who has strayed over from Fifth Avenue, leading an evil-faced poodle, gray as a wasp's nest and as nervous, on an expensive string. And I am equally the lady with bright orange hair and muscles knotted high in the calves of her shapely, still agile legs, who taught Hilary ballet that summer she was fourteen, or thought she taught her, for actually Hilary needed to be taught nothing, having learned it all sometime, somewhere, before. I am also, being adult, the police officer who apprehended Hilary, except Hilary could never be apprehended. She was beyond arrest or incarceration, for the walls of any prison would disappear if she laid the palm of her hand against the stone.

The story begins on a Thursday, the second day of the summer ballet course, when a wealth of sunshine was poured out hot over the trees and lawns and the asphalt bowers of the playgrounds. Hilary had eaten her sandwich and drunk her milk, and before the ballet would begin again she wanted to get to where the flotillas of sailboats and schooners would be blowing across the waters of the lake. She wore a short blue dress over the black legs of her leotard, and her pink satin toe shoes were slung across her shoulder by their knotted strings. Her light hair was wrenched away from her scalp into a glossy ponytail, and her eyebrows were jet black and seemingly as perishable as the markings on a night-flying moth.

As she ran across the slope below those benches where the old men bend over their chessboards in the sun, the violent and unexpected battle began. Balloons of every color, swollen with water, sped from the bushes toward the benches, and smacked wide open on the players, drenching their clothes, their hair, and their crumpled faces. Under this multi-colored barrage, they leapt to their feet, and knights, castles, kings, queens, bishops, and pawns rolled to the sidewalk or

language & characterization

were flung into the sewer opening of the inner avenue. The old men shook their fists and whimpered imprecations.

"Where are they? Where are they?" one old man cried out as he spun around, but there was no one to answer.

"You never know when they're going to strike! They make fools even out of the police!" cried out another, kneeling to retrieve the chess pieces with his veined and faltering hands.

Except for the old men and the passing traffic and the stirring of squirrels, there was no sign of life. Even Hilary was gone, having seen the bare legs fleeing from ambush, and running with them in surprise. When they had scattered in a dozen different directions, she found herself standing with three boys in the circle of the zoo, and for a moment none of them could speak because of the wild beating of their hearts. They had halted before the bars of the elephants' yard, and Hilary saw that the clothes the boys wore had been worn too long, and their shirts were torn like paper. The three of them were as thin as deer, and the backs of their necks were stained brown either by the sun or by the climate of the place their people had come from. The tallest carried a bootblack box on a strap across one shoulder, and the smallest had longish black hair, and the side of his face was of great delicacy and beauty. It might have been carved from the ivory tusk that man had relieved the elephants of some time before, giving them nothing in recompense except this small enclosure of captivity. Beyond the bars, the elephant hides appeared coarser and drabber than ever in contrast with the smallest boy's pure face.

"Do you prefer elephants to zebras or zebras to elephants?" Hilary asked the three of them when her heart had quieted. But it was only the tallest boy who turned his head to look at her, his chest rising and falling, rising and falling, with the laboring of his breath. He said hooded cobras were better than zebras or elephants, and his accent turned to music these words he spoke. The other two had cautiously locked the doors of themselves and drawn the blinds down as they stood looking through the bars. "I like armadillos best," Hilary went on saying. "I saw a lot in Mexico last summer."

"I don't know what that animal is," said the tallest boy; and the middle-sized boy, fragile as a wasp, with dark, narrow shoulders hunched up around his ears, gave Hilary a quick, sly glance.

"It's a mail-clad mammal. It has a coat of armor all over it," she was explaining, her curved hands shaping the way the armor fitted on.

"That would be good," the tallest boy said. He shifted the strap of the bootblack box on his shoulder. "It would be good to be like that," he said.

"You'd have to feed on roots and reptiles to preserve your armor," Hilary said. Because of the mask of wariness he wore, the features of his face were difficult to determine. His hair was like a thick black cap pulled down to join his eyebrows, and the narrow space left between scalp and brows was deeply engraved with the lines of his concern. It went through Hilary's mind then that he was perhaps twelve years old, and the others younger, but he had been so many things for such a long time that his face would have great trouble being young again. "Would you want to live on nothing but worms and carrion?" she asked him, as if speaking to a child.

"I wouldn't mind what I ate if I could be armored," he said, his voice low, the accent altering the sound of the words on the summer air.

"Let's go look at the camels," Hilary said. She was suddenly uneasy, for there were his eyes, two mortally stricken and savage beasts, crouching in pain in the darkness of their lairs.

They set off together, two by two, passing the fox and the coyote cages, and when they came to the peanut and popcorn stand, the two who had not yet spoken abruptly took on their separate identities.

"This here's Giuseppe!" cried the delicate-boned and beautiful boy, pushing the other one into Hilary's arms as he danced up and down. "He wants peanuts, nothing but peanuts!" His teeth were white in the ivory mask of his face, and his eyes were thickly lashed. "He's got a big hole inside him and all the peanuts in the world can't fill it up!"

"Maybe two bags would, just maybe!" Giuseppe said. He had swollen, golden eyes set far to the sides of his skull, and his voice was high and wasplike when he spoke. "Jorge, he likes popcorn. He steals it from the pigeons! I seen him stealing it yesterday!" he said, his teeth grown long and venomous.

Hilary took her wallet from the pocket of her dress, and she bought them what they wanted. The seals were barking hoarsely behind them in the pool, and the boy with the shoeshine box walked up the macadamized path alone.

"Are you brothers? Are any of you brothers?" Hilary asked, catching up with him.

"We're none of us brothers," he said. They could smell the camels, like bad butter, on the air ahead. "Jorge there, he's from Puerto Rico. Giuseppe's people, they're from Italy. My father and mother, they were born in Spain." Whatever he said, it was as if he carried within him a small harp on which the sun, and the breeze, and his own sorrow played. "My name's Federico. They named me after a Spanish poet the cops killed back in Spain," he said.

"If you'd like some popcorn," Hilary said, holding the waxed bag out to him, "I haven't touched it yet." But he shook his head.

"I only eat reptiles and carrion," he said.

There was no time left even for the camels, for in twenty minutes the ballet would begin again. The smell of them, and the sound of the seals' voices, grew fainter and fainter as Hilary and Federico climbed the steps toward the traffic of the avenue. Federico shifted the strap of his bootblack box higher on his shoulder, and he might have been speaking of something as casual as the way the grass grew between the trees, or of the tunnel of sidewalk shade that was waiting at the top. But what he was saying was that Giuseppe's brother had drowned in the Bronx two weeks ago. It was a kind of reservoir that he'd fallen into, he said, with a big fence around it, and nobody could get over the fence in time.

"There was a cop there, and even the cop couldn't get off his horse quick enough and get over the fence," Federico said, his voice low, the words he spoke playing like music in the beginning of the leafy shade.

"So what?" Jorge, the beautiful, said, coming behind them up the steps.

"He kept on crying for help for a long time, but nobody could get over the fence," Federico said. "People just stood there looking at him."

"Sometimes people are like an audience," Hilary said, not wanting to hear Giuseppe's brother crying out. "You keep on waiting, and sometimes they don't even applaud," she said, her pale mouth chewing the popcorn fast.

"So what?" Jorge said again.

"And what do you do if they don't applaud?" Federico asked.

But it was Jorge, the delicate-featured, the jet-black-lashed, who answered.

"Then they pull the curtain down on you—quick, like that," he said. He stood beside them on the sidewalk now, making a baseball out of his popcorn bag, and aiming it at a pigeon strolling by. "I saw a kid killed yesterday. A horse was running away with her up near 72nd Street, and she fell off and cracked her head wide open on a rock. She was dead like that," he said, and he snapped his fingers. "I got real close. I touched her hand. It was cold like stone."

"That's nothing," said Giuseppe, his long teeth slyly smiling. He had come so quietly among them that they had not known he was there. The cars passed before them on the avenue, and Hilary waited at the curb, waited either for the light to change from red to green, or else for the terrible story to be told. "There was a kid downstairs from us," he was saying, the waspish shoulders hunched up to his ears. "I guess she was something like six months old. And this man—maybe he was her father, except her name was Angela Talleferico, and he had another, different name—he used to get drunk, and he'd beat her when she cried. And one night she kept on crying, and he picked her up by her feet and smashed her a couple of times against the wall. They had his picture in the paper, resisting arrest."

"They kill rabbits like that where I come from in Puerto Rico," Jorge said, and he did a step or two of his casual, gypsy dance. "It's a quick way to die," he said, and Hilary suddenly cried out:

"Stop saying these things! Stop saying them!" Her face was white, and her teeth were clenched. "I don't want all the children in the world to die!" she cried out above the sound of the heedless traffic.

"Well, they have to just the same," Giuseppe said quietly, and he smiled his venomous, slow smile.

"All of them," Jorge said, walking on the edge of the curb as if balancing on a tightrope. "All of them, except for me," he said.

"The poet they named me after, he died, but they never found his body," said Federico. He did not look at Hilary, as if not to see the tears coming down her face. "He wrote a poem telling he was going to be killed. He said they would never find his body. And it was true," he said.

"Maybe God took it," said Giuseppe, the wasp. With his thin crooked arms, he made the motion of great wings flapping across Fifth Avenue.

"You didn't say what your name is," said Federico after a moment.

When she told him, he said the letters of it over twice. And then the light changed, and she lifted one hand and pointed to where the ballet-school sign hung, halfway up the side street, partly in shadow and partly in sun.

"I have to go there and dance," she said, and she crossed the avenue alone, without looking back at them, wanting never to see any one of them again. Her head was down, and her heart was filled with grief, and the taste of tears was salty in her mouth.

That was Thursday, and on the next Tuesday Hilary came back to the city again to work on the *pas de chat* and the *entrechat* and the *arabesque*, and the rest of the rigmarole that the lady with bright

language & characterization

orange hair tried to teach the young. When Hilary walked out of the ballet school for the noontime recess, Federico and Jorge and Giuseppe were waiting there beneath the canopy. In spite of the heat, she wore the tight black leotard, and carried over her shoulder on their knotted strings were the same pink toe slippers, somewhat soiled and frayed. But this time her dress was yellow, and her hair fell open across her shoulders to her waist, and she held her lunch in a small brown paper bag.

"Isn't your hair hot?" was the first thing Jorge said. He was even more delicate-boned, more gazelle-eyed, more ebony-hoofed, than he had been before.

"No, it isn't," Hilary said, and she swung the length of it sideways, as if out of the reach of his hand. She did this without thought or intention, not knowing that the outcry of children who had died by violence would be there forever between them, only not to be mentioned aloud again or acknowledged in any way. If Federico had spoken in warning then, telling her that a shadow hung over the streets, the parks, the avenues, the reservoirs, the bridle paths, even in clearest sunlight, if he could have said this to her in musical words, she might have taken them dancing elsewhere, perhaps back on a train into suburbia, where the grass springs green and fresh in the horse's paddock, and the cricket voices are as bright and separate as stars. But Federico did not speak. So instead Hilary went on saying: "If we're going to talk, let's think of the most interesting possible things to say, not about the weather."

Giuseppe began at once by saying there were coins in the fountain across from the Plaza. Jorge was dancing backward down the street before them as they walked, and he said that people made wishes when they threw the coins in the water, so you could make wishes the same way when you took them out. He said that he and Giuseppe had made two dollars and ninety-five cents that morning in the subway; saying they could walk through maybe ten or twelve subway cars on their hands when it wasn't the rush hour; saying they carried the nickels and dimes and quarters that people gave them in their mouths so they wouldn't fall out of their pockets. He said they stood on their heads on the express-stop platforms, because that way you covered two trains at a time, while they played their mouth organs upside down; saying that when they learned to juggle they'd be in big-time money.

"Where do you keep the nickels and dimes and quarters when you're playing the mouth organs upside down?" Hilary asked.

"In our ears," Jorge said; and how they could laugh with all that lay behind them and all that still lay ahead, it is difficult to say; but, except for Federico, they laughed out loud. Even Hilary laughed as Jorge danced backward down the street, speaking to her of rain and shine, and now and yesterday, and what they did winter and summer. "In winter we keep them in our earmuffs, and in summer in our snorkels," he said.

"We went every day except Sunday to the door of the ballet school and waited," Giuseppe said, his shoulders hunched to his golden ears, his face scarred by his furtive, insect-smiling.

"That's not very interesting. That's like talking about your hair being hot," said Jorge, the supple. But Federico did not speak.

"There's going to be a competition at the ballet school," Hilary said suddenly. "They told us that today."

"For dancing the best?" Jorge asked, and he spun himself three times into the air.

"For the best ballet a student writes," said Hilary. She looked at the side of Federico's face, at the lowered head, and the hair jerked down in a black iron helmet to his brows. He carried the bootblack box on a strap over his shoulder as he had carried it before, but today he seemed a little taller. He might be thirteen, or even fourteen, she thought, and she liked it better that way. "I want to do something like *Petrouchka*. I want to have organ-grinders, and monkeys, and things like that in it, ordinary things, not swans or angels," she said.

Jorge skipped to the right and then to the left in his backward dance to avoid the people passing by.

And now Federico spoke. "Did you ever make up a ballet before?" he said.

"I made one out of a miracle play once," she said, and she wanted to tell him then that she had made up a dance of the forest-trees. Each tree was exactly like the others, swaying and murmuring with leaves, she wanted to say to him, until it stepped out from the others and danced in the spotlight alone. And then you could see that one tree had birds' nests in its hair, and the boughs of another were filled with fruit, and another had honeycombs packed in its trunk, and another had mistletoe at its crest, like a lighted chandelier. "I made it up for the first graders to dance," she said.

"I don't know what is a miracle play," Federico said.

"It has something to do with religion," said Hilary, "and it has to have magic come to pass in the end."

Being a prisoner bound hand and foot by his own silence, Federico could not tell her that whoever had come close to the Spanish poet whose name he bore had been baptized by the dark waters of his magic. These were the words in which his father had described him.

language & characterization

"Wherever he went, that poet always found a piano," Federico said. "Even when he was running from the cops, he played."

They had come to the traffic light, and Jorge turned himself the right way around to cross Fifth Avenue. The four of them walked clear of the trees together, past the open carriages halted in a row. The long bony faces of the horses between the shafts were masked to the eye sockets in their feed bags, and pigeons walked in and out beneath them, pecking swiftly at the grains that fell. The cushioned seats of the carriages were older than time, but neatly brushed and mended, and shiny-handled whips stood upright at the dashboards, alert as antennae for any promises that might be on the air.

"Someday we're going to cut all the horses loose and race them up to 110th Street," Jorge said. "We'll go faster than cars, faster than jets. There's big-time money in horse racing."

They crossed through the surf of heat to the shoreline of the little square, and the shimmering waves ran liquid to the curb with them, but came no further, for here the trees made their own cool grove of shade, and the fountain waited. Hilary sat down on the curved edge at the brink, and took the squat milk carton and straw and the sandwich from her paper bag. Federico slipped the strap of the bootblack box from his shoulder, and set the box down on the paving, and he stooped to look into the water held in the crescent of stone.

"I thought of writing a shoeshine ballet," Hilary said, beginning to eat. "We'd have to have ten or twelve more shoeshine boys."

"I could get them," Federico said, looking up quickly. "I have friends. I have enemies, too," he said with pride. "The poet had many friends. One of his friends was a matador. He got killed in the bull ring." For the moment he said this, the javelins were laid aside, and the armor was unbuckled. "He wrote a poem about the death of his friend. My father said the poem many times in Spanish to me. My father said it was the best poem he wrote because it had the most *duende*. The *duende* does not come to a poet unless it knows that death is there." If he could have remembered the exact words his father had said, he would have put them into English for her, saying that all one knows of the *duende* is that it burns the blood like powdered glass. He would have told her that Spaniards have said that the *duende* is not in the fingers, not in the throat, but that it surges up from the soles of his feet. He would have whispered across the trembling water: "For those who have *duende*, it is easier to love and to understand, and also one is certain to be loved and understood." But he could not manage to say these things. "If you put *duende* into the shoeshine ballet, then it would be good. It would not be an ordinary dance," was all he was able to say.

Jorge had already sprung on his dark quick legs into the fountain, and his toes sought out the coins at the bottom and flipped them up into his open palm. Giuseppe, striped yellow and black by sunshine and shade, and drained now of his venom, hovered above the surface like a dragonfly. If there were any adults passing, they did not see them, for their eyes, concerned with the vision of something else, had wiped the sight of children away.

"I wish for all the elephants and foxes and coyotes and camels to get out of their cages, and the eagles and ostriches," Jorge said, with the wishing-coins held in his hand.

"I wish for all the cops and the cops' horses to be turned to stone, and everybody not standing in the fountain," Giuseppe said, his mouth stretched grinning in his face, his long teeth hanging out.

"Jump into the fountain quick and be saved!" Jorge cried to Hilary and Federico, but they gave no sign that they had heard. Federico was watching Hilary's finger trace the plan for the ballet up and down, and back and forth, across the stone.

"It could begin with the bombing of old men playing chess," she was saying. "It could begin with a hundred balloons of every color being thrown across the stage."

"Maybe we ought to start practicing now," said Jorge, leaping from the fountain.

"That part doesn't need any rehearsal," Hilary said, "and there wouldn't be any water in the balloons, but the old men would shake their fists at us just the same. There'll be a dance for boys standing on their heads," she went on with it, "and a dance for boys walking on their hands through a subway train. We'll need eight or ten more acrobats for that."

"I'll get the acrobats, but they're rivals of the shoeshine boys," Giuseppe said.

"Thursday, I'll stay in town after my classes," said Hilary, "and we can begin to practice. The last dance of a ballet has to be like a climax. We'll find some very dramatic music for it. It will be the dance of the knives, the switch-blade knives," she said. "In the end every boy will lay his knife down on the grass."

As she finished speaking, a sudden hush fell on them, and after a moment Federico put the question softly to her.

"Our knives. What do you mean to say, our knives?" he asked.

"Don't all boys carry knives?" she cried a little wildly, not knowing how the thought had come to her. "You must admit that the ballet has to have some meaning. All ballets do. So the stage will get

language & characterization

slowly darker and darker, until it is about like dusk, and the boys will kneel and lay their knives down on the grass."

None of them moved. They remained quite silent, looking at her face. And then a stranger's voice summoned them back from where they were.

"Hey, boy," it called out, "I want a shine."

Federico got to his feet, and picked up his box by its canvas strap, and Giuseppe and Jorge stepped back into the fountain to get on with what they had to do. The stranger was leaning against a tree, and he fitted the sole of his shoe into the iron foothold as Federico kneeled before him. The top of the shoeshine box was open now, and from where she sat Hilary could see on the light wood of the inside of it, the name "Hilary" written in shoe polish black, ineffaceable, and strong.

Hilary was the first to get to the meeting place in the park on Thursday. It was five o'clock, and the members of the ballet troupe had not yet begun to assemble on the slope below the benches where the old men played. But after a moment they began to come up the path, or emerge from under the trees, or else come running down the slope. Some of them carried shoeshine boxes, and some were Negroes; some were olive-skinned, and some were white as slugs. Three or four of them turned themselves upside down at once and stood on their heads as they waited, and one of them played a harmonica, but not loud enough to attract the attention of anyone passing by. At first there were ten, and then fifteen, and at last there were twenty boys, some chasing each other across the grass on silent feet, some shadowboxing, some simply waiting. It was almost as if it was the wraiths of boys who had drifted, in the beginning of evening, to this appointed place. Even the old men at their chessboards did not interrupt their games to glance down to where they were. But Hilary was uneasy in their muted presence until Federico and Jorge and Giuseppe came up from the iron jungle of the playground, and then she knew there was no reason to fear.

"Have you got the balloons?" Jorge asked at once. His eyes were black-lashed, his delicate bones more pliable, his beauty even more eloquent than before.

"Have you got enough peanuts to go around?" Giuseppe said.

"I didn't bring anything for anyone," Hilary said. "It isn't going to be like that. First we decide on the different roles, and then we practice the ballet steps. In the end, if we win the competition, there'll be prizes and things to eat," she said.

But how to describe the rehearsal that now got under way is

not an easy thing to do. However it came about, within a few minutes the lot of them were twisting and turning, and swinging and bopping, with Giuseppe playing on the harmonica the music of *Petrouchka*, playing it over and over as Hilary hummed it aloud. Jorge led the boys who walked on their hands, making them clap their feet together; and Federico danced the steps that a matador dances, his chest thrust out, his shoeshine box hanging from his shoulder, leading the bootblacks like him who, day after day, kneeled before men with shoes to be cleaned. As they followed the pattern he stamped in the grass, their tempers were running hot in their blood, but Hilary, the actress of international renown, the musical genius of sweet precocity, was not aware that this was taking place. That they had come to dance for peanuts, or the slap of water-filled balloons, or for some act of violence as reward, had nothing to do with the music of Mozart or Stravinsky, or with the *duende* of a Spanish poet whose last name Federico could not recall. It was six o'clock when the murmur of their discontent became an orchestration for bass violins, but still Hilary did not recognize the deep-voiced prophecy it made.

They had come to the moment for the final dance, for the climax of renunciation, and Hilary, her high, narrow cheekbones flushed, jumped up from where she had been kneeling on the grass. Her voice could scarcely be heard in the vast auditorium of the park as she called out in heedless pleasure to them:

"It was very good! It was better than any ballet I've ever seen! This is almost the end. This is where I come in for the first time, and you must all stop dancing when I come on the stage!"

But they had already ceased to dance.

"Have you got the balloons with you?" one voice shouted out. "What are we getting out of this?" another asked, as if he had looked down in bewilderment and suddenly seen his empty hands. The sky, like a planetarium cleared for stars, was filled with the blue and lingering dying of the light. "We ain't jumping up and down here for our health!" cried another voice from the receding limbo where they stood, their features wiped away, and their color gone, in the slowly falling dusk.

"This is the final part!" Hilary said. "Don't be impatient! This is where you take your knives out, because the ballerina asks you to, and you lay them down, each making up a separate dance!"

And now the roar of their voices was like a tempest rising, and Federico pushed his way through the wild storm to where Hilary stood. He took the switch-blade knife from the back pocket of his chinos, and whatever they may have thought he had in mind, he laid it down, with a sweep of his arm, before her. This was the last gesture he was to be permitted for all eternity, for the leaping, screaming mob closed in on them.

"So the Hooded Cobra dies!" they cried in fury. "The Hooded Cobra dies!"

The sirens of the police cars keened in pain, and the ambulance shrieked out like a mother for him, as his blood ran black across the trampled grass. The park was empty. The old men had folded their chessboards and gone home, and there were no children anywhere. He had been cast off by friend and enemy, by life itself, except for the little girl who sat with the iron helmet of his head held close against her heart. "The knife and the cartwheel, the razor and the prickly beards of shepherds, the bare moon . . . religious images covered with lace work," went the words of the poet whose name he had been given; "in Spain, all these have in them minute grass-blades of death." His knife lay there, with no blood on its blade, as the cops leaned over to take her hands away from him.

"Stop crying," said the one who apprehended her. "If you get mixed up in things like this, it has to end this way."

commentary

Kay Boyle

Of this story Miss Boyle said in a letter of January 1, 1965:

"The Ballet of Central Park" is a story I had wanted to write for some time, the outline and details of it being quite clear in my mind since 1960, when one of my daughters was taking ballet lessons in New York. A great deal of elimination of character and incident, unfortunately, had to take place before the actual writing was begun. I sometimes wonder—but this is true of everything I have written—if I have not left out the really tremendously actual and moving things that made the story important enough to set down on paper. For instance, there were six or eight boys involved in the real story from the outset, all very different in character, and a number of them boot-blacks. In the actual story, the high spot of the drama was the theft of one of the boot-black's shoeshine kit, and the plot proceeded from that. This somehow never got into my writing of the story, although I started out with the intention of developing that incident. The old men playing chess whom the boys bombard with water-filled balloons was not a part of the actual happening. These old men, and the water-filled balloons, were transferred in the writing from a San Francisco Park to Central Park in New York. Thus, with the opening dramatic incident established, the final dramatic incident had to be considered. In the story as it actually happened there was no killing, but there could have been a killing. For me, the obligation to make a convincing inevitability out of a remote possibility helps to make a story what it should be.

"The Ballet of Central Park" was accepted as it was written, except that the editors suggested—once the story was in galley proof—deleting the Dostoevsky quote. They believed it added nothing to the story, and I think they were absolutely right. In fact, on reading the proof I was a bit perplexed as to why I had brought Stavrogin in. The explanation is, I suppose, that I wanted to make clear my point, my belief, that children are never to blame, and that we who are adults in the present violent world are, in Stavrogin's words, the guilty and the condemned. I feel now that the quote not only did not serve to stress or clarify this point, but that it confused the story. And—this is possibly much more serious—it held up the telling of a story that I had already stated I was anxious to tell as quickly as possible.

While throwing considerable light on the creative process, Kay Boyle's remarks regarding the differences between the actual events behind "The Ballet of Central Park" and the tale itself lie outside the scope of the extant manuscript materials, which are valuable principally

language & characterization

because they say something about the craft of rewriting. For example, the selected passages show the author shaping her style to include colorful specific details and to exclude whatever she deemed unnecessary. Thus in Passage I Hilary's ballet slippers eventually become "pink satin toe shoes" and her hair "light," while the progressively more elaborate "hieroglyphic" reference finally disappears. Miss Boyle may have indicated her attachment to the latter by developing it through several versions, but as an artist she ultimately decided to excise it, for, like the Stavrogin section cut from the previous paragraph, it "added nothing to the story."

None of Miss Boyle's other descriptions in "The Ballet of Central Park" is as obvious as the "hieroglyphic" reference. Characterization by means of surface details, which are explicit and nondramatic, generally succeeds less well than characterization by means of dialogue and action, which are implicit and dramatic. Nevertheless, Miss Boyle, like most professional writers, manages to use the method of "telling" effectively. Passages II and III illustrate this.

Hilary's character undergoes very little development between the "Notes" for Passage II and the Published Version, the most significant addition being the phrase, "having learned it all sometime, somewhere, before." Instead, Passage II focuses on the development of the narrator's character. Through skillful elaboration of surface details, this figure gradually becomes more fully realized as the embodiment of the adult world. One of the three potential roles mentioned at the outset—the "passerby" leading an "evil-faced poodle"—evolves rather markedly. She grows into an "elderly lady, twisted out of shape" (Draft #6) and then into "that idle lady" who "has chosen to trap the look of youth for a little longer" and who "has strayed over from Fifth Avenue" (Published Version). Thus, taking her cue from the notion of "poodle," Miss Boyle creates a representative of the wealthy class out of a mere "passerby." Her selfish indifference serves to comment on the adult world that the narrator embodies.

The third passage consists of three paragraphs, the first of which shows no important alterations between Draft #1 and the Published Version. With the exception of increasingly complex character descriptions, the essentials of the other two are present at the starting point also. Jorge is merely the "smallest" boy in Draft #1, but in Draft #2 he is the "sharpest" as well. Draft #3 calls him "quick and beautiful" with "small white teeth" and the Published Version—

more strongly influenced by an earlier passage—"delicate-boned and beautiful" with teeth "white in the ivory mask of his face" and eyes "thickly lashed." Giuseppe, who accuses Jorge of stealing popcorn from the pigeons (#3 and Published Version), experiences a similar metamorphosis. From "clean and unmarred" (#1), his teeth become "long and venomous" (#3 and Published Version), and from preceding "swollen" eyes and depicting the child's whole body (#2 and #3), his waspishness eventually culminates the affected sentence and pertains only to Giuseppe's voice (Published Version). There is a simple explanation for this. The Draft #3 phrase, "fragile as a wasp, with dark, narrow shoulders hunched around his ears," had already been used. The aim of Passage III is to describe the two boys as precisely as possible through their physical appearance and at the same time to distinguish between them by stressing the most salient aspect of each. Therefore, while Jorge grows steadily more beautiful, Giuseppe becomes uglier and uglier.

Miss Boyle approaches characterization dramatically in Passage IV, where both direct and indirect speech are employed to develop Federico. Fittingly, the single Draft #2 allusion to the latter's voice, "Whatever he said, it was as if music had started playing, as if he carried within him a small harp on which the sun, and the breeze, and his own sorrow played," inspired two additional vocal references: "might have been speaking of something as casual" and "the words he spoke playing like music" (Published Version).

In both of the reproduced versions, which are essentially alike, direct and indirect speech support the idea of Federico's "sorrow." Taken together, the two statements about the police create an air of resigned irony, just as the statement, "I only eat reptiles and carrion," stands as a bitterly humorous allusion to Hilary's armadillos. The sole instance of indirect speech—Federico's account of the drowning—also contributes to the presentation of his melancholy character while simultaneously relieving a long stretch of direct speech.

A crucial difference between the use of dialogue in Miss Boyle's story and Miss Welty's should be noted. Each has a first-person narrator, but whereas the dialogue of "Where Is the Voice Coming From?" remains internal—i.e., inside the narrator's mind—the dialogue of "The Ballet of Central Park" remains external—i.e., outside the narrator's mind. As a result, the murderer's wife seems to be a creature of her husband's imagination and the children seem to have independent existences.

language & characterization

Passage V continues the development of Federico through direct and indirect speech, an example of the first being his comment, "It would be good to be like that," and an example of the second being the narrator's report, "He said hooded cobras were better than zebras or elephants." But in this passage the author also employs action—that other component of drama, that other way of "showing" as opposed to "telling."

Draft #8 contains three instances of "looking," which are expanded in Draft #10 and then revised and intensified in the Published Version. There Miss Boyle sharply contrasts Federico's accessibility with the inaccessibility of Jorge and Giuseppe by juxtaposing the open way Federico looks at Hilary and the notion of the other two peering from behind the "blinds" of their own inner prisons through the "bars" of the elephants'. Giuseppe is further characterized by furtiveness as he gives Hilary "a quick, sly glance." This and the previous juxtaposition serve not only to contrast very different natures, but also to establish Federico's special relation to the girl.

III

characterization

James Jones

James Jones was born in Robinson, Illinois, on November 6, 1921. A few months after graduating from high school, he entered the Army, where he served between 1939 and 1944, receiving the Bronze Star and the Purple Heart and witnessing the Japanese bombing of Pearl Harbor. Mr. Jones has studied at the University of Hawaii and New York University. His first novel, From Here to Eternity, *won the National Book Award for 1951; other novels include* Some Came Running *(1957),* The Thin Red Line *(1962), and* Go to the Widow-Maker *(1967).*

The Pistol *was published by Charles Scribner's Sons in 1958. Its eleven short chapters describe Pfc. Richard Mast's (Slade's) efforts to retain a weapon, which, had the enemy not attacked, would normally have been turned in, and which he and the other men equate with salvation. Attempts to appropriate Mast's pistol involve a number of individuals and range from theft through trickery, abuse of rank, barter, force, and betrayal. When the supply clerk—that "personification of absolute, inexorable, impersonal Authority"—finally comes for the weapon, an Irishman named O'Brien shouts, "You got no right! It ain't fair!" O'Brien,* The Pistol's *second most important character, is introduced in Chapter II, which has been transcribed below both in its second draft and its published state. His initial appearance entailed some interesting revisions.*

THE PISTOL

Chapter Two

As he made up his full-field pack and stuffed things into the one barracks bag they were being allowed to take, he thought of maybe packing the pistol away, so no one would see it. If he did, maybe nobody would remember it. But if the Japs were on the beaches, already, he would want it immediately. And if they dropped their packs going into action and the pistol was in his pack-- . . .

Knowing better, knowing he was taking a real chance of eventually losing it, he decided to gamble and wear it anyway. Luckily it was a regulation holster and not the kind the MPs wore. All he had to was unhook it off the web pistol belt and hook it into his rifle cartridge belt. The extra clips he stuffed into the pocket above it. He packed the brassard and lanyard in the barrqcks bag with the pistol belt. Then, wearing his tin hat with a jauntiness he did not entirely feel when he thought about what might be in store for them, he carted everything downstairs to the yard and, sweating heavily, sat down with the rest of his squad to wait. First Sergeant Wycoff had certainly been right about the time. There was almost another hour and a half to wait, and it was nearly four o'clock before the personnel trucks of the Regiment began to move.

On the way down to the beaches he received only one comment on the pistol. A guy in the same truck but brom another squad, a huge heavy-bearded black Irishman of twenty-two named O'Brien, asked him enviously where did he get the pistol?

"That?" Slade said coolly, but with his mind working swiftly. "Oh I've had that a long time. Bought it off a guy."

The Pistol

CHAPTER TWO

The second floor squadroom was alive with movement of men kneeling and straining at packstraps, men stooping to stuff barracks bags with extra clothes. Moving out! As he rolled his own pack, Mast thought once again about packing the pistol away so no one would see it. If he did, maybe nobody would ever remember it. But if the Japs were on the beaches, already, he would want it immediately. And if the company dropped their packs going into action as they surely would, and the pistol was in his pack— . . .

Well aware that he was taking a real chance of eventually losing it back to the supply room, Mast decided to gamble and wear it anyway. What good would it do him, what protection, lying in a barracks bag or pack? Luckily it was a regulation holster and not the kind the MPs wore. All he had to do was unhook it off the web pistol belt, hook it into his rifle cartridge belt, and stuff the extra clips into the cartridge pockets above it. The brassard and lanyard he packed in the bottom of the barracks bag with the pistol belt. Then, wearing his tin hat with a jauntiness he did not entirely feel when he thought about what might be in store for them, Mast carted everything downstairs to the yard where the company was slowly forming. Sergeant Wycoff had certainly been right about the time. There was another full hour and a half to wait, and it was nearly three o'clock before the personnel trucks of the Regiment began to move.

On the way down to the beaches in the trucks Mast received only one comment on the pistol. A Private 1st Class in the same truck but from another platoon, a huge blue-jowled black Irishman of twenty-two named O'Brien, asked him enviously where did he get the pistol?

"That?" Mast said coolly, but with his mind working swiftly. "Oh, I've had that a long time. Bought it off a guy."

O'Brien moved his big dark face inarticulately, wrinkling his broad forehead and moistening his lips, then flexed his hamlike hands a couple of times where they dangled from his knees. He stared at

characterization

But that was the only comment. Nobody else noticed, not even his own squad leader. Everyone was too concerned with thinking about what they might find on the beaches. If the Colonel knew that the Japs had not landed, he might have told the Company Commander. But if he had, the Company Commander had not told his troops. Perhaps nobody knew. At any rate, the men in the truck did not. And as the convoy, moving bu fits and starts, wound down off the high central plateau of the island, there were places between the hills where they could see clearly far away below them the smoking shambles of Pearl Harbor and Hickam Field. The

the holstered pistol hungrily, almost abjectly. Then he turned his huge dark head with the pale green eyes and stared off levelly from the back of the open truck with its hastily mounted MG on the cab roof, toward where the sea was. Mast had seen him engaged in some tremendous, almost Herculean fist fights since he had been in the company, but he did not look tough now. He turned back to Mast. "Want to sell it?" he said huskily.

"Sell it? Hell, no. That's why I bought it."

O'Brien reached one big-fingered hand up and unbuttoned his shirt pocket and pulled out a wad of bills. "Made some money on craps last night," he said almost wistfully. "Give you fifty bucks for it."

Mast was astonished, and did not think he had heard right. He had had no idea his new possession would be so valuable,—not to anyone but himself. But there was O'Brien, and there was the money. Nobody else in the truck was paying any attention.

"No," Mast said. "Nosir. I want it for myself."

"Give you seventy," O'Brien said quietly, almost beseechingly. "That's all I got."

"No dice. I told you. That's why I bought it in the first place. So I could have it for myself."

"Well, hell," O'Brien said hopelessly, and slowly put his useless money back in the pocket and buttoned the flap. Unhappily he clutched his rifle, and out of the broad, dark, brooding face with its pale green eyes stared off in the direction of the sea again.

But that was the only comment. No one else noticed the pistol apparently, not even Mast's own squad leader. They were all too concerned with thinking about what they might find on the beaches. Mast could not help feeling rather smugly sorry for O'Brien, somewhat the same feeling a man who knows he has salvation experiences for one who knows he has not; but Mast did not know what he could be expected to do. There was only one pistol. And through fate, or luck, and a series of strangely unforeseeable happenings, it had been given to him, not O'Brien.

Mast and O'Brien were not the only ones who kept looking off toward where the sea was. If the colonel knew that the Japanese forces had not landed, he might possibly have told the Company Commander. But if he had, the Company Commander had not seen fit to tell his troops. Perhaps the truth was that nobody knew. At any rate, the men in the truck did not. And as the convoy, moving by fits and starts, wound its way down off the high central plateau of the island, there were places between the hills where the men could get clear glimpses far away below them of the smoking shambles of Pearl Harbor and Hickam Field. The sight made them

characterization

sight made them even more thoughtful. And as far as they could see, a miles-long line of trucks was worming its way down bumper to bumper, carrying them at a pace an ordinary man could walk, toward Honolulu and they knew not what.

Actually, long before they ever reached the city everybody knew the Japanese had not landed. The word was shouted back from truck to truck, traveling far faster than the trucks themselves went forward. But the knowledge reassured nobody. If they didn't land today, they would tomorrow, or the next day. And going through the city there was very little friendly response by the men in the trucks to the wildly cheering civilians who only a week or so before had wanted nothing to do with soldiers except take their money. And John Slade could not help but think of Kipling's Tommy Atkins.

The method in which the trucks had been loaded back at Schofield by Regimental Order was planned in advance so that the men and equipment for each beach position would be loaded all on the same truck, or trucks. Consequently, the little section of the miles-long convoy which was Slade's company (whose sector ran from the Wailupe Naval Radio Station east through Koko Head to Makapuu Head), having split off from the main trunk highway and made its way through the city on back roads, found itself alone out on Kamehameha Highway going east, its trucks peeling off one by one from the head of the column as it came abreast of their positions, until finally only four were left: the four trucks for the company's last and biggest position at Makapuu Point, one of which was Slade's. The effect was weird, if not downright enervating: from a huge, powerful convoy of men and vehicles they had dwindled down to just four trucks, alone, moving along a deserted highway between the mountains and the sea and filled with thirty-five puny men and eighteen puny machineguns, all that was left apparently, to fight the war alone against the entire might Imperial Japanese war machine. Or so they felt. Slade could not help feeling a shiver, in spite of his pleasure over his new pistol.

Makapuu Head, and Point, was acknowledgedly the worst position in the company sector. For one thing, there were no civilian homes within miles and hence no civilians to be admired by and bum food off of. For another, it was at the very extreme end of the company chow line and by the time

even more thoughtful. As far away as they could see, a miles-long line of trucks was worming its way down bumper to bumper, carrying them at a pace a man could walk, toward Honolulu and they knew not what else.

Actually, long before they ever reached the city everybody knew the Japanese had not landed. The word was shouted back from truck to truck, traveling far faster than the trucks themselves went forward. But the knowledge reassured nobody. If they didn't land today, they would tomorrow, or the next day. And going through the city there was very little friendly response by the men in the trucks to the wildly cheering civilians who only so recently as last night had wanted nothing to do with soldiers except take their money.

The method in which the trucks had been loaded back at Schofield by Regimental Order was planned in advance so that the men and equipment for each beach position would be loaded all on the same truck, or trucks. Consequently, the little section of the miles-long convoy which was Mast's company (whose sector ran from Wailupe east through Koko Head to Makapuu Head), having split off from the main trunk highway and made its way through the city on back roads, found itself alone out on Kamehameha Highway going east, its trucks peeling off one by one from the head of the column as it came abreast of their positions, until finally only four were left: the four trucks for the Company's last and biggest position at Makapuu Point, one of which trucks was Mast's. The effect was weird, if not downright enervating: From a huge, powerful convoy of unnumbered men and vehicles they had dwindled down to just four trucks, alone, moving along a deserted highway between the mountains and the sea and filled with thirty-five puny men and eighteen puny machineguns, all that was left apparently, to fight the war alone against the entire might of the Imperial Japanese war machine. Or so they felt. Mast could not help feeling a shiver, in spite of his pleasure over his new pistol.

Makapuu Head, and Point, was acknowledgedly the worst position in the company sector. For one thing, there were no civilian homes within miles, such as the majority of the company's positions had, and hence no civilians by whom to be admired, and from whom to bum food. For another, it was at the very extreme end of the company chow line and by the time the little weapons carriers that the little weapons carriers that brought the food got to them, the food itself in the big containers was so cold the grease would be congealed on top of it. For a third, Makapoo (as they came to call it) was the only position in the company sector large enough to have a true autonomous military organization; most of the positions had four, or five, or even seven, men and were run by a single sergeant or corporal; not Makapoo: it had thirty-five, its own private lieutenant, three sergeants, and at least five corporals. And for a fourth, Makapuu Point was the very hub and apex of what the Islanders preferred to called the "Windward" side of Oahu. Jutting far out into the sea all by itself, there was nothing--not a single rock, stick or leaf--between it and San Francisco; and the wind that poured against the Pali and shot straight up (strongly enough to keep more than one would-be suicide from obtaining more than a couple of broken legs by a fall of a couple of hundred feet), poured across it also, a living river of air, a tidal ocean. "Windward" was a pretty soft term for such a wind if you had to live in it without shelter, and never at Makapoo were you free of it. Even in the pillboxes cut into the living rock in November, the wind seeped in like water and made chilling eddies of air among the shivering men who tried to sleep there.

And if these were not enough to earn Makapoo its title of "A-hole of the Universe", for a fifth thing, there was not a single building there to take shelter in; nor was there enough loose dirt on top the solid rock to drive a tentpeg into. This was the beach position John Slade, with his customary luck, had managed to get himself assigned to; and this was the beach position they scrambled out of the trucks that first day to try and make, first, militarily defensible, and then second, livable.

The first week of this attempt was hectic, what with the Japanese invasion expected every day, and consisted mainly (after getting the MGs set up in their proper fields of fire in the pillboxes) of putting up barbed wire which as often as not the sea washed away, and of having one's shelterhalf and blankets blown off of one during the night by the wind. Consequently there was very little sleep. No matter how tightly and carefully a man might wrap up, the wind, testing here, trying there, eventually would find a loose corner somewhere with which to begin its endless and seemingly diabolical tug of war.

brought the food got to them, the food itself in the big aluminum pots was so cold the grease would be congealed on top of it. For a third, Makapoo (as they came at once to call it) was the only position in the company sector large enough to have a truly autonomous military organization; most of the positions had four, or five, or even seven, men and were run by a single sergeant or corporal; not Makapoo: it had thirty-five, its own private lieutenant, six sergeants, and at least four corporals. And, as every soldier knows, a sergeant who has an officer observing him does not act at all the same as a sergeant who is on his own.

For a fourth thing, Makapuu Point was the very hub and apex of what the Islanders preferred to call the 'Windward' side of Oahu. Jutting far out into the sea all by itself, there was nothing between it and San Francisco, and the wind that poured against the Pali and shot straight up, strongly enough to keep more than one wouldbe suicide from obtaining more than a couple of broken legs by a fall of more than a hundred feet, poured across it also, a living river of air, a tidal ocean of it. 'Windward' was a pretty lax term for such a wind, if you had to live in it without relief. And at Makapoo you were never free of it. It never ceased. Even in the pillboxes cut into the living rock in November, the wind seeped in like water and made chilling eddies of air among the shivering men who tried to sleep there.

And if these were not enough to earn Makapoo its title of 'A-hole of the Universe', for a fifth thing, there was not a single building there to take shelter in; nor was there enough loose dirt on top the solid rock to drive a tentpeg into. This was the beach position Richard Mast, with his customary luck, had managed to get himself assigned to; and this was the beach position they scrambled out of the trucks that first day to try and make, first, militarily defensible, and then second, livable.

The first week of both of these attempts was hectic, what with the Japanese expected every day, and also ridiculous. It consisted mainly (after having first got the MGs set up in their proper fields of fire in the pillboxes) of putting up all day barbed wire which far more often than not the sea washed away, of standing guard half the night, and of having one's shelterhalf and two blankets blown off of one during the rest of the night by the wind. There was consequently very little sleep. No matter how tightly and carefully a man might wrap up, the wind, testing here, trying there, eventually would find a loose corner somewhere with which to begin its endless and seemingly diabolical tug of war. There was not room enough for most of the men to sleep 'indoors', if the rock floors of the pillboxes could

characterization

But even all of this, together with the anticipated invasion, did not stir up half as much exictement at Makapoo as Slade's loose pistol, once it became known generally that he had it. Everybody wanted it.

be called that, and most of them had to lie down outside on the stony ground in the full force of the wind. No one had thought to try to provide sleeping shelter for the men.

But even all of this discomfort, together with the excitement of the anticipated invasion and the bad news about the Philippines, did not stir up half as much interest at Makapoo as Mast's loose pistol, once it became known generally that he had it. Everybody wanted it. In the first five days after the attack Mast had no less than seven separate offers to buy it, as well as two nocturnal attempts to steal it from him as he slept. He could not remember having had so much attention since he first came into this company over a year ago.

Quite plainly O'Brien had talked about it. About this free-floating, unrecorded pistol loose at Makapoo in Mast's hands. Out of his hunger for it, plus his lack of success in getting hold of it, O'Brien had talked about it to somebody, if not everybody. How else would anyone know? And Mast began to realize his error in having lied about it and said he'd bought it. He had done that out of sheer instinct, and because he did not want it brought to the attention of the supply room that he still had it; and after two years in the Army Mast was cynically suspicious that there existed more than one man who would go to the supply room and tell, just simply because he himself did not have one. And for the purpose he had used it, the lie had sufficed. The supply room apparently was still totally unaware it had a pistol missing. But in succeeding, the lie had created other problems. It had, in effect, thrown the possession of Mast's pistol open to the field: anyone who had it, owned it.

Actually, Mast was willing to accept possession of his pistol under those circumstances; or any other circumstances. Having worn and cared for it those days since the attack had made it his in a peculiar way that he could not possibly have felt that Sunday when he knew he had to turn it back in twenty-four hours. And from there, it was only one step to believing that he *had* bought it after all, the only logical step to take, in fact. He knew of course that somewhere there existed a paper with his signature on it saying that he owed God, or the Army, one pistol. And while the knowledge registered with him, it also somehow did not register. He *had* bought it. He could even, when pressed, remember the face of the man from the 8th Field Artillery who had sold it to him. So in one way the pistol had become what everyone believed it was. And Mast was prepared to defend it on those terms. From any source of jeopardy.

The offers to buy it ranged in price from twenty dollars to sixty dollars, none as high as the seventy dollars O'Brien had offered him under the stress of that first day. O'Brien himself was out of the

characterization

It was interesting to speculate upon just why everyone was so desirous of possessing this particular pistol, and Slade did speculate on it, a little. But he was so busy working, trying to find some sleep, and trying to protect and keep his pistol now that he had it, that he really had very little time left to speculate on anything. Perhaps, also, he had not yet, at nineteen, acquired the equipment with which to speculate deeply enough to find the real reason. All he knew was that everyone wanted it, wanted it badly, and that he was having a hard time keeping it. And after someone, whom he never did see or identify, tried to sneak it out of the holster one night while he slept, he slept after that with it tucked in his belt under his buttoned shirt. This made for more difficult sleeping, but then sleeping at Makapoo was difficult at best, and he didn't care. Now that he had his pistol he meant to keep it. The sense of personal safety that it gave him, the awareness that here at last was one object which he could actually depend on, the almost positive knowledge that it would one day actually save him, all of these comforted him as he lay rolled up in his two blankets and one shelterhalf with the rocky ground jabbing him in the flanks or as he toiled backbreakingly all day long at the never-ending job of putting up barbed wire. The world was going to hell in a basket, but if he could only hold on to the pistol, remain in possession of that extra margin of safety its beautiful blued-steel pregnant weight offered him, he could be saved, could come through it.

Obviously, a lot of other people seemed to feel the same way.

bidding now, having lost nearly all of his seventy dollars in a poker game in one of the pillboxes. Poker was just about the only recreational facility left them now, and since it was clear that money was not going to be of use to any of them for some time to come, almost everybody who had any cash played; and the young lieutenant in charge of the position was powerless to stop it. And usually, whenever anyone won a wad of money, the first thing they did was go to Mast and make an offer for his pistol. Mast, naturally, refused them all.

As for the two attempts to steal it, Mast was lucky in being able to circumvent them both. The first occurred on the third night after the attack. Up to then Mast had been used to sleeping with his cartridge belt, and the holstered pistol, under his head for a sort of makeshift pillow and he woke up from a fitful sleep in the unceasing ear-beating wind to feel his belt, with the pistol on it, being stealthily withdrawn from under his head. He made a grab for it, caught it and yanked, and retained his pistol. But when he raised up to look, all he could see in the moonless darkness was the retreating back of a crouched running figure, its footfalls silent because of the loudly buffeting wind. After that, he decided to sleep with his belt on, around his waist. And after someone, whose retreating back he could also see but not identify, tried two nights later to sneak the pistol out of its holster while he again slept, he slept after that with the pistol itself tucked into his waist belt under his buttoned down shirt and zippered field jacket while still wearing the riflebelt outside. This made for difficult sleeping but then sleeping at Makapoo was difficult at best, and he didn't care. Now that he had his pistol he meant to keep it.

It was interesting to speculate upon just why everyone was so desirous of possessing this particular pistol, and Mast did speculate on it, a little. Everybody had always wanted pistols of course, but this was somehow becoming a different thing, he felt. But he was so busy working all day long, trying to sleep at night, and above all trying to keep and protect his pistol, that he really had very little time left to speculate on anything.

Certainly, a lot of it had to do with the fact that it was free, unattached. All the members of the machinegun platoon at Makapoo carried pistols too, but theirs had been assigned to them and so nobody tried to steal them. It was pointless, because the serial numbers were registered to them. But because Mast had bought his (Had he? Yes! He had. He distinctly had.), instead of signing a requisition for it, it was unrecorded and therefore anyone who could come into possession of it would own it.

characterization

It was strange. Even to Slade, it was strange, and almost funny, when he thought about it. Across the swing of the wheeling planet America was girding herself for war, and at the same time cleaning up the debris and burying her dead, and taking stock of the damage done her. In Hawaii the citizenry were buttoning down their minds and hearts to hardship and the inevitable invasion everyone anticipated. In Europe and in Asia world-shaking events were taking place the effects of which would never be erased from the slate of humanity. And all this time at Makapuu Head on the Windward side of Oahu thirty-five men, that is, everyone below the rank of Staff sergeant, connived and fretted and conspired over the salvation inherent in one single free-floating unrecorded pistol, and spent most of their free time worrying about how to get possession of it.

And yet, despite that very strong point, there seemed to be something else, something Mast, certainly, could not put his finger on. Everybody seemed to be getting frantic to possess his pistol. And Mast was unable to account for it, or understand it.

All Mast knew was the feeling that the pistol gave him. And that was that it comforted him. As he lay rolled up in his two blankets and one shelterhalf at night with the rocky ground jabbing him in the ribs or flanks and the wind buffeting his head and ears, or as he worked his arms numb to the shoulder all day long at the never-ending job of putting up recalcitrant barbed wire, it comforted him. Thy rod and thy staff. Perhaps he had no staff—unless you could call his rifle that—but he had a 'rod'. And it would be his salvation. One day it would save him. The sense of personal defensive safety that it gave him was tremendous. He could even picture the scene: lying wounded, and alone, his rifle lost, himself unable to walk, and a Jap major bearing down on him with a drawn saber to split him in half: then his pistol would save him. The world was rocketing to hell in a bucket, but if he could only hold onto his pistol, remain in possession of the promise of salvation its beautiful blued-steel bullet-charged weight offered him, he could be saved.

On September 14, 1964, James Jones said: "At one time in my career, while writing THE PISTOL, which I knew would be a short novel, I carefully and deliberately saved every page of manuscript that I worked on." Chapter II exists in 1st Draft, 2nd Draft, First Full Draft and First Completed Draft stages. The 2nd Draft has been reproduced rather than the 1st Draft because three pages have disappeared from the latter while the single reference to O'Brien is essentially alike in both. The 1st Draft reads:

On the way down to the beaches he received only one comment on it. A guy in the same truck but from another squad named O'Brien, a heavy-bearded black Irishman of twenty-two, asked him enviously where did he get the pistol?

The Published Version of Chapter II runs to about thirty-one hundred words and the 2nd Draft version to about seventeen hundred words. This fourteen-hundred word discrepancy may be attributed partly to the handling of O'Brien whose role in the Published Version is much larger than it is in the 2nd Draft. For instance, while the 2nd Draft follows the above quoted passage with Mast's brief response, the Published Version goes on to give an elaborate description of O'Brien, several lines of dialogue concerning his offer to purchase the pistol, and a passage treating Mast's feelings toward him. That Mr. Jones was aware of the need for such dialogue during the composition of the 2nd Draft is indicated by the marginal notation "ASKS TO BUY IT" wedged between "Bought it off a guy" and "But that was the only comment."

There are no further references to O'Brien in the 2nd Draft, but the Published Version contains two, the passage beginning "Quite plainly O'Brien had talked about it" and the passage beginning "The offers to buy it ranged in price from twenty dollars to sixty dollars. . . ." And, except for minor changes in the phraseology of the First Full Draft and the First Completed Draft and the absence of the "Quite plainly" passage in the former, these stages are very different from the 2nd Draft, which they succeed, and very similar to the Published Version, which they precede. Thus, the major revisions of the O'Brien material were incorporated as early as the First Full Draft.

Although the subsequent O'Brien material is new, it grows out of the single short paragraph appearing in the 2nd Draft. One aspect intro-

duced there—the Irishman's size—has been greatly elaborated, so that the Published Version contains descriptive phrases like "big dark face," "broad forehead," "hamlike hands," "huge dark head," "big-fingered hand," and "broad, dark, brooding face." Another aspect—his envy of Mast's pistol—has been motivated by a helplessness the author expresses principally through adverbs: "inarticulately," "hungrily," "abjectly," "huskily," "wistfully," "quietly," "beseechingly," "hopelessly," and "unhappily." No wonder Mast feels "smugly sorry" for the unlucky O'Brien, whose "lack of success" in buying the weapon causes him to talk about it later and whose money finally vanishes in a poker game!

The reason Mr. Jones elaborated on the size and gave motivation to the envy of O'Brien is clear. After the 2nd Draft he emerges as Mast's opposite—his brawn being set over against the high-school graduate's brains—and consequently the novel's next most significant figure. And the reason Mr. Jones chose Chapter II to do this in is also clear. Chapter III must be prepared for because it dramatizes the conflict. There O'Brien makes "the first open attempt" to steal Mast's symbol "of an obscure personal safety." He possesses the pistol momentarily. Soon Mast, who outsmarts him, gets the weapon back. To no avail, though, since ultimately brawn and brains stand impotent before that "personification of absolute, inexorable, impersonal Authority."

Of course, the Published Version of the chapter under consideration differs from the 2nd Draft in ways which have nothing to do with the characterization of O'Brien. Two should be mentioned briefly, the first affecting the chapter's last third and the second its conclusion. Between the paragraph beginning "But even all this discomfort," where offers to purchase and efforts to steal the pistol are cited, and the paragraph beginning "All Mast knew," where the Japanese major is alluded to, the Published Version provides much information not contained in the 2nd Draft on the relation of Mast and the others to Mast's weapon. By the same token, the ending of the 2nd Draft—"It was strange," etc.—has been completely eliminated.

IV

characterization & structure

Bernard Malamud

Bernard Malamud was born on April 26, 1914, in Brooklyn, New York. He holds an A.B. degree from C.C.N.Y. and an M.A. degree from Columbia. He has taught English for several years and is currently a member of the faculty of Bennington College. During 1956–57, Mr. Malamud was a Partisan Review Fellow in fiction; during 1958, he received the Rosenthal Award of the National Institute of Arts and Letters and the Daroff Memorial Award; during 1959, he won the National Book Award for fiction. Mr. Malamud was one of the eleven recipients of the first Ford Foundation grants to creative writers and he has also had a Rockefeller grant.

His books include The Natural *(1952),* The Assistant *(1957),* The Magic Barrel *(1958),* A New Life *(1961), and* The Fixer *(1966). "Idiots First" is the title story of his first volume of short stories since* The Magic Barrel. *A comparison of the published piece and an earlier version called "A Long Ticket for Isaac"—both of which are ironic treatments of Abraham's willingness to sacrifice his son—brings to light many important revisions treating the interrelated problems of characterization and structure.*

A LONG TICKET FOR ISAAC

Mendel Gellis arose from his deathbed, muttering as he weakly drew on his sour and embittered clothes. In the dark he fished in a drawer amid odds and ends and counted the crumpled dollars. Eight where he needed fifty. Had he breath he would have screamed. Seized with trembling he sat for half an hour on the edge of the twisted bed.

"Isaac." He spoke softly but his son, playing with salted peanuts on the kitchen table, heard. After a while he disengaged himself and appeared. Mendel, in loose hat and long overcoat, still sat on the bed. Isaac gazed uncomfortably, his ears and eyes small, hair graying thickly down the sides of his head. He remained, with open mouth, mute.

Afterwards he nasally said, "Sleep, Papa."

"No," muttered Mendel. With a relentless effort he rose.

Isaac followed him out of the bedroom.

"With the hat and coat," said Mendel.

Isaac returned for his clothes, then they went together slowly down the stairs.

"Hungrig," Isaac mumbled.

"Eat then the peanuts."

Isaac munched those in his fist.

At the outer door, Mendel held his son back as he peered cautiously into the street. Then he waited in the vestibule, fighting weakness and nausea. Again he peeked out and once more waited.

"Isaac," he whispered, "you remember Mr. Ginsberg that he came to see me yesterday and also today two times?"

Isaac tittered nervously.

"You know the one I mean?"

Bernard Malamud

Idiots First

The thick ticking of the tin clock stopped. Mendel, dozing in the dark, awoke in fright. The pain returned as he listened. He drew on his cold embittered clothing, and wasted minutes sitting at the edge of the bed.

"Isaac," he ultimately sighed.

In the kitchen, Isaac, his astonished mouth open, held six peanuts in his palm. He placed each on the table. "One . . . two . . . nine."

He gathered each peanut and appeared in the doorway. Mendel, in loose hat and long overcoat, still sat on the bed. Isaac watched with small eyes and ears, thick hair graying the sides of his head.

"Schlaf," he nasally said.

"No," muttered Mendel. As if stifling he rose. "Come, Isaac."

He wound his old watch though the sight of the stopped clock nauseated him.

Isaac wanted to hold it to his ear.

"No, it's late." Mendel put the watch carefully away. In the drawer he found the little paper bag of crumpled ones and fives and slipped it into his overcoat pocket. He helped Issac on with his coat.

Isaac looked at one dark window, then at the other. Mendel stared at both blank windows.

They went slowly down the darkly lit stairs, Mendel first, Isaac watching the moving shadows on the wall. To one long shadow he offered a peanut.

"Hungrig."

In the vestibule the old man gazed through the thin glass. The November night was cold and bleak. Opening the door he cautiously thrust his head out. Though he saw nothing he quickly shut the door.

"Ginzburg, that he came to see me yesterday," he whispered in Isaac's ear.

Isaac sucked air.

"You know who I mean?"

Isaac waggled his fingers under his chin.

"This is right," said Mendel. "He has a big beard which is black." He lowered his voice. "Be careful."

Frightened, Isaac stared at his father.

Mendel quickly explained, "A young person like you he don't bother. Only me he is interested now."

Isaac broke into weeping, making mewling sounds.

"Don't cry, Isaakil. Maybe he won't come."

Isaac wiped his eyes with the back of his hand, and they went, after a last look, into the street.

"But I want you should tell me if you see him," Mendel warned.

It was suppertime. The street, and stores along it, were empty, but the windows lighted their way to the corner. There they crossed the street and, with coat collar raised against the cold wind, made their way up the block. Isaac spied the pawnbroker's shop and joyously held up three fingers. Mendel, despite his weariness and pain, smiled and nodded.

They went under the golden balls into the shop. The pawnbroker, who wore black horn-rimmed glasses, was at supper in the rear of the store. He craned his neck, then settled back to finish his tea. He came forward, patting thick lips with a pocket handkerchief.

Isaac gazed with awe at the sparkling rings, watches, cameras, banjos and horns. Racks of clothing crowded the store.

Mendel, breathing heavily, fumbled with his watch chain, unhooked it and silently held forth the worn gold watch, his hand shaking.

The pawnbroker, already disappointed, raised his glasses and screwed in the watchmaker's eyepiece. He turned the watch over once and said, "Five dollars."

Removing the glass, he returned the watch to Mendel.

Mendel wet his cracked lips. "Not ten?" he asked.

"Five."

"Cost me sixty dollars."

"Forty years ago," said the pawnbroker.

Mendel explained, "I need for my son to buy him a train ticket. Costs fifty dollars the ticket. I got maybe seven."

"Frankly, my stock is overloaded. This is the best I can do."

Isaac combed his chin with his fingers.

"That's the one, with the black whiskers. Don't talk to him or go with him if he asks you."

Isaac moaned.

"Young people he don't bother so much," Mendel said in afterthought.

It was suppertime and the street was empty but the store windows dimly lit their way to the corner. They crossed the deserted street and went on. Isaac, with a happy cry, pointed to the three golden balls. Mendel smiled but was exhausted when they got to the pawnshop.

The pawnbroker, a red-bearded man with black horn-rimmed glasses, was eating a whitefish at the rear of the store. He craned his head, saw them, and settled back to sip his tea.

In five minutes he came forward, patting his shapeless lips with a large white handkerchief.

Mendel, breathing heavily, handed him the worn gold watch. The pawnbroker, raising his glasses, screwed in his eyepiece. He turned the watch over once. "Eight dollars."

The dying man wet his cracked lips. "I must have thirty-five."

"So go to Rothschild."

"Cost me myself sixty."

"In 1905." The pawnbroker handed back the watch. It had stopped ticking. Mendel wound it slowly. It ticked hollowly.

"Isaac must go to my uncle that he lives in California."

"It's a free country," said the pawnbroker.

Isaac, watching a banjo, snickered.

"What's the matter with him?" the pawnbroker asked.

"So let be eight dollars," muttered Mendel, "but where will I get the rest till tonight?"

"How much for my hat and coat?" he asked.

Isaac, looking in the show cases, laughed.

Mendel handed the pawnbroker the watch. "Take for five." He said sadly, "What is the time don't interest me more."

The pawnbroker went behind his cage and wrote out a ticket.

Mendel watched him write. "You could use maybe my coat?"

"No," said the pawnbroker. He slipped the ticket out with a five dollar bill.

Isaac laughed again.

"What's the matter with him?" the pawnbroker asked.

Mendel didn't answer. He urged Isaac away from the show cases and they finally left.

Outside, Mendel located a scrap of paper in his pants pocket and strained to read an address by the light of the pawnbroker's window.

"Come," he said to Isaac, "we must take now the trolley."

"Hungrig," Isaac said, making movements with his mouth.

"Later. Now is not time."

They walked up another block, crossed an intersection, and entered a small treeless park.

Here a stranger followed them, a dumpy man with shoulders as broad as an ox. He wore a cap and mackinaw, and his black bushy beard seemed to sprout from his whole face. Isaac saw him first and let out a mournful cry. Mendel, drained of blood, raised his white wasted arms, and with an anguished wail, flailed them at Ginsberg.

"Gut yuntif," murmured Ginsberg, standing out of reach.

Mendel shrieked with all the force at his command.

"Don't be a fool," Ginsberg shouted. "You ain't got so long. Take it easy now."

But Mendel went on shrieking, and a policeman came running.

"What's wrong here?" he wanted to know.

Mendel was done in, but he and Isaac pointed to Ginsberg. Ginsberg dove into some bushes. The policeman hunted frantically but couldn't find him.

Isaac helped his limp father to a bench. Mendel gasped and moaned.

The policeman returned. "What happened here?"

"No sale." The pawnbroker went behind the cage and wrote out a ticket. He locked the watch in a small drawer but Mendel still heard it ticking.

In the street he slipped the eight dollars into the paper bag, then searched in his pockets for a scrap of writing. Finding it, he strained to read the address by the light of the street lamp.

As they trudged to the subway, Mendel pointed to the sprinkled sky.

"Isaac, look how many stars are tonight."

"Eggs," said Isaac.

"First we will go to Mr. Fishbein, after we will eat."

"Bad man," said Isaac.

"Did he hurt you, Pop?"

"No," Mendel got out.

"Better go home, you look all tired out. In case I find him I'll notify you."

He took their address. When he had gone, Mendel snatched five second's rest, then with Isaac's help, boarded a trolley. They rode for thirty minutes.

At the city limits Mendel asked directions from a passer-by.

"Fishbein? Oh him--he lives about six blocks in that way." He tipped his hat and went on. They walked the six long blocks, buffeted by wind.

At last they stood in front of the huge many-storied house--unmistakable.

"A palatz," murmured Mendel.

Isaac's mouth hung open.

After precious time wasted searching for the bell, Mendel repeatedly struck the massive door with the flat of his hand. At last, Fishbein's secretary, a pompous man with long sideburns, let them in, although against his will. The high-ceilinged foyer was huge, with many pictures on the walls, a thick, flowered rug at foot, and an iron-railed marble staircase.

"Who comes at such a time?" the secretary said crossly. "Now is no time for charity."

"You'll be so kind," Mendel said meekly. "Tell Mr. Fishbein, comes to see him Mendel Gellis."

"Come back in the morning. Mr. Fishbein eats now."

"He should eat in peace, but we don't eat so we will wait till he finishes."

"No," said the secretary. "Tomorrow morning--tomorrow you'll come, and tomorrow Mr. Fishbein will talk to you."

Mendel shook his head. "Tomorrow is too late."

"Tomorrow," said the secretary, flushing with anger.

Mendel sank to the floor, so did Isaac.

"Don't try dirty tricks here," shouted the secretary. "I'll telephone the police."

"Look in my face," said Mendel, "and tell me if I got time till tomorrow."

The secretary stared at him, then at Isaac and went up the stairs.

They got off the train in upper Manhattan and had to walk several blocks before they located Fishbein's house.

"A regular palace," Mendel murmured, looking forward to a moment's warmth.

Isaac stared uneasily at the heavy door of the house.

Mendel rang. The servant, a man with long sideburns, came to the door and said Mr. and Mrs. Fishbein were dining and could see no one.

"He should eat in peace but we will wait till he finishes."

"Come back tomorrow morning. Tomorrow morning Mr. Fishbein will talk to you. He don't do business or charity at this time of the night."

"Charity I am not interested—"

"Come back tomorrow."

"Tell him it's life or death—"

"Whose life or death?"

"So if not his, then mine."

"Don't be such a big smart aleck."

"Look me in my face," said Mendel, "and tell me if I got time till tomorrow morning?"

The servant stared at him, then at Isaac, and reluctantly let them in.

characterization & structure

In two minutes a door opened and Fishbein, short but stout philanthropist, ran heavily down, his napkin tucked under a tuxedo coat button. He stopped on the fifth step from the bottom and looked over the rail at Mendel and Isaac, who had risen from the floor.

"Who comes on a Friday night to a man that he has guests, to bother him?" Fishbein said in a high hoarse voice.

"This I am very sorry," said Mendel humbly, "But if I don't come tonight, I can't come tomorrow. This is my last time."

"What do you mean your last time?"

"Tomorrow--" Mendel answered, nodding at Isaac as if he were joking, "--I will be dead."

"What kind talk is this?" Fishbein's voice had risen higher. "Who says you will be dead?"

"I say."

"Ginsberg--" said Isaac.

Fishbein paid no attention to him. "How are you so sure, if I may ask?"

"Don't ask. Take my word."

"So what you now requesting?--the funeral expenses you should spend them before you die?" Fishbein broke into a little cackle.

"This boy," said Mendel quietly, taking Isaac by the arm, "is my son Isaac. He is a wonderful boy--God bless him--but he was born already like this."

Tears sprang into his eyes. He fumbled for a handkerchief but found none. Since Fishbein did not offer his napkin, he wiped his eyes with his coat sleeve.

Isaac listened in rapt attention.

"He is thirty-five years," Mendel went on. "A job he can't keep. I take care on him. Seven years ago died his mother, and now I am very sick. I am dying. I come to you, Mr. Fishbein, that you should give me maybe forty dollars to help him."

After studying Isaac, Fishbein replied, "What good is forty dollars for such a person? How long will help him forty dollars?"

"This is not to take care on him. We need the money to buy a train ticket he should go to my Uncle Meyer, that he lives far away in another city. In case happened to me something, promised Uncle Meyer to take care on Isaac."

The foyer was a vast high-ceilinged room with many oil paintings on the walls, voluminous silken draperies, a thick flowered rug at foot, and a marble staircase.

Mr. Fishbein, a paunchy bald-headed man with hairy nostrils and small patent leather feet, ran lightly down the stairs, a large napkin tucked under a tuxedo coat button. He stopped on the fifth step from the bottom and examined his visitors.

"Who comes on Friday night to a man that he has guests, to spoil him his supper?"

"Excuse me that I bother you, Mr. Fishbein," Mendel said. "If I didn't come now I couldn't come tomorrow."

"Without more preliminaries, please state your business. I'm a hungry man."

"Hungrig," wailed Isaac.

Fishbein adjusted his pince-nez. "What's the matter with him?"

"This is my son Isaac. He is like this all his life."

Isaac mewled.

"I am sending him to California."

"Mr. Fishbein don't contribute to personal pleasure trips."

"I am a sick man and he must go tonight on the train to my Uncle Leo."

"I never give to unorganized charity," Fishbein said, "but if you are hungry I will invite you downstairs in my kitchen. We having tonight chicken with stuffed derma."

"All I ask is thirty-five dollars for the train ticket to my uncle in California. I have already the rest."

"Your uncle? How old is he?"

"Uncle Meyer--a long life to him--is now eighty years."

"Eighty," Fishbein cried. "Eighty years, and you sending him this boy? What can a man eighty do for such a boy?"

"Where is open the door, there we go in the house," Mendel answered. "Is by my Uncle Meyer open the door, but costs fifty dollars the train ticket. I got now maybe twelve. If you will kindly give thirty-eight, God will bless you your whole life, and everything you got now you will soon have double."

"Headaches I got now," answered Fishbein. "I got headaches from everybody that they come to me for money. Take my advice, mister, and don't waste your life for this boy. For him the best thing will be a home where they will take care on him. Let me give you my personal card. Tomorrow morning go in this home that I will write down the name of it and leave your boy there, they should learn him a trade or something. This is what he needs more than a eighty-year uncle with his crooked foot in the grave."

"Tomorrow morning is too late," said Mendel. "Please Mr. Fishbein, what is to you thirty-eight dollars? Nothing. What is to me? To me is everything. Enjoy yourself to give me everything."

"Private contributions I am not making--only to institutions. This is my policy."

Mendel gazed at him, then sank to his knees. His voice trembled. "Don't say to me no, Mr. Fishbein. If you can't spare thirty-eight, give then twenty."

"Mr. Levinson," the philanthropist called hoarsely.

The secretary appeared at the top of the stairs.

"Show this party where is the door."

"This way, if you please," said Levinson, solemnly descending.

Isaac helped his father rise.

"Take him to an insitution," Fishbein called over the rail. "This is my last advice."

He turned and ran up the steps. They were soon outside the house, buffeted by winds.

The walk to the trolley was unbearable. Mendel, breathless, jumped at shadows. The wind blew mournfully though leafless trees. Isaac, too, was nervous.

"Who is your uncle? How old a man?"

"Eighty-one years, a long life to him."

Fishbein burst into laughter. "Eighty-one years and you are sending him this halfwit."

Mendel, flailing both arms, cried, "Please, without names."

Fishbein politely conceded.

"Where is open the door there we go in the house," the sick man said. "If you will kindly give me thirty-five dollars, God will bless you. What is thirty-five dollars to Mr. Fishbein? Nothing. To me, for my boy, is everything."

Fishbein drew himself up to his tallest height.

"Private contributions I don't make—only to institutions. This is my fixed policy."

Mendel sank to his creaking knees on the rug.

"Please, Mr. Fishbein, if not thirty-five, give maybe twenty."

"Levinson!" Fishbein angrily called.

The servant with the long sideburns appeared at the top of the stairs.

"Show this party where is the door—unless he wishes to partake food before leaving the premises."

"For what I got chicken won't cure it," Mendel said.

"This way if you please," said Levinson, descending.

Isaac assisted his father up.

"Take him to an institution," Fishbein advised over the marble balustrade. He ran quickly up the stairs and they were at once outside, buffeted by winds.

The walk to the subway was tedious. The wind blew mournfully. Mendel, breathless, glanced furtively at shadows. Isaac, clutching his peanuts in his frozen fist, clung to his father's side. They entered a

characterization & structure

At the trolley stop, as they were huddled behind a telegraph pole, Mendel said bitterly, "Isaac, if you are someday a rich man, give always help to poor people."

"Hungrig," moaned Isaac.

After the long car ride they dragged themselves into a cafeteria. Isaac had coffee with rolls. Mendel, ashen, sitting with coat collar raised, ate nothing.

He noticed an empty chair at the table and asked Isaac to remove it.

Isaac, looking over his father's shoulder, whimpered.

"Gut yuntif." Ginsberg stepped forward and seated himself in the chair.

Mendel clutched at his heart. "Not now," he wailed.

Ginsberg shrugged. "Has got to go sometime everybody."

"Not now, not now."

"How long must I wait?" Ginsberg said impatiently. "I got enough work to do."

"But who will take care on Isaac if I die now?"

"I saac will take care on himself. Where you want to die--here, or you want to die in your bed? If in bed, come, I will go home with you."

"I will not die here and I will not die in bed."

Ginsberg scowled through his bushy beard. "This kind talk I don't like."

Mendel sat stupified. Isaac was unable to drink his coffee and whimpered softly.

"So will be here or there?" Ginsberg asked sternly. "A bed is more comfortable."

Mendel cried out, "I won't die, because I am already dead."

Some of the customers at the other tables turned to look at him.

"Speak lower," hissed Ginsberg. "What do you mean you are dead?"

Mendel's lips trembled. "For thirty-five years now I am dead."

"Oo wah," said Ginsberg sarcastically. "So why not thirty-six?"

"Thirty-five is how old is Isaac."

Ginsberg stopped in the middle of a remark. Isaac smiled at him craftily. Ginsberg removed his cap and scratched his bald spot.

small park to rest for a minute on a stone bench under a leafless two-branched tree. The thick right branch was raised, the thin left one hung down. A very pale moon rose slowly. So did a stranger as they approached the bench.

"Gut yuntif," he said hoarsely.

Mendel, drained of blood, waved his wasted arms. Isaac yowled sickly. Then a bell chimed and it was only ten. Mendel let out a piercing anguished cry as the bearded stranger disappeared into the bushes. A policeman came running, and though he beat the bushes with his nightstick, could turn up nothing. Mendel and Isaac hurried out of the little park. When Mendel glanced back the dead tree had its thin arm raised, the thick one down. He moaned.

They boarded a trolley, stopping at the home of a former friend, but he had died years ago. On the same block they went into a cafeteria and ordered two fried eggs for Isaac. The tables were crowded except where a heavyset man sat eating soup with kasha. After one look at him they left in haste, although Isaac wept.

"So what you want from me, tell me?"

"Nothing. Just leave me alone one more day."

"A whole day is too long."

"Please."

"I can't."

"Why you can't?"

"Don't ask me why. I can't."

He put on his cap and stood up. "I will wait till midnight--positively not more."

Mendel broke out in a cold sweat. "What can a sick man do until midnight?" He begged for more time but Ginsberg had departed.

Isaac resumed eating. Tears dripped into his coffee. Mendel tried to apologize but couldn't and looked away.

The hands of the cafeteria clock were pointing at five after ten. Startled, Mendel rose.

"Come, Isaac."

Isaac raised his coat collar and they hurried out of the cafeteria.

In the street, where could they go? Mendel had another address on his slip of paper, but it was too far uptown. They stood in a doorway, shivering, Mendel overwhelmed by misery.

Where can I go, where? Then he remembered the furniture in the house. It was old and broken but maybe could bring a few dollars. And there were some other odds and ends that might be worth a few cents. They went again to the pawnbroker's to talk to him, but an iron gate was drawn across his place of business.

They waited in another doorway.

"Tired," Isaac moaned.

Across the street stood an ancient brick synagogue.

"We will go inside," said Mendel.

It was closed but he pounded on the door.

The sexton appeared, holding a lit candle. He was frightened by Isaac, but calmed himself when he faced Mendel.

Mendel's words fell forth, detailing his troubles.

The sexton sighed. "Personally, I can't help you, I am a very poor man. But maybe can help you the rabbi."

"Where lives the rabbi?" Mendel asked.

Mendel had another address on a slip of paper but the house was too far away, in Queens, so they stood in a doorway shivering.

What can I do, he frantically thought, in one short hour?

He remembered the furniture in the house. It was junk but might bring a few dollars. "Come, Isaac." They went once more to the pawnbroker's to talk to him, but the shop was dark and an iron gate—rings and gold watches glinting through it—was drawn tight across his place of business.

They huddled behind a telephone pole, both freezing. Isaac whimpered.

"See the big moon, Isaac. The whole sky is white."

He pointed but Isaac wouldn't look.

Mendel dreamed for a minute of the sky lit up, long sheets of light in all directions. Under the sky, in California, sat Uncle Leo drinking tea with lemon. Mendel felt warm but woke up cold.

Across the street stood an ancient brick synagogue.

He pounded on the huge door but no one appeared. He waited till he had breath and desperately knocked again. At last there were footsteps within, and the synagogue door creaked open on its massive brass hinges.

A darkly dressed sexton, holding a dripping candle, glared at them.

"Who knocks this time of night with so much noise on the synagogue door?"

Mendel told the sexton his troubles. "Please, I would like to speak to the rabbi."

"We have a new one he lives uptown, a young man. But the old rabbi that he is now retired, Reb Zissleman, he lives next door." The sexton pointed to an old house. "But he is also a poor man, and sick, I don't know what he can do for you."

"Everybody is a poor man," said Mendel.

He went with Isaac to the rabbi's house and rang the bell. After a long interval an old woman came out in her night dress.

"Who rings so late the bell?" she complained.

"If you must ring, you must ring," Mendel apologized.

"Veh is mir. Yascha," she called.

Reb Zissleman appeared in his nightshirt and skull cap. He was a heavy man, with white skin and milk-white beard. His white feet were bare.

Mendel hastily related his errand.

The rabbi listened in dismay. "Dear friend," he said, "I have nothing. You see what is my house." He pointed inside. There were two rooms, the furniture piled high in heaps.

"We live like worms," complained his wife. "The doctors take every penny."

"I got now in my pocket twelve dollars," Mendel said, heavy-hearted. "I need more thirty-eight."

"Who's got so much money," said the old woman, scandalized.

"God will give to you," said the rabbi.

"In the grave," said Mendel. "Come, Isaac."

The old rabbi stared after them. "Wait," he called.

"Yascha," screamed his wife.

"Go, Gittel," he sighed. "Get for them how much money they need."

"Yascha, are you crazy?"

"Go," he said.

"No," she wailed.

"Go get." He pointed inside.

After a while she went into the bedroom.

"A glass tea with lemon?" asked the rabbi.

"No," Mendel answered wearily. "Thanks. Is too late."

Gittel returned with some crumpled one-dollar bills.

"Yascha, you need a coat."

"Take," he said to Mendel.

"The rabbi is an old man. He sleeps now. His wife won't let you see him. Go home and come back tomorrow."

"To tomorrow I said goodbye already. I am a dying man."

Though the sexton seemed doubtful he pointed to an old wooden house next door. "In there he lives." He disappeared into the synagogue with his lit candle casting shadows around him.

Mendel, with Isaac clutching his sleeve, went up the wooden steps and rang the bell. After five minutes a big-faced, gray-haired bulky woman came out on the porch with a torn robe thrown over her nightdress. She emphatically said the rabbi was sleeping and could not be waked.

But as she was insisting, the rabbi himself tottered to the door. He listened a minute and said, "Who wants to see me let them come in."

They entered a cluttered room. The rabbi was an old skinny man with bent shoulders and a wisp of white beard. He wore a flannel nightgown and black skullcap; his feet were bare.

"Vey is mir," his wife muttered. "Put on shoes or tomorrow comes sure pneumonia." She was a woman with a big belly, years younger than her husband. Staring at Isaac, she turned away.

Mendel apologetically related his errand. "All I need more is thirty-five dollars."

"Thirty-five?" said the rabbi's wife. "Why not thirty-five thousand? Who has so much money? My husband is a poor rabbi. The doctors take away every penny."

"Dear friend," said the rabbi, "if I had I would give you."

"I got already seventy," Mendel said, heavy-hearted. "All I need more is thirty-five."

"God will give you," said the rabbi.

"In the grave," said Mendel. "I need tonight. Come, Isaac."

"Wait," called the rabbi.

He hurried inside, came out with a fur-lined caftan, and handed it to Mendel.

"Yascha," shrieked his wife, "not your new coat!"

"I got my old one. Who needs two coats for one body?"

"Yascha, I am screaming—"

"Who can go among poor people, tell me, in a new coat?"

"Yascha," she cried, "what can this man do with your coat? He needs tonight the money. The pawnbrokers are asleep."

"So let him wake them up."

"No." She grabbed the coat from Mendel.

He held on to a sleeve, wrestling her for the coat. Her I know, Mendel thought. "Shylock," he muttered. Her eyes glittered.

Gittel handed over the money. Mendel quickly counted twenty dollars. "Please, rabbi," he said anxiously, "costs the ticket fifty dollars."

"So how much you need more?"

"Eighteen."

Gittel shouted, "Who's got eighteen dollars? You making from us beggars."

"Give eighteen dollars," the rabbi commanded.

She wept but returned with eighteen one-dollar bills and thrust them at Mendel.

"For ten years now he needs a new coat."

"Who can come among poor people in a new coat?" the rabbi said.

Mendel counted the eighteen dollars, making a total of thirty-eight.

"I got in my pocket thirteen," he confessed, "but Isaac will need extra a dollar to eat on the train."

It was after eleven by the rabbi's alarm clock so they left hastily.

At the station Mendel bought the ticket. Isaac laughed at the length of it.

Mendel led him to the tracks. "I explained you already what to do, Isaac. So soon leaves the train, go to sleep. In the morning will come a man that he sells sandwiches and coffee. Eat but get change. When comes your stop, the conductor will tell you. When gets there the train, will be waiting for you on the station Uncle Meyer. He saw you when you were a boy nine years, but he will recognize you. Tell him I send him best regards."

Isaac nodded.

The rabbi groaned and tottered dizzily. His wife cried out as Mendel yanked the coat from her hands.

"Run," cried the rabbi.

"Run, Isaac."

They ran out of the house and down the steps.

"Stop, you thief," called the rabbi's wife.

The rabbi pressed both hands to his temples and fell to the floor.

"Help!" his wife wept. "Heart attack! Help!"

But Mendel and Isaac ran through the streets with the rabbi's new fur-lined caftan. After them noiselessly ran Ginzburg.

It was very late when Mendel bought the train ticket in the only booth open.

There was no time to stop for a sandwich so Isaac ate his peanuts and they hurried to the train in the vast deserted station.

"So in the morning," Mendel gasped as they ran, "there comes a man that he sells sandwiches and coffee. Eat but get change. When reaches California the train, will be waiting for you on the station Uncle Leo. If you don't recognize him he will recognize you. Tell him I send best regards."

But when they arrived at the gate to the platform it was shut, the light out.

Mendel, groaning, beat on the gate with his fists.

"Too late," said the uniformed ticket collector, a bulky, bearded man with hairy nostrils and a fishy smell.

He pointed to the station clock. "Already past twelve."

"But I see standing there still the train," Mendel said, hopping in his grief.

"It just left—in one more minute."

"A minute is enough. Just open the gate."

"Too late I told you."

Mendel socked his bony chest with both hands. "With my whole heart I beg you this little favor."

"Favors you had enough already. For you the train is gone. You shoulda been dead already at midnight. I told you that yesterday. This is the best I can do."

"Ginzburg!" Mendel shrank from him.

"Who else?" The voice was metallic, eyes glittered, the expression amused.

"For myself," the old man begged, "I don't ask a thing. But what will happen to my boy?"

Ginzburg shrugged slightly. "What will happen happens. This isn't my responsibility. I got enough to think about without worrying about somebody on one cylinder."

"What then is your responsibility?"

"To create conditions. To make happen what happens. I ain't in the anthropomorphic business."

"Whatever business you in, where is your pity?"

"This ain't my commodity. The law is the law."

"Which law is this?"

"The cosmic universal law, goddamit, the one I got to follow myself."

"What kind of a law is it?" cried Mendel. "For God's sake, don't you understand what I went through in my life with this poor boy? Look at him. For thirty-nine years, since the day he was born, I wait for him to grow up, but he don't. Do you understand what this means in a father's heart? Why don't you let him go to his uncle?" His voice had risen and he was shouting.

Isaac mewled loudly.

"Better calm down or you'll hurt somebody's feelings," Ginzburg said with a wink toward Isaac.

"All my life," Mendel cried, his body trembling, "what did I have? I was poor. I suffered from my health. When I worked I worked too hard. When I didn't work was worse. My wife died a young woman. But I didn't ask from anybody nothing. Now I ask a small favor. Be so kind, Mr. Ginzburg."

The ticket collector was picking his teeth with a match stick.

"You ain't the only one, my friend, some got it worse than you. That's how it goes in this country."

"You dog you." Mendel lunged at Ginzburg's throat and began to choke. "You bastard, don't you understand what it means human?"

They struggled nose to nose, Ginzburg, though his astonished eyes bulged, began to laugh. "You pipsqueak nothing. I'll freeze you to pieces."

His eyes lit in rage and Mendel felt an unbearable cold like an icy dagger invading his body, all of his parts shriveling.

Now I die without helping Isaac.

A crowd gathered. Isaac yelped in fright.

Clinging to Ginzburg in his last agony, Mendel saw reflected in the ticket collector's eyes the depth of his terror. But he saw that Ginzburg, staring at himself in Mendel's eyes, saw mirrored in them the extent of his own awful wrath. He beheld a shimmering, starry, blinding light that produced darkness.

Ginzburg looked astounded. "Who me?"

His grip on the squirming old man slowly loosened, and Mendel, his heart barely beating, slumped to the ground.

"Go," Ginzburg muttered, "take him to the train."

characterization & structure

Mendel embraced his son. "Isaakil, be good to people, then they will love you."

The train pulled in. Mendel turned for a last look. Isaac sat hunched at the edge of the seat, his face strained in the direction of his journey.

Mendel unpinned a hidden dollar from his inside pocket and sent a telegram to Uncle Meyer. Although there were still a few minutes left, he hurried forth to seek Ginsberg.

"Let pass," he commanded a guard.

The crowd parted. Isaac helped his father up and they tottered down the steps to the platform where the train waited, lit and ready to go.

Mendel found Isaac a coach seat and hastily embraced him. "Help Uncle Leo, Isaakil. Also remember your father and mother."

"Be nice to him," he said to the conductor. "Show him where everything is."

He waited on the platform until the train began slowly to move. Isaac sat at the edge of his seat, his face strained in the direction of his journey. When the train was gone, Mendel ascended the stairs to see what had become of Ginzburg.

commentary

Bernard Malamud has written, "I do have a manuscript—a version of years ago—of 'Idiots First,' which though an unsuccessful short story, at least achieves the virtue of being a past first step of a better piece of work." The most extensive revisions occurring between Mr. Malamud's "version of years ago" or "A Long Ticket for Isaac" and the published story of "Idiots First" concern characterization and structure. The published story is "a better piece of work" than the "unsuccessful" earlier draft, because the published story attains better organization and presents more subtly and complexly the character of Mendel and the character whose name appears in the earlier version as Ginsberg and in the published story as Ginzburg. These developments are interrelated.

The action of "A Long Ticket for Isaac" proceeds from Mendel's house to the pawnshop, the park, Fishbein's house, the cafeteria, the rabbi's house, and the train station. Throughout numerous explicit references are made to Mendel as a dying man. From the first sentence to the statement "In the grave" much later, they pervade it, but especially during the episode at Fishbein's house. There are also numerous implicit references to Ginsberg as the angel of death: at Mendel's house; in the park; and at the cafeteria, where Ginsberg's role is most clearly implied. Eventually, Mendel hurries forth to seek him, who keeps his promise to "wait till midnight."

But whereas numerous explicit references are made to Mendel as a dying man in "A Long Ticket for Isaac," "Idiots First" commences with words like "fright" and "pain," the import of which does not become fully apparent prior to the transition between the cafeteria and the rabbi's house. The baldest statements made at Fishbein's house have been deleted; others have been softened. And while the dying-man references have been eliminated or toned down so that the ultimate extent of Mendel's malady is withheld until he speaks to the sexton, the implicit references to Ginzburg as the angel of death have been sharply reduced. Mr. Malamud has cut the affected dialogue at Mendel's house by half and Isaac's remarks at Fishbein's house altogether. The meeting between Ginzburg and Mendel in the park is much shorter in the published version than in "A Long Ticket for Isaac," and the long cafeteria episode now contains fewer than fifty words. During the train-station scene Ginzburg's role becomes clear.

The preliminary draft is as anticlimactic structurally as it is obvious in the presentation of character, for the crowning event—the meeting between Ginsberg and Mendel—occurs before the story's termination, which at this stage of the writing consists of merely Mendel's instructions to Isaac and his hurrying forth to seek Ginsberg. In addition, whatever force a precipitate climax might have had has been dissipated by splitting the Ginsberg-Mendel confrontation into two scenes: the park and the cafeteria. That Mr. Malamud was aware of its anticlimactic aspect even during the composition of the preliminary draft would seem to be suggested by a marginal notation beside the line, "At the station Mendel bought the ticket." This notation reads: "End with cafeteria dialogue."

"Idiots First," like "A Long Ticket for Isaac," employs a spatial type of structure, but, as with the interrelated treatment of character, changes were made in the published piece to augment suspense and dramatic impact. Besides being considerably shorter, the park and the cafeteria scenes now follow the episode at Fishbein's house in rapid succession, thus helping to form the transition between it and the rabbi's house. This paves the way for a single confrontation scene at the end of the story (train station), to which the earlier version devotes about 175 words and the published piece nearly 900 words.

Although the borrowed material is slight quantitatively and different qualitatively, the climax of "Idiots First" does draw upon three scenes of "A Long Ticket for Isaac," these being the park, the cafeteria, and the train station. However, it is the fresh material Mr. Malamud added to the end of "Idiots First" that has especial importance, for through this the characters of Mendel and Ginzburg are deepened. The first evolves toward more than a gentle, humble father with a determined sense of responsibility. Challenging "the cosmic universal law" by asking ". . . where is your pity?" and attacking Ginzburg physically while asking ". . . don't you understand what it means human?" he comes to represent the superior morality and compassion of mankind over the gods. But Ginzburg's evolution toward more than an indifferent emissary of fate is even more complex. Between the moment the angel of death appears as "the uniformed ticket collector" and the moment Mendel attacks him, malice replaces disdain, and between the moment of the attack and the moment Ginzburg stares into Mendel's eyes, rage replaces malice.

characterization & structure

Then, seeing "his own awful wrath" mirrored there, he relents, astounded to discover that he is "in the anthropomorphic business" after all.

Partly as a concomitant of the subtler presentation of Mendel and Ginzburg, "Idiots First" became a more unified story than "A Long Ticket for Isaac," and partly as a concomitant of the dramatic ending which emerged from this tighter structure, Mendel and Ginzburg became richer characters.

V

characterization, structure, & setting

Wright Morris, who was born in Central City, Nebraska, during 1910, has received three Guggenheim Fellowships, a grant from the National Institute of Arts and Letters, and the National Book Award (1957) for his novel, The Field of Vision *(1956). He has taught at Haverford, Sarah Lawrence, Swarthmore, the University of Utah, and is currently Professor of English at San Francisco State College. Mr. Morris' books include* My Uncle Dudley *(1942),* The Man Who Was There *(1945),* The Inhabitants *(1946),* The Home Place *(1948),* The World in the Attic *(1949),* Man and Boy *(1951),* The Works of Love *(1952),* The Deep Sleep *(1953),* The Huge Season *(1954),* Love Among the Cannibals *(1957),* The Territory Ahead *(1958),* Ceremony in Lone Tree *(1960),* What a Way to Go *(1962),* Cause for Wonder *(1963), and* In Orbit *(1967).*

One of the author's recent works, One Day, *treats the events in the lives of several characters on Friday, November 22, 1963, the day President John F. Kennedy was assassinated. These characters, whose pasts become known through a series of flashbacks, are related to*

Wright Morris

each other by virtue of their mutual residence in Escondido, California, and to the assassination by being contemporary Americans. While the action is also described from the point of view of Ignacio Chavez, Wendell Horlick, Evelina Cartwright, Luigi Boni, Miriam Horlick, Sheriff McNamara, and Holmes, Alec Cartright and Harold Cowie emerge as the two principal figures.

An important episode involving Harold Cowie and occurring at Matamoros, Mexico, about midway through the novel gave rise to some interesting revisions regarding characterization, structure, and setting. Whereas the first draft of this episode breaks off without any ending, "the crucial second draft," which has been transcribed up to the ending in abridged form, "embodies the contrasting treatment of the Cowie-Concepcion love scene, the chapters climax." A comparison of the two fully transcribed second-draft endings and of the later with the Published Version indicates what Mr. Morris had to confront.

second draft of matamoros episode up to ending (abridged)

ONE DAY

That sensible girl who still sent him clippings of the march of science in the bee culture, had taken Cowie's measure, that summer, and given him up. When confronted with the facts she was accustomed to say it was all for the best. Cowie - twenty-three that summer with two years of medical school to finish - had taken the funds reserved for his education and did what he could to get away from it all. As it happened, he did not have far to go. On the advice of a colleague, a young man named Wilde who was specializing in venereal diseases, Cowie bought a second hand car, boots that laced to his knees, pills for purifying water, and went to Mexico. From Wilde he had letters to several Mexican friends. and a few words of advice. "If you get her with a baby, Cowie," he said, "don't let her waddle out into the fields and have it. That's for the greeks. You know how many women a year they lose?"

. . . He liked Mexican cigars, he drank a good deal of Mexican beer. The beer, perhaps, like the heat and the light aggravated a problem he had while driving: he inclined to doze a bit at the wheel. On the long hot drive from Oaxaca to Puebla, where the soil was often red as the blood of martyrs, his car left the road on a curve and cut across a field just plowed by an oxen. The huge beast was less than ten yards away when the car stopped. . . . He crossed a bridge where the Indians, like giant insects, crawled about on the steel girders, chipping off the paint with sharply pointed rocks. About ten miles farther, or it might have been twenty - everything in Mexico seemed to be <u>about</u> one thing or another - he glanced up to see an Indian napping on the slope of a curve. A red cloth, as if he might have been bleeding, lay across his knees. A moment later the car banked on the curve and Cowie swung wide to avoid a row of boulders, before he saw, directly in his path, a huddle of men. One drank from a gourd tipped over his head. They remained in the huddle as if they lacked the will to separate. The brake pedal Cowie pushed to the floor gripped only one wheel, that on the right front, dragging the car against Cowie's efforts into the men. In that moment he realized that when the car had left the road he had broken something, and that his chronic dozing at the wheel, as was only just, would now cost him his life. Of other lives he did not think. One man leaped, the rest he struck broadside, as if the car was swung like a paddle, tossing them aside like fragments of a broken pot. . . . Unable to move his hands from the wheel - they appeared to grip it, disembodied - Cowie stared through the windshield, one half of it shattered, at the bus that approached from the south, an overload of passengers clinging to the top and the rear. Although the dozing flaGMan had awakened it did not cross his mind to wave it. What more could be possibly happen? A good deal. As it swung around the corner the bus careened to the left, to avoid the bodies, spilling Indians from the rear and the top, then righted just in time to smash headlong into Cowie, the glass breaking like a crest of spray before his face. . . .

So it began, the strange love story of Harold Cowie. Two men were dead, four seriously injured, a car was demolished. Harold Cowie's injuries were peculiar, but slight. His hands were broken, he had several cuts on his head. The ankle of the foot he had applied to the brake pedal was sprained. . . . Dr. Kaspar had placed three fingers on his forehead, as if in prayer. Well enough Cowie understood that he was stupefied by human ignorance. "A bone we can fix, right? he said. Cowie's bandaged head had wagged slowly, "but we cannot fix - " he put a hand on his head "when something is broken in here! You have a soft head. It is your head that hurts, is that not right?"

Lupita Gonzalez, who heard that, wondered what was wrong with his head that it hurt so, but Cowie understood Dr. Kaspar only too well. One question only. Was guilt felt by the head or the heart? In either case it was not so easily repaired. His bones healed, the pain let up, his fingers wiggled at the tip of the casts, but there was no change in the condition of his guilt. The word accident did not do for Cowie what it did for the mother who had lost a son, what it did for the daughter who had lost a brother. Quite the contrary, it merely aggravated his guilt. His laziness, his dozing, would one day cost him something - and this was it.

If one went back - as he had the time to do, napping half the day and awake half the night - it was his refusal to face certain facts that had brought him to Mexico Otherwise the sensible girl in his life would have married him. He didn't mention such things to Dr. Kaspar, of course, but he often hinted at them to Dr. Carrillo, a man who was also not a little soft in the head. . . . With Cowie his eyes would pass over the street, cobbled like a stream bed, the cafe where shabby hens scratched the bit of terrace, the square with its gravel paths, dying tree of India, the fountain that dripped like an illness, the tile benches too hot in the sun, too cool in the shade, the tne bell tower of the church, grass sprouting between the tiles, where pigeons strutted, the clock that tolled no recognizable hour, the door hung with curtains like a stage entrance, then sweeping the view as if it were veiled his eyes came back to where they were seated, a blacony with a railing where a caged bird had been put to sun.

. . . Cowie took it as an example of the Mexican taste for the macabre, like the skulls and bones eaten by children, and the fantastic birds and animals made of paper. . . . The voice of Lupita, the child who put her lips to the wires and spoke to it, would sometimes persuade the creature to open an eye. Was it dead or alive? That was the question Dr. Carrillo answered with his characteristic shrug. It applied, obviously, not merely to Chiquita, wired to her perch, nor to the specatcle of Matamoros, but to all that the eye surveyed from the balcony. Including Dr. Carrillo? Especially. Cowie found it an all inclusive shrug.

Until the arrival of Cowie, this bird, Chiquita, was the pet and prize of Senora Gonzales, a widow, mother of two daughters and one son. This son, a boy of twenty-three, had been killed in the accident on the highway. It was not clear if the deaths had been caused by Cowie, or the bus. That seemed to all concerned an unimportant detail. The Indian with the flag had frankly admitted he had fallen asleep at the switch, and this crime was no crime since it had been the hour for the siesta. Nature was nature, just as fate was fate. Cowie had been an instrument in God's mysterious plan. Part of that plan was that he should be carried, like a sack of wase parts, up a long flight of stairs to the balony of the woman whose son he had destoryed. No other accomodations were available. The Tuxtla Hotel, just off the Plaza, offered the only rooms suitable for travelers, and Senora Gonzalez was the owner of the Hotel. That Cowie should be brought there was no accidnet. Dressed in black, her large eyes more luminous than usual, the first gaze she turned on Sowie was that of pity and recognition. Through them, His will was made manifest. Cowie was filled with remorse, with gratitude, and especially with guilt. In; this crisis it proved to be a godsend that he neither understood nor could speak the language, the eyes, especially those of Senora Gonzalez, were expressive enough. The gathering of the family at Cowie's beside, which took place the first evening, had left the impression that he was attending his own wake. The pity in their glances was all for him. The older girl, whose name was Concepcion, covered her face in the manner of the Indian women, showing no more than a remarkably luminous pair of eyes. Cowie had felt these eyes would see through him. That her lips would show hate. But no, quite the contrary, she showed only her eyes out of shame since her face was covered with a terrible acne. Over this she wore an ointment put on so thickly it looked like pigment. But that Cowie saw later, not at the time. He was able to gather, to piece together, from his tourists spanish and Concepcion's English, that this tragedy in a mysterious way had linked them together, and he was to feel, while he was with them, at home. Cowie's physical discomfort was not small, but it was nothing compared with his guilt and remorse. That night established the pattern of his recovery: he spent it wide awake.

Cowie lay on a bed that occupied about a one-third of the balcony. If there were no guests, which was not unusual, it was used by the gonzalez family, who brought out chairs and waited for the cool of the evening. . . . The door to the balcony had been removed.

At the south end of the balcony, veiled by a screen, was the apartment of the Lopez family. . . . Dolores treated him like sick child, but intimated he was a man. "You need a woman!" she would say, lifting his bottom to insert the bedpan, then turning to wipe the film of perspiration from his bloodless face. . . .

characterization, structure, & setting

Neither Senora Gonzalez, nor her daughters, went down to the street. It was neither place for a matron, a child, or a young woman. A few men and Indians, male and female, crossed the Plaza during the day, and in the evening a few girls appeared walking arm in arm. They circled the Plaza in one direction, while loose clusters of boys circled it in the other, exhanging furtive or bold glances as they passed. The accompaniment of chatter did not carry to Cowie, thanks to the jukebox that throbbed in the room just below. It began with the conclusion of the siesta and lasted until ten or eleven. The records had been worn so that one mariachi throbbed like another. The hoarse voices blended with the strings, The racket was that of some disordered machine. Nevertheless, it gave to the scene a reality it lacked during the daytime: the throb of the machine created vibrations in the springs of his bed. Dr. Carrillos pills, given to Cowie to kill the pain and promote sleep, had their use in gently stupefying his nerves. . . . He was not all there. But for Matamoros that was more than enough.

He might have been tied to the top of a bus and eventually tranported to the border - but to what purpose? Had he not come for what he had found? To get away from it all - was that not precisely where he was? The road to Oaxaca bypassed the town and at night he could see the lights of the cars, but no sensible tourist ever stopped. . . . In a way he could not describe he had not merely gotten away from it all, but from that object he took for granted: himself. Cowie was always giving up, that had not changed, but one might say that in Matamoros Harold Cowie gave up what he had never known he had.

Unable to feed himself, what food Cowie consumed he had to be fed. At the start it was Dolores who naturally believed that after a good woman, what a man needed was food. Patiently, as with a spoiled child, she fed him, and forced fed him, fried beans. In the evening her place would be taken by Lupita, Senira Lopez's youngest daughter. She poured his tea, and splattered them both as she spooned his soup. Lupita wore dresses and blouses that were hand-me-downs from her sister, whose bottom was rounder, and the same might be said of her bust. . . .

Of the oldest daughter, Concepcion, Cowie saw little In the evening she came out for the air, but sat with her back to him. She wore her hair in a style Cowie had seen in Spanish paintings, swept up to a peak at the rear, with a few rather silly curls on the forehead. She wore a shawl but her neck and shoulders were usually exposed. Not brown at all, but of the whitness that had gone sallow in the mother, Concepcion was a shade paler than the flesh above the cast on Cowie's leg. At her side the copper-toned Lupita looked almost black. UNless the light above the corner bar was on, which had no shade, and burned like a warning, Cowie saw no more of her face than the profile against the dim light behind her, candles burning under a picture of our Lady of Guadaloupe. This profile was remarkable in how familiar it seemed, and impersonal, like the silhouette cutouts on boxes of candy. A symbol of beauty. A symbol of womanhood. In such light the heavy coating of ointment that concealed her cheeks like shaving lather was invisible. Unpredictably, and without warning, as if it had no purpose but to expose her, the light above the bar would flash yellow into her face. Too late she would hide behind her fan. This disturbed Cowie, since the eyes that troubled her were his own. . . .

Was it possible those pills kept Cowie awake? When the street, like the blacony, had emptied, the only sound that came to Cowie was that of billiard balls in the back of one of the bars. There were seldom voices. Did the men play in earnest, or alone. Dr. Carrillo, carrying the paper he had read like a proofreader, would give it a wag toward Cowie then go off across the Plaza, slapping it on the bench where an Indian usually slept. So dead he looked, his hat on his face, it seemed miraculous to find him alive in the morning, a faggot broom in his hands, a bandanna concealing his face. This was against the morning chill, certain vaporous spirits, and the coldness of air on bad teeth. He looked to Cowie like a bandit cleaning up after a good nights work.

. . . The shabby plaza with its dripping fountain, the Indian curled up like an ashtray, seemed to be a collection of symbolic objects, hints toward a meaning that escaped him. . . . Several nights had passed, too many, before it occurred to Cowie that the bell, sounding the hour, had nothing whatsoever to do with the clock. Not a thing. It operated in a world, and on a time, of its own. So did Cowie, oddly enough, since he felt no connection with the time on his wrist: it might have been one of the many clocks that ornament a wall in railroad stations, advising the traveler what time it was somewhere else. The clock itself, due to its age, sometimes ran and sometimes stopped, o that the time it told was not that in Matamoros, but nobody seemed to care. Thinking to amuse the child, Cowie had pointed this out to Lupita. Was it his spanish? She seemed to have trouble grasping that the bells and hands of the clock were meant to go together. It made her smile. But it was at Cowie, not with him. A clock might behave that way somewhere else, but why should it do so in Matamoros. Why indeed? So Cowie began to feel himself. If one ignored the ridiculous time on the clock's face a more sensible time seemed to emerge. It stood - to speak theatrically - ready and waiting in the wings. The steps of the cathedral, flooded with light so it could be seen from the Oaxaca highway - seemed to be the stage, the perfect setting, for a time that seemed less arbitrary than the time on the clocks' face, or the time on Cowie's wrist. But why bother? There was this problem of Cowie's guilt. There was this phememonon described as an accident. No sense could be made of human events if one accepted the time on the clocks face, every clock told time that was out, the wrong time. Cowie preferred to believe that a time existed wherein it wa;s known, and could be explained, that on a certain day, at a certain instant, he would round a determined corner and be responsible for the; the deaths of two men. Better that than that such lives were snuffed out with meaning. Better guilt than accidents.

That Cowie lacked the wit to explain this meant no more than that he lacked the talent. So did the child who could not read the clock. There were other clocks to be read. Clocks without hands. The mind sensed this time, but could not spell it out. In this ignorance man lived the victim of a false time, and a life that might appear to be meaningless. For what could be said of a life snuffed out? That it made sense up to that moment? Impossible. All the more horrible then the witless accident that destroyed it. No, there was not time if it relied on such a word as accident. That was just a way of saying that for some men, time was out. The whole of life was a game which they saw from the bench.

It almost goes without saying that during the day Cowie

was free of these impressions. He accepted the simple, sensible time he read on his watch. . . .

A moment later Dr. Carrillo, with his mornings mail in his pocket, would stop by to have a look at Cowie, take his pulse. He came up with his shoes tracking in water from the wet cafe terrace, where a boy named Jaime flushed it down with a hose. . . . No, all of that playing around with water, with hoses and with mops, was the behaviour of children. . . .

Although guessed at more of this than he followed, he understood it pleased Dr. Carrilo to tell him. With somebody to listen, he was quite willing to talk. As a young man he had come to Matamoros to bring health to its suffering people. This statement needed no comment. Not so much as a Carrillo shrug. As for native superstiotons, would he like to hear something? Cowie had peered from beneath a loose bandage. They had lost fewer than Carrillo himself had acquired. It was something that Cowie would never understand, but if he were to live in Matamoros, he would end up as superstitous as the rest. One fine day Carrillo would find him with a hose, flusing off the terrace, or with a bucket mopping down the steps.

Did he possibly realize that such a prospect appealed to Cowie? No, it seemed unlikely. He feared it too much himself. This dread of matamoros, or so it seemed to Cowie, had a stimulating effect on Carrillo. . . .

It seemed of little consequence at the time that the family Lopez, the mother and her two daughters, would be seated in the room that the sun made cheerful in the morning. Of Senora Lopez, bent over her sewing, little more other showed than the part in her hair. When she glanced up it was merely to blink and rest her eyes. The child, Lupita, often used this period to speak to the bird Chiquita, put water in her bath, empty the pan in her cage. It was unusual, but not unheard of, for the creature to peep. One note, no more. If the perch were given a nudge the bird might drop to the floor of the cage, hop like a toy, then gargle a bit of water in the plucked throat. All but naked it would dip in the water, shudder faintly, then pretend to preen. The polished beak was like a kernel of dried corn.

MATAMOROS EPISODE

Whether the night seemed unreal, or sur-real, was a question that hung in balance until the appearance of the sleep walker. An arched doorway without a door, opened out on the corridor that led to the stairs, the floor of yellow tile, the railing along the stairs lined with plants. These were the stairs that Dolores daily slopped with water and mopped, Some of the plants had died for lack of it, but never mind. Dolores used a door at the top of the stairs that Cowie assumed led to kitchen, When it stood open he sometimes heard her tuneless singing, or the squawk of a doomed turkey. Senora Lopez came and went by the door on the balcony.

From the stairs, at Cowie's back, that is, came this figure in a trailing nightshift, the barefeet making no sound at all on the tile. A lump rose and blocked Cowie's throat. Was it his heart? Owl-eyed and speechless he watched this figure, vague as an appartion, pass within a yard of him and walk boldly to the balcony rail. A female. That certainly. The light from a street lamp defined her figure. Plainly it was not that of the goat-legged dolores. The bust was ample. Could it be Senora Lopez? Fear that he might break the spell and be the cause of a new revolution made of Cowie a sleep walker himself. His mouth dried. The bed vibrated to the beat of his heart. When she spoke he understood that

MATAMOROS EPISODE

After a few days the faunlike Lupita took both Cowie and Carrillo for granted: she wore only her nightshift, one of her sisters that hung so low she tripped on it, her unbraided hair hanging to sweep the small of her back. If she leaned over the wall so that her feet left the floor she was able to see the white dome Ixtclaccihuatl, the sleeping woman, floating above the morning veil of mist. Senora Lopez, in a quilted robe that puffed out like a flight suit might open the screen to warn Cowie against los aires. And what was that? Carrillo would exchange a glance with Cowie. It was not merely against the morning chill that the peons draped themselves like bandits. No, they were keeping out evil sprits. Did it matter if Carrillo called it consumption and the indian an evil spririt? Not much. In either case he wasted away and coughed.

It seemed to be for the light - she let a rebozo rest lightly about her shoulders - that led Concepcion to do her sewing near the dooreay. She did the sort of thing Cowie thought of as tatting, needlework in cloth that was stretched on a frame. All that one saw of her was the back of her neck, and the gold ornaments at her ears. The lobes were pierced. The light was good enough to see that. Mother and daughter looked much the same bent over their sewing, their shoulders rounded, their black hair gleaming up auburn lights from the sun.

In what way did Cowie first sense that Dr. Carrillo's fluent sermons were not for him? It took time, of course. But gather it he did. For one thing, it seemed perfectly clear that Cowie did not understand them. The moral strain was elevated. The Spanish fluent and complicated. For another, he directed his remarks not so much toward Cowie, captive in his bed, as toward those who had more to do than merely listen, but listen they did. Lupita followed this harangue in the classical manner of a child exposed to uplift, her eyes wandering, one nail fingering a scab on

characterization, structure, & setting

Was it customary for people to be sleep talkers? In Matamoros it was. Like Cowie, it was the night she preferred. a question had been put. Did not the night make the ugly beautiful? Was that put to Cowie? Apparently it was, since she turned as if for an answer. Did he agree with that? she repeated. His mouth bone dry, he had nodded. She had moved from the railing to staand beside his bed. He felt the warmth of her body before she ran her hand through his hair. Not once but two, three times, gripping the locks at the rear. As part of his getting away from it all, he had let his hair grow,. Her eyes on him she had put a question he did not clearly follow, but he understod it. Very plainly he understood what he had been asked. Did the night which could make Matamoros beautiful, do the same for her? He stared at, but he could not see her face. The layer of oinment was gone or he would have smelled it, he knew that. In her hair some of the pale light from the street was trapped. Once more, speechless, his head had nodded, and she had let go of the grip on his hair, cupped her face in his hands, and put her lips to his mouth. That was all. It was wrong to say that he had been kissed. Then she released him, smoothed his hair, and went off down the corridor she had come out of, the draft chill on Cowie's perspiring face when she opened the door.

her knee. Senora Lopez, without lifting her eyes, showed in many ways that she was attentive, using the pauses to snip at frayed ends with her shears, and open up a seam. From her lips a length of thread often dangled, as if she meant to pull a tooth. Infrequently her gaze, dull with sewing, would rest on the bowed head of her daughter, a lovely sight indeed so long as it concealed her face. It was Concepcion, however, speechless as usual, who made on Cowie a curious impression. That of her presence. That of being all ears. Her eyes were never raised, but there were moments when she seemed a figure in a painting. Her hands idle. A stillife pattern of light and sahde. One could see that the mother had once had very beautiful arms.

This took time, almost forever, but once Cowie had grasped it he saw the events he had suffered were not meaningless. It was possible, indeed, for him to make them meaningful. An accident could be shaped to save, rather than merely destory lives. Here in this tomb, this life-less Matamoros, a lover and his beloved had been figures in a mural, or the captives of a spell, until Cowie had come along. He was the only one to see it, the only one free to act. The rules of the game in Matamoros kept Dr. Carrillo on his leash, just as it kept the blighted Concepcion in her cage. The freakish and comical intrusion of Cowie made it possible to crack this pattern. To open, for a moment, the doors of the cage. To do this Cowie, his bed, and his balcony were perfectly located for such an occasion. The lovers could meet. Cowie could keep the watch at the foot of the stairs. When it was over he would not be squeamish about taking his place in a bed, transformed, to put it mildly, by meaningful events.

All Cowie had to do was impress on the lovers that he had grasped the situation. That was not easy. Perhaps that was what they feared? Since it would not be hard to tipoff Dr. Carrillo, Cowies problem was the shy beloved. How get her attention? It was seldom he caught her eye. His only chance seemed the evining when they came out on the balcony for the coolness, or, with her sister as an escort, she took a turn around the Plaza, buying the ice cream sticks they would munch on when they returned. Cowie was usually asked if he wanted something, and as a rule he didn't. It was Lupita who ran the errand, not Concepcion. But if Cowie needed money, which was seldom, the traveler's

characterization, structure, & setting

A ghostly lover? Could she behave like that in her sleep? Like <u>that</u>, perhaps, but this was not merely a ghostly lover. Nor did he soon return a ghostly kiss. Whether <u>she</u> was alseep or not was immaterial - the question was, what about Cowie? What about the lover with his hands in the plaster casts? This took some doing, as well as dreaming, some of it stranger than the Matamoros night, some of it so strange it had not Cowie preferred to let it pass as a dream. Those phantasies a bed-ridden man will have in the twilight between sleeping and waking, where the beloved ghost just might materialize in the plaster arms. Love stories incline to be strange, and nothing suits them better than to lie beyond the telling of it. Such was Cowie's. A story so strange he did not believe it himself.

check was given to Concepcion, and on one occasion she had given him the money personally. That had been strange, many dirty bills and silver, and she had gripped the coins in such a manner that when they were dropped into Cowe's palm they were so moist many of them stuck together. To kill the smell of the ointment she wore a very strong perfume.

On the weekend a carnival set up around the Plaza, with a ferris wheel, four or five sideshows, rings to be/tossed, balls to be thrown, and games with darts. A music box that little Indians took turns cranking made a racket that was meant to be that of the marimba. Its pitch was determined by the energy and speed of the crank. The ferris wheel, a rig with six seats that wobbled dangerously when loaded, brought the eyes of the spellbound merrymakers just above the level of Cowie. He may/have appeared to them as a being from another world. Several times during the evening the gasoline motor stopped, leaving some of the passengers high in heaven, This seemed better than the ride. They shouted taunts to those peering up from below. The sideshow that attracted the greatest attention featured a two-headed woman, vividly painted in on a banner that hung at the front. A great beauty she was, with each head sensibly coiffed with her rebozo, the faces wearing the expression of the Virgin of Guadaloupe. Before that feature men, women and children stood in line. Closer at hand, lit up by lanterns that transformed the gamblers into bandits, adults only, and only caballeros huddled with their fists full of pesos. Into the gambling wheel, spun like a top, the gambler would hurl three feathered darts, then wait to see what numbers he had turned up. It was quite a sight, and obviously no one in Matamoros thought of sleeping, The family Lopez had an excellent view from the balcony. To croos the Plaza, if one cared to, it was necessary to detour around it. using the side streets to the north and the west. There were of course fire crackers. An Indian who had got

Cowie let it be known that he wanted money, but it was Lupita who took the check from him. He watched the sisters stroll around the square, passing the cafe where Dr. Carrillo, the paper folded on the table, did the crossword puzzle. He raised his eyes. Concepscion concelaed her face behind her fan. Without his intervention, Cowie wondered, would that burlesque go on forever? Perhaps. In

Two, three times a week, the spectral lover would come down the hall, stand a moment at the rail, then materialize in Cowie's plaster embrace. Aside from its strangeness, what could be more maddening. He was not unlike an amorous inhibited pelican. With the tips of fingers, no more, he could appreciate her virtues. To that extent the lover was ghostly. Ravish her he could not. It came as a shock to Cowie when he realized she had ravished him. Another shock was its thoroughness: she was not without experience. While the mist was like woodsmoke in the Plaza and before the first donkeys clopped in from the country, Cowie would sit shivering without his sheet while he went over the bed for long strands of her hair, proof he did not need that she had been there. Nor did that strategem fool Dolores. That face that seemed to have but one pig-like expression was a mask of sublety when she slapped his pillow, and rolled him on his face to change the sheet. One might have thought she had been there herself: that was how she looked. In the morning she wore Concepcion's curlers in her hair for ornaments.

Matamoros it was not at all strange. It waited on an accident like Cowie to drop one wire to spark another - if that occurred everyone would accept the inevitable. Cowie had told Lupita to buy them all an ice cream, a Matamoros version of the popsicle, and she ran up the stairs ahead of her sister to give one to Cowie, then run with one to her mother. So that Concepcion came along with the coins. Cowie had prepared himself, when she extended her hand he actually gripped it, that is, he tried to, but she had jerked it free as if he had pinched her, throwing a fistfull of bills and coins into the air. The awful racket it made brought both Lupita and her mother to the balcony door, where they watched Lupita, crouched on her knees, crawling around to pick them up. What had happend? She had tripped in the dark. There was nothing to trip on, nothing, but the dark was a godsend, since Cowie's face burned like a fever and he knew it was red. It took time to round up the money. Many matches were struck. When Concepcion approached him with the money Cowie was so shamefaced he could hardly accept it: he could not believe the pressure of her fingers on the palm of his hand. Was it possible? Unmistakeable. It had been as deliberate as the grip Dr, Carrillo made on his pulse. He had been so startled he stared at her face. The eyes returned his gaze.

So there was hope after all! She understood! And he had been so distracted he forgot about the ice cream that melted into a puddle in his lap. The evening cooled, Senora Gonzalez hooded the bird cage and took it in with her, and some time later the throbbing of the jukebox could not be felt in the springs of Cowie's bed. In the quiet he could hear the click of the billiards at the rear of the cantina. The man who liked to bang his cue was playing. The butt thumping the floor. This time was no time at all for Cowie, as if the early event had stunned him. Dr. Carrillo, weary of the puzzle had gone off across the plaza and into the shadows, the slap of his rolled up paper echoing from the dark. One event remained. The last bus to Puebla. Never before had Cowie watched the bent hands of the clock in their witless movement. Now they held the secret of a time of an event, that he awaited. What event, what accident, delayed more than usually the last bus. On time, of course, it never was. But _in_ time it somehow managed. _In_ time it would surely turnup. But when was that. Time

characterization, structure, & setting

During the increasingly unreal day there were many things to dwell on, most of them with wonder. One worth mentioning was the extent to which Cowie looked forward to the future. The future? More concretely, he looked forward to losing his casts. One might as well admit, as he did, to the way the lower man in him had been aroused. The ghostly lover was ample. He lusted for that amplitude. With a rather fixed stare, as if his thoughts were elsewhere, he would watch her movements through the screened doorway, the round ess of her shoulders when she bent over her sewing, her bottom when she stooped. If there was anything she lacked it was an angle, every contour was a curve. This amplitude would go soft in time but not Cowie hoped, before he possessed it. The memory of it in his hands as well as his eyes. Oddly enough, he gave her face little thought. During the day it wore its familiar mask of ointment. Something of the odor of it, of course, was there at night. Otherwise she smelled, as did Dr, Carrillo, of hot peppers and guacamole, the taste of it giving flavor to her lips. This streak of lechery in his nature uncomplicated by the higher more respectable emotions - gave Cowie something more than cause for wonder, but he attributed his fall to the southern climate, the strangeness of the night, and the beloved's latin temperament. It could also be said, in part, that his hands were tied. He was the ravished, not the ravisher. Could he help what happened to him at night? To what extent the ghostly lover preyed on other guests he gave some random thought, but not much. No, it called for something out of <u>this</u> world, like himself. Someone who would go off just as mysteriously as he had appeared, taking not a jot more than he had received.

after time Cowie checked his watch. To what end, since he had no idea when she appeared - what time it was. From the hall at his back, leading to the stairs, she came to stand framed in the doorway. To see her he had to twist around his head. He was able to do that, having no idea what he would see. Her hair was down. She wore only a cloak of light? The faintly luminous ointment was not on her face. She spoke his name, then came forward to take his head in her arms, his face pressed close between her breasts. With both hands she gripped his hair as if to lift his head from his shoulders, tipped it upward, and placed her lips on his mouth. And Cowie? Is it necessary to say? Isnt this the point, precisely, where the good clean books and the movies ended, where Rin Tin Tin rubbed noses with Lassie, if not much else? Precisely, but that was not for Cowie. At the point of suffocation - or so it seemed - he gasped for air. A mistake, since with the air he was faintly aware of what had happened. Worse yet, he had recovered the powers of speech.

"But - " he said, both of his hands were full of the hair that hung to her waist, "but Carrillo, Dr. Carrillo!"

She moved his head away to look at his face. What did she see? He saw nothing. Like a whiff of salTS he inhaled the strong scent of her perfume.

"Jaime?" she said, "<u>Jai</u>-me?"

Cowie was spared his answer. His head was shaking Plainly she had a mind shaking it off. No sound was made, none, except the panting her effort caused her, and the straw-like creak of the bed. When she released him Cowie felt most of his hair must be in her fingers. But no, it wasn't. He saw they were pressed to her own face. In some chidlish book, luminous with moonlihgt and his own imagination, had he seen, or had he dreamed, of such a strange lady Godiva, her shame exposed to the world but concealed from herself. Was she weeping? No, she merely seemed to be gathering her forces. Her face thrust to almost touch his own, the scent of the ointment activated, she hissed into his face words that he mercifully could not fathom, mere shadows of the substance that would kill. Sensing that she added one more, good in any language. "Buffooooon!" she said. her feet slapping she was gone. In his hair she left the strength of her fingers on his lips the taste of her mouth, in his nostrils the talcum'd

characterization, structure, & setting

Everyday he held up his hands to Dr. Carrilo, but the first cast to come off was the one on his leg. That produced more problems than it solved. He was able, and encouraged, to get up and hobble about. What reason was there, therefore, for him to stay? The fingers of his plaster hand would button his fly, and pull on a shirt. While thinking this over he effected a hobble and complained that his foot was still large for his shoe. Nobody seemed to mind. Dr. Carrillo merely shrugged and took him off the pills to promote his sleep.

Did that explain it? It didn't, of course, but with the pills went his assuramce that his luck would not change. What more could happen? Nothing more, but considerably less., Two, three four nights went by without a sign of his ghostly lover. What did he feel? He seemed to feel little more than anxiety. Interminable waiting. His mouth his eyes and his ears wide open. Nothing broke the spell of the night but the witless bells. As a knowledgeable man he reasoned this might be dictated by her period: but he did not believe it. No, he had the intimation, common to lovers, that perhaps his luck was running out. Had she taken his measure? Ruefully he could only admit that she had. Her measure - and how correct the term was - had eluded him.

scent of her powdered breasts. Back to her bed she had certainly taken samples of his hair. Was it possible that Cowie's generous act to provide her with a lover was a familiar artful doge for himself? That seemed too strong But it crossed a mind he took some pride in keeping open. An artful dodger. Didn't that describe his flight on the bus? Would Jaime Carrillo have gone off down the stairs, carrying his shoes? Somewhere between Matamoros and Puebla Cowie waited for fate to save him from himself, to interven in such a way that such a dodge would be impossible. This was not at all unlikely. The bus was given to breakdowns. so it might return him. The bus itself would break down. The southbound bus would pick him up. Or the bus might continue into Puebla where the law, alerted, would be be waiting for him, pick him up for absconding, and return him to Concepcion in chains. That would settle the matter. She would recognize the hand of fate herself. When she came to him aGAIN Dr. Carrillo's name would not be on his lips.

But the bus hammered through the night, tires that should have blown out held their air, like new ones, and there was nothing at the station in Puebla but the bus for Mexico City. He took it. And that settled that. From Mexico city he sent a money order to generously cover his expenses, folded in a sheet of paper on which he had written one word. Buffoon. Adios, he said, and signed it Buffoon.

published version
ending of the matamoros episode

It was for the light, of course, that Concepción sat near the doorway. She did the sort of thing Cowie thought of as tatting, needlework in cloth that was stretched on a frame. One saw the part in her hair, and the gold loops dangling from her pierced ears. Something about that disturbed Cowie, but pleasurably. It hardly mattered in what way Cowie first sensed that Carrillo's discourse was not for *him*. The moral strain was elevated. The Spanish fluent and complicated. Concepción Lopez, without lifting her eyes, showed in many ways that she was attentive, using the pauses to snip at frayed ends with a small pair of shears. From her lips a thread often dangled, as if she meant to pull a tooth. Infrequently her gaze, dull with sewing, might rest on the head of Cowie, who was careful to wear an expression of sympathetic concern. Did she grasp that he *understood?* He felt that she did. The dappled light in the room led one to forget the lather of ointment that covered her face, and see only her luminous eyes, her beautiful arms.

Was it by accident that Carrillo's discourse had a special effect on Cowie? Could he help but see himself as the link in this broken chain? With Cowie there a connection was established. Words and looks were communicated. Dr. Carrillo had taken a new lease on his buried life. In the cemetery of Matamoros something miraculous might happen, was indeed about to happen as if the scene had arranged itself. Here in this tomb a lover and his beloved had been like figures in a mural, or birds in separate cages, until Cowie had been brought to join them. Was it possible to speak of this as an *accident?* Not to Cowie. Nothing seemed clearer than the series of events that resulted in his stay in Matamoros, his entombment, no less, so that others might arise from the grave.

Very pretty, certainly, but how was it to be arranged?

What Cowie had to do was impress on the lovers that he had a full grasp of the situation. Even more. That he had the key to their cage. What better place could be imagined than his balcony—if not his bed? The lovers could meet. He could keep the watch at the foot of the stairs. If flight was called for, he would be the one to see them off on the bus.

Flight would take money. Money happened to be something he had. Every night he gave coins to Inez—Dolores had proved to have gaps in her memory—to buy cigarettes, ice cream in paper cups, or the Mexican type of popsicle with the stick that sometimes entitled the lucky consumer to another one free. Concepción preferred popsicles to paper cups. But what good was all that? Inez was too young to be an accomplice. Cowie was willing but helpless the weekend the carnival set up in the Plaza, with a small ferris wheel, three tent-size side shows, rings to be tossed, darts to be thrown. A music box that little Indians took turns cranking made a racket that was meant to be like a marimba, the pitch determined by the speed of the crank. The ferris wheel, a rig with six wagging compartments, wobbled dangerously when loaded, and brought the eyes of the spellbound merrymakers on the level of Cowie's. He appeared to them as a being from another world. Several times during the evening the motor stopped, leaving the passengers secure in heaven. This seemed better than the ride. They jeered and shouted taunts at the fools below. This was such an occasion that Inez, with Concepción as her escort, was given money to spend and allowed to walk in the Plaza. Both Señora Lopez and Cowie kept an eye on them. Whenever the child bought something she would turn and wave. The wobbly ferris wheel she was forbidden to ride, but she could eat ice cream, drink orange crush, throw darts at the balloons and wave to Cowie. Of Concepción Cowie saw only the eyes. Were they often directed at him? So he felt. This seemed to him strange since Dr. Carrillo sat, as usual, on the moist café terrace, drumming his nails on the table and rocking his glass of warm beer. It seemed to Cowie he lacked the Latin lover's temperament. Even Cowie felt the urge to mingle with the crowd, and brush close to her.

He had given Inez a bill to change so he would have small coins for the shrewd Dolores, and Inez had given this fistful of money to Concepción. Cowie saw this take place. Did it make his heart beat faster? It did. When Señora Lopez signalled them to return by rapping her fan on the balcony rail, Cowie's mouth went dry as if he were the lover himself. When she passed him the coins he must do, or say something. But what? He lacked the words. Perhaps he should simply blurt out the word *mañana*. Was there any doubt to lovers what such a word meant? The child Inez was the first to arrive, waving a balloon and a string of firecrackers she would have to wait for a fiesta day to shoot off. Concepción followed, and seemed to forget the money clutched in her hand until Cowie spoke to her. What did he say? Her name, not a word more. Admittedly, of course, it was not a common name. *Concepción.* So he called it, and she threw up her arms as in a seizure. Both arms! The one with the coins threw them with a clatter against the ceiling, from where they fell like a rain of silver on the floor. What a racket it made! Some rolled into the hallway, some reached the stairs. Not one single sound did she utter, nor did she seem to be aware of what had happened. While the coins were still falling and rolling she went off. Had she perhaps thought Cowie was asleep? Had he spoken out like a voice of the dead? God knows. What voice he had he lost. Nor could he sleep. As his eyes accustomed to the darkness he could see the silver coins in the corners: what did he think of? That ridiculous sand pile of his childhood. That first place where having lost something he had given up.

Thank God for the carnival down in the street nobody had heard the rain of coins, not even Dr. Carrillo who sat slouched as if asleep. The feeble, flickering bulbs on the ferris wheel seemed part of the sky they ornamented, a spiralling nebula operating on a coughing gasoline motor. The seats were vacant, however. The jeering revelers had run out of pesos. Not visible to Cowie, a reveler sang while he relieved himself at the foot of the stairwell, water-music with a strong Latin beat. Was it over so quickly? Somewhere he could hear the dry scratch of a faggot broom. Unobserved by Cowie Dr. Carrillo had got himself off. Was it in Cowie's head, or the floor, that the jukebox continued to throb? A faint buzzing persisted in his ears. So he had no idea, none, how long she had been standing in the hallway, or what it was that led him to turn his head. The doorway framed her. Was she clad in more than her hair? To Cowie's eye she wore only a cloak of light. He said nothing, dry-mouthed he sat there with his head twisted on his shoulders. She spoke his name, then came forward to take his head in her hands. With both hands she gripped his hair as if to lift his head from his shoulders, tipped it upward, and placed her lips on his mouth. And Cowie? Did he resist her? Or was this not the point where resistance ended? Of what was he conscious? Of the odor of the ointment. His mouth sealed he was obliged to breath through his nose. At the point of suffocation—or so it seemed—he gasped for air. A mistake: with the inhalation he recovered his powers of speech.

"Look—" he blurted, "Look, Dr. Carrillo—"

She gave a twist to his head to look at his face. What did she see there? His head was shaking. Perhaps she had in mind changing the expression. He felt that large gobs of his hair would pull out by the roots.

"Jaime?" she whispered, "*Jai*-me?"

Cowie was spared an answer. His head was wagging as if she meant to shake it off. She made no sound, not a one, except the panting her effort caused her, and the cart-like creak of the legs of the bed. When she released him Cowie felt most of his hair must be in her hands. But it wasn't. He saw they were pressed to her own face. In some child's book, luminous with moonlight and his own imagination, had Cowie seen, or had he merely dreamed of such a strange demon lover, her shame concealed from the world but revealed to herself. Was she weeping? No, merely gathering her forces. Her face thrust to almost touch his own, the scent of the ointment activated, she hissed into his face words that he mercifully couldn't fathom. Did she sense that? Perhaps. She added one more good in any language. "Bufff-*foooon!*" she cried, and again from the doorway, "Buf*foooooooooon!*" In his hair she left the strength of her fingers, on his lips the taste of her mouth, in his nostrils, alas, the talcum'd scent of her breasts.

Was that all? Anything can and often must pass as a love story. It is not what happens, which is always the same. It is what might have happened, which is always unique. Such details are important. They make it possible for unlikely people to be lovers. And who is likely? Not Harold Cowie. It is enough that we know that something *might* have happened. It is this that makes it easier for bachelors and spinsters to generate love stories than those who are married. Marriage is a custom. Love is a condition. Anybody who knows anything knows that. Customs are immortal but conditions change from hour to hour, from day to day. Who can believe, for example, in the love story of those who are married for half a century? It strains the mind. Worse, *there* they are. Old friends form a withered garland of age around them. Why must pictures be taken? It makes the dream of love impossible. If only *one* is there, never mind how absent, the missing beloved can be imagined. We can accept it as the gleam in the fading eye. Back there, way back there, something might have happened—just as it did in Matamoros. Back there when Concepción, Cowie and the Matamoros night were young.

That is where we left Cowie, still back there. Most of the night was still before him. It seemed a blank, however, strongly scented, until in the hills southwest of the city he heard the horn of the Oaxaca Puebla bus. The curves were bad. The driver tooted the horn and then trusted his luck. That night he was something more than three hours late. On such small things fate hangs if you are a person like Harold Cowie. The toot of the horn must be for him, who else? How otherwise explain the lateness of the bus? One could hardly believe it was Cowie who rose up like a man possessed. The horn that he heard might have been Gabriel's. His left foot, still sheltered by the cast, would not go into the shoe. Nor could he, with one hand still in a splint, tie the laces of the other. But all of that actually proved to be helpful: it saved him time. The odd shoe went into the pocket of his raincoat, and the coat went over pants, shirt and pajamas. Anywhere else a man in such disarray might be an object of interest, but not in Matamoros.

On the stairs, where he felt a touch of panic, Cowie bruised the toes sticking out of his cast. A strange sight they were, at the best, all of the nails still black. He was there on the corner, however, when the lights of the bus swept the street, the motor hammering like the rim of a flattened tire. Would they actually make it out of town? Cowie had his doubts. The bus driver knew him—night after night Cowie alone was awake to greet him. And now he was leaving? Cowie shook his head. No, no, he lied, just a trip to the doctor. The motor pounding like his heart, the bus left for Puebla.

Had there ever been such a night? Not in the life of Cowie. An hour before dawn the bus lights went off and they parked off the road waiting for the daylight. Nearby cocks crowed. The braying of a burro, it seemed to Cowie, expressed man's fate. A desperation no longer quiet lamented the very burden of living. But with the dawn the motor started, they went hammering off.

If he allowed himself to think, and he did, that Concepción's ointment concealed her true emotions, he was also aware of a disturbing ambivalence in his own. That way she raised her arms, fussing with her hair, the front of her blouse glistening with needles. How it was the light itself seemed to penetrate the pink lobes of her ears. If he could trust his memory he had often wondered how such a lobe would taste. Now he knew. Having the flavor of her lips in his mouth. If one saw only her eyes, they were nevertheless quite remarkable. Before he had grasped Dr. Carrillo's intentions, Cowie had sometimes thought, that is, he had been thinking, that a fine complexion was not quite all there was to a woman. Not some women. Not one like Concepción. Away with him he had taken the taste of her lips: back to her bed she had taken sample locks of his hair. Was it remorse he felt, or guilt? Or more plainly put, was it self-disgust? With the sun in his face Cowie's generous impulse to provide the poor girl with a suitable lover, was it little more than an artful dodge for Cowie himself? A way out. A respectable sensible way to give up. That was perhaps too strong—but it crossed the mind he took some pride in keeping open. Cowie the artful dodger. The pajama-clad lover who fled under the cover of night. Would Dr. Jaime Carrillo, the crippled rebel, have gone off down the stairs with one shoe in his pocket? the talcum of the lover's breasts powdering his nose? That seemed unlikely. That was a talent more often found north of the border. Hopefully, as they approached Puebla, Cowie waited for fate to save him from himself, for the Matamoros law, or the next of kin, horsemen with masks like Pancho Villa, to come across the landscape like a dust cloud, halt the bus, and kidnap Cowie. That fate seemed attractive, but he didn't deserve it. Nothing happened. They arrived in Puebla four hours late. It seemed only just that Cowie would be seized by the uniformed Indians who stood there, smoking, or by the gentleman who plainly carried a pistol under his coat. No one could fail to recognize Cowie, but neither did anyone seem to care to. He ate tortillas, drank warm Carta Blanca, and listened to a concert on the marimba. The bus for Mexico City carried him off. From the P.O. station behind Sanborn's restaurant he sent a money order to cover his bill to Señorita Concepción Lopez folded in a sheet of paper on which he had written *Adios*, and signed it Buffoon.

commentary

In a letter of November 7, 1964, Wright Morris discussed the following problem:

> The climax proved to be crucial—a highly unorthodox latin romance. This had to be resolved within the scene itself (one version) and in terms of the demands of the novel (the final version). As I note, I was helped, rather than hindered, by the development of the story. This persuaded me to recast the love scene, and I feel that the scene itself profits.

The first version of the climax of the Matamoros episode occurred during the second draft. It may be summarized briefly. Wearing only a nightshift, Concepción enters Cowie's room. She asks if the night does not "make the ugly beautiful," and he nods. After running her hand through his hair and putting her lips to his mouth, she departs. We are told that their love story is strange. She would come to ravish him often, stimulating a "streak of lechery" he attributes to "the southern climate, the strangeness of the night, and the beloved's latin temperament." Then, when Cowie has affected a hobble enabling him to remain in Matamoros, Concepción abandons him, which he interprets as a change of luck due to her having taken his "measure." Of this version, Mr. Morris wrote:

> . . . I am still free to resolve the scene within its own terms. (I do not as yet know what the future holds for Cowie) As the result testifies, this is more of a hindrance than a help. My sense of the scene is better (I know what it will take) when I know Cowie better.

That Mr. Morris had come to "know Cowie better" by the time he composed the second version of the climax of the Matamoros episode is clear from a synopsis of its action. The author sets the scene through references to the nightshift, Ixtclaccihuatl, and los aires. We see Concepción and her mother sewing and we learn Dr. Carrillo's "sermons" are directed toward them and a younger sister, Lupita. Concepción impresses Cowie as particularly attentive. This leads him to feel that his automobile "accident" has been neither meaningless nor altogether destructive. He will free these lovers from their "spell," from local social taboos by providing vigilance and a place to rendezvous. But first he must "tip off" the "shy beloved," which can best be done at night. Then a carnival arrives and Cowie, watching Concepción and Lupita stroll past Dr. Carrillo, becomes more and *more convinced that the "accident" of his presence will cause everyone to "accept the inevitable." Later, Concepción squeezes his hand, but he misinterprets her advance as a token of awareness. A passage ensues describing nocturnal noises and desolation. "What event, what accident," Cowie wonders, could be delaying the last bus. The sudden appearance of Concepción supplies the answer. Attired in only "a cloak of light," she kisses him. He gasps for air, stammers, "but Carrillo, Dr. Carrillo!" She shakes his head angrily, shouts "Buffooooon!" and exits. We discover that both Cowie's "generous act" and "flight" are "artful" dodges. "Fate" does not intervene to "save him from himself," so he sends back a money order "to generously cover his expenses."*

The all-encompassing difference between the two versions is a structural one. While the first begins with Concepción's initial visit and moves on to her subsequent ravishments and ultimate desertion of Cowie, the second builds up very slowly to an abortive seduction, then gives considerable space to Cowie's desertion of Concepción. The new material establishes a fuller, more definitive main character. In the first version, Cowie is physically passive; he rationalizes his physical desires; he feels unlucky. But in the second version these traits—altered, expanded, and deepened—become inextricable. A spiritually as well as physically passive Cowie disguises a spiritual as well as physical attraction to Concepción by romanticizing himself into a sort of knight destined to free her and her lover, who are under a "spell." When the truth of their feelings and his can no longer be ignored, he flees, realizing that he is a fool.

The structural difference between the two second-draft versions of the ending which enabled Mr. Morris to alter, expand, and deepen certain elements of his anti-hero's makeup was in turn the result of having come to "know Cowie better." The love scene—"recast" to embody "the development of the story" and to conform to "the demands of the novel"—is a good example of the fictional part shaped by the fictional whole. "A loner" like the assassin Lee Harvey Oswald, Cowie gave up when merely a child because his pet chameleon disappeared in a sandpile. "The inventor of the meaningful accident," he understands that the murder of President Kennedy expresses impotence, that Oswald has displaced a man "who could act" and "who represented the maximum of human connections." But if the impotence of Oswald and another important figure, Alec Cartwright, leads to protests with anarchic results, Cowie's takes

characterization, structure, & setting

the form of an equally destructive aloofness which the Matamoros episode and its climax dramatize.

Besides the details of the opening passage, the fresh material in the two later versions on the carnival, the evening, the money, and the flight creates a more specific setting whose atmosphere is now grotesquely comic. More important, these details also reflect the principal character's situation and state of mind.

The Published Version eliminated two rather significant aspects of the natural setting from the opening passage of the second version—"the white dome of Ixtclaccihuatl" and los aires—while elaborating on the idea of Matamoros as a tomb. In addition, it intensified and clarified the sewing-harangue tableau, which shows Cowie's ambivalent feelings of attraction and repulsion toward Concepción.

Both later versions emphasize the ferris wheel, since the ferris wheel most vividly exhibits the symbolic relationship between Cowie and the carnival. A passive observer, "a being from another world," he is a sort of freak experiencing a nightmare. And both versions further particularize the environment with details of the evening, but the sole objects among these that reveal Cowie's psyche—"the bent hands of the clock" and "his watch"—appear only in the second.

The money material which accompanies the carnival material belongs directly to the ending's revised structure, for it treats the lovers' involvement through action. Nevertheless, this action does enable Mr. Morris to present various aspects of the Plaza, including the café where Dr. Carrillo sits.

While the flight material, as rendered in the second version, is also devoted to showing Cowie's makeup by means of action, the Published Version adds to this structural dimension the dimension of place. Thus, the bus horn "might have been Gabriel's" and the burro's braying "expressed man's fate." Following these properties of the natural setting, which voice the anti-hero's fatalism, is a token of the social setting: "Cowie waited for fate to save him from himself, for the Matamoros law, or the next of kin, horsemen with masks like Pancho Villa, to come across the landscape like a cloud of dust. . . ."

Finally, a number of changes with no direct bearing on the interdependence of characterization, structure, and setting in the climax of the Matamoros episode should be mentioned. Dolores of the first version has been dropped in the second version, where Lupita (Inez) appears and where Concepción, Dr. Carrillo, and Señora Lopez play larger roles. Two additions between the second and the Published Version should also be mentioned. One, taken from the novel as a whole, is the reference to "that ridiculous sand pile" of Cowie's childhood, "that first place where having lost something he had given up." The other, based upon the allusion to "love stories" in the original ending, is the long digression concerning "what might have happened."

VI

characterization, structure, & symbolism

F. Scott Fitzgerald

F. Scott Fitzgerald was born in St. Paul, Minnesota, on September 24, 1896, and died in Hollywood, California, on December 21, 1940. He attended Princeton University from September, 1913, to October, 1917, without graduating. His works include This Side of Paradise *(1920),* Flappers and Philosophers *(1920),* The Beautiful and Damned *(1922),* Tales of the Jazz Age *(1922),* The Vegetable *(1923),* The Great Gatsby *(1925),* All the Sad Young Men *(1926),* Tender Is the Night *(1934),* Taps at Reveille *(1935), and* The Last Tycoon *(1941).*

The holograph or pencil draft of the author's masterwork, The Great Gatsby, *is among the F. Scott Fitzgerald Papers at the Princeton University Library. There are many differences between Chapter I in it and Chapter I in the first edition published by Charles Scribner's Sons, but the most important involves the paragraph concerning the "Dutch sailors' eyes" and the paragraph concerning "the dark fields of the republic." Before Fitzgerald finished the pencil draft, he had transposed the chapter's ending to the ending of the entire novel. Among the results of this structural change are a sharper and richer characterization of Nick and Gatsby and an expansion into greater symbolic significance of the iterative or recurrent image, green light.*

THE GREAT GATSBY

Chapter I

In my younger and more vulnerable years my father told me something that I've been turning over in my mind ever since.

"When you feel like critisizing anyone," he said, "just remember that everyone in this world hasn't had the advantages that you've had.

He didn't say anymore but we've always been unusually communicative in a reserved way and I understood that he meant a great deal more than that. In consequence I'm inclined to reserve all judgements, a habit that has opened up many curious natures to me and also made me the victim of not a few collossal bores. The abnormal mind is quick to detect and attach itself to this quality when it appears in a normal person, and so it came about that in college I was unjustly accused of being of politician, because I was privy to the secret griefs of wild, unknown men. Most of the confidences were unsought--frequently I have fiegned sleep, preoccupation or a hostile levity when I realized by some unmistakeable sign that an intimate revelation was quivering on the horizon--for the intimate revelations of young men or at any rate the terms in which they express them vary no more than the heavenly messages which reach us over the psychic radio. Reserving judgements is a matter of infinite hope. I am still a little afraid of missing something if I forget that, as my father snobbishly suggested and I snobbishly repeat, a sense of the fundamental decencies is parcelled out unequeally at birth.

And, after boasting this way of my tolerance, I come to the admission that it has a limit. Conduct may be founded on the hard rock or the wet marshes but after a certain point I don't care what it's founded on. When I

The Great Gatsby

CHAPTER ONE

In my younger and more vulnerable years my father gave me some advice that I've been turning over in my mind ever since.

"Whenever you feel like criticising any one," he told me, "just remember that all the people in this world haven't had the advantages that you've had."

He didn't say any more, but we've always been unusually communicative in a reserved way, and I understood that he meant a great deal more than that. In consequence, I'm inclined to reserve all judgments, a habit that has opened up many curious natures to me and also made me the victim of not a few veteran bores. The abnormal mind is quick to detect and attach itself to this quality when it appears in a normal person, and so it came about that in college I was unjustly accused of being a politician, because I was privy to the secret griefs of wild, unknown men. Most of the confidences were unsought—frequently I have feigned sleep, preoccupation, or a hostile levity when I realized by some unmistakable sign that an intimate revelation was quivering on the horizon; for the intimate revelations of young men, or at least the terms in which they express them, are usually plagiaristic and marred by obvious suppressions. Reserving judgments is a matter of infinite hope. I am still a little afraid of missing something if I forget that, as my father snobbishly suggested, and I snobbishly repeat, a sense of the fundamental decencies is parcelled out unequally at birth.

And, after boasting this way of my tolerence, I come to the admission that it has a limit. Conduct may be founded on the hard rock or the wet marshes, but after a certain point I don't care what

came back here from the east last autumn I felt that I wanted the world to be in uniform and at a sort of moral attention forever; I wanted no more riotous excursions with priveledged glimpses into the human heart. It was only Gatsby himself that was exempted from my reaction, Gatsby who represented everything for which I have an unaffected scorn. There was, after all, something gorgeous about him, some heightened sensitivity to things as if he were related to one of those intricate machines that register earthquakes ten thousand miles away This sensitivity had nothing to with that flabby unethical impressionability which is dignified under the name of the "creative temperment"--I have always felt the same disgust toward the artist that I do for that other nessessary evil, the garbage man--it was an extraordinary aliveness to life, an alert vitality such as I have never found in any human person and which it is not likely I shall ever find again. No--Gatsby turned out all right at the end; it is what preyed on Gatsby, what foul dust floated in the wake of his dreams that temporarily closed out my interest in the abortive sorrows and unjustified elations of men.

My family have been substantial people here in this middle-western city for three generations. The Carraways are something of a clan and we have a tradition that we're decended from the Dukes of Buccleuch, but the actual founder of my line was my grandfather's brother who came here in '51, sent a substitute to the civil war and started the wholesale hardware business that my father carries on today.

I never saw this great-uncle but I'm supposed to look like him--with special reference to the rather hard-boiled painting that hangs in father's office. I graduated from New Haven in 1915, just a quarter of a century after my father, and a little later I participated in that delayed Teutonic migration known as the great war. I enjoyed the raid so thoroughly that I came back restless. Instead of being the warm center of the world the middle-west now seemed like the ragged edge of the universe--so I decided the go East and enter the bond business. Everybody I knew was in the bond business so I suppossed it ought to be able to support one more man. All my aunts and uncles talked it over as if they were choosing a prep-school for me and finally said "Why--yes" with very grave, hesitant faces. Father agreed to finance me for a year and after various delays I came east, permanently, I thought, in the spring of twenty-one.

it's founded on. When I came back from the East last autumn I felt that I wanted the world to be in uniform and at a sort of moral attention forever; I wanted no more riotous excursions with privileged glimpses into the human heart. Only Gatsby, the man who gives his name to this book, was exempt from my reaction—Gatsby, who represented everything for which I have an unaffected scorn. If personality is an unbroken series of successful gestures, then there was something gorgeous about him, some heightened sensitivity to the promises of life, as if he were related to one of those intricate machines that register earthquakes ten thousand miles away. This responsiveness had nothing to do with that flabby impressionability which is dignified under the name of the "creative temperament"—it was an extraordinary gift for hope, a romantic readiness such as I have never found in any other person and which it is not likely I shall ever find again. No—Gatsby turned out all right at the end; it is what preyed on Gatsby, what foul dust floated in the wake of his dreams that temporarily closed out my interest in the abortive sorrows and short-winded elations of men.

My family have been prominent, well-to-do people in this Middle Western city for three generations. The Carraways are something of a clan, and we have a tradition that we're descended from the Dukes of Buccleuch, but the actual founder of my line was my grandfather's brother, who came here in fifty-one, sent a substitute to the Civil War, and started the wholesale hardware business that my father carries on to-day.

I never saw this great-uncle, but I'm supposed to look like him—with special reference to the rather hard-boiled painting that hangs in father's office. I graduated from New Haven in 1915, just a quarter of a century after my father, and a little later I participated in that delayed Teutonic migration known as the Great War. I enjoyed the counter-raid so thoroughly that I came back restless. Instead of being the warm centre of the world, the Middle West now seemed like the ragged edge of the universe—so I decided to go East and learn the bond business. Everybody I knew was in the bond business, so I supposed it could support one more single man. All my aunts and uncles talked it over as if they were choosing a prep school for me, and finally said, "Why—ye-es," with very grave, hesitant faces. Father agreed to finance me for a year, and after various delays I came East, permanently, I thought, in the spring of twenty-two.

The natural thing was to find rooms in the city but it was a warm season and I had just left a country of wide lawns and friendly trees, so when a young man at the office suggested that we take a house together in a commuting town I jumped at the idea. He found the house, a weather beaten cardboard bungalow at a hundred a month, but at the last minute the firm ordered him to Washington and I went out to the country alone. I had a dog, at least I had him for a few days until he ran away, and an old Dodge and a Finnish woman who made my bed and cooked breakfast and dinner and muttered Finnish proverbs to herself over the 1906 electric stove.

And so with the sunshine and the great bursts of leaves growing on the trees--just like things grow in fast movies--I had that familiar conviction that life was beginning over again with the summer. There was so much to read for instance and so much fine health to be pulled down out of the young breath-giving air. I bought a dozen volumes on money and banking and investment securities and they stood on my shelf in red and gold like new money from the mint, promising to unfold the shining secrets that only Morgan and Midas and Maecenus knew. And I had the honorable intention of reading many other books besides. I was rather literary in college--one year I wrote a series of very solemn and absurd editorials for the Yale News--and now I was going to bring back all such things into my life and become again that most limited of all specialists, the "well-rounded" man.

It was entirely a matter of chance that I should have rented a house in one of the strangest communities in North America. It was on that slender riotous Island which extends itself due east of New York and where there are, among other natural curiosities, two unusual formations of land. Twenty miles from the city a pair of enormous eggs, identical in contour and separated only by a courtesy bay, jut out into the most domesticated body of salt water in the Western hemisphere, Long Island Sound. They are not perfect ovals--like the egg in the Columbus story they are both crushed flat at the contact end--but their physical resemblance must be a scource of perpetual wonder to the gulls that fly overhead. To the earth dwellers a more amazing phenomenon is the dissimilarity they manifest in every way except shape and size

The practical thing was to find rooms in the city, but it was a warm season, and I had just left a country of wide lawns and friendly trees, so when a young man at the office suggested that we take a house together in a commuting town, it sounded like a great idea. He found the house, a weatherbeaten cardboard bungalow at eighty a month, but at the last minute the firm ordered him to Washington, and I went out to the country alone. I had a dog—at least I had him for a few days until he ran away—and an old Dodge and a Finnish woman, who made my bed and cooked breakfast and muttered Finnish wisdom to herself over the electric stove.

It was lonely for a day or so until one morning some man, more recently arrived than I, stopped me on the road.

"How do you get to West Egg village?" he asked helplessly.

I told him. And as I walked on I was lonely no longer. I was a guide, a pathfinder, an original settler. He had casually conferred on me the freedom of the neighborhood.

And so with the sunshine and the great bursts of leaves growing on the trees, just as things grow in fast movies, I had that familiar conviction that life was beginning over again with the summer.

There was so much to read, for one thing, and so much fine health to be pulled down out of the young breath-giving air. I bought a dozen volumes on banking and credit and investment securities, and they stood on my shelf in red and gold like new money from the mint, promising to unfold the shining secrets that only Midas and Morgan and Mæcenas knew. And I had the high intention of reading many other books besides. I was rather literary in college—one year I wrote a series of very solemn and obvious editorials for the Yale News—and now I was going to bring back all such things into my life and become again that most limited of all specialists, the "well-rounded man." This isn't just an epigram—life is much more successfully looked at from a single window, after all.

It was a matter of chance that I should have rented a house in one of the strangest communities in North America. It was on that slender riotous island which extends itself due east of New York—and where there are, among other natural curiosities, two unusual formations of land. Twenty miles from the city a pair of enormous eggs, identical in contour and separated only by a courtesy bay, jut out into the most domesticated body of salt water in the Western hemisphere, the great wet barnyard of Long Island Sound. They are not perfect ovals—like the egg in the Columbus story, they are both crushed flat at the contact end—but their physical resemblance must be a source of perpetual wonder to the gulls that fly overhead. To the wingless a more interesting phenomenon is their dissimilarity in every particular except shape and size.

I lived at West Egg, the--well, the less fashionable of the two, though this is a most superficial tag to express the bizarre and not a little sinister contrast between them. My house was at the very tip of the egg, only a hundred yards from the sound, and squeezed between two huge places that rented for twelve or fifteen thousand a season. The one on my right was a collosal affair by any standard--it was a factual imitation of some Hotel de Ville in Normandy! with a tower on one side, spanking new under a thin beard of raw ivy, and a marble swimming pool and more than forty acres of lawn and garden. It is was Gatsby's mansion. Or rather, as I didn't know Gatsby yet it was a mansion inhabited by a gentleman of that name. My own house was an eye-sore, but it was a small eye-sore and it had been overlooked, so I had a view of the water, a partial view of my neighbors lawn and the consoling proximity of millionaires--all for fifty dollars a month.

Across the courtesy bay the white palaces of fashionable East Egg glittered along the water and the history of the summer really begins on the evening I drove over there to have dinner with the Tom Buchanan's. Daisy Buchanan was a cousin of mine and I'd known Tom in college. And once just after the war I spent a week with them in Chicago.

Her husband, among various physical accomplishments, had been one of the most powerful ends that ever played football at New Haven--a national figure in a way, one of those men that reach such an accute limited excellence at twenty that everything afterwards savours of anti-climax. His family were enormously wealthy--even in college his spending capacity was a matter of scandal--but now he'd left Chicago and come East in a fashion that rather took your breath way: for instance he'd casually brought down a string of polo ponies from Lake Forest. It was hard to realize that a man in my own generation was wealthy enough to do that.

Why they came east I don't know. They had spent a year in France, for no particular reason, and then drifted here and there unrestfully wherever polo was played and people were rich together. This was a permanent move Daisy said over the telephone, but I didn't believe it--I had no sight into Daisy's heart but I felt that Tom would drift on forever seeking a little wistfully for the dramatic turbulence of some irrecoverable football game.

F. Scott Fitzgerald

I lived at West Egg, the—well, the less fashionable of the two, though this is a most superficial tag to express the bizarre and not a little sinister contrast between them. My house was at the very tip of the egg, only fifty yards from the Sound, and squeezed between two huge places that rented for twelve or fifteen thousand a season. The one on my right was a colossal affair by any standard—it was a factual imitation of some Hôtel de Ville in Normandy, with a tower on one side, spanking new under a thin beard of raw ivy, and a marble swimming pool, and more than forty acres of lawn and garden. It was Gatsby's mansion. Or, rather, as I didn't know Mr. Gatsby, it was a mansion inhabited by a gentleman of that name. My own house was an eyesore, but it was a small eyesore, and it had been overlooked, so I had a view of the water, a partial view of my neighbor's lawn, and the consoling proximity of millionaires—all for eighty dollars a month.

Across the courtesy bay the white palaces of fashionable East Egg glittered along the water, and the history of the summer really begins on the evening I drove over there to have dinner with the Tom Buchanans. Daisy was my second cousin once removed, and I'd known Tom in college. And just after the war I spent two days with them in Chicago.

Her husband, among various physical accomplishments, had been one of the most powerful ends that ever played football at New Haven—a national figure in a way, one of those men who reach such an acute limited excellence at twenty-one that everything afterward savors of anti-climax. His family were enormously wealthy—even in college his freedom with money was a matter for reproach—but now he'd left Chicago and come East in a fashion that rather took your breath away: for instance, he'd brought down a string of polo ponies from Lake Forest. It was hard to realize that a man in my own generation was wealthy enough to do that.

Why they came East I don't know. They had spent a year in France for no particular reason, and then drifted here and there unrestfully wherever people played polo and were rich together. This was a permanent move, said Daisy over the telephone, but I didn't believe it—I had no sight into Daisy's heart, but I felt that Tom would drift on forever seeking, a little wistfully, for the dramatic turbulence of some irrecoverable football game.

characterization, structure, & symbolism

And so it happened that on a warm windy evening I drove over to East Egg to see two old friends who, in reality, I scarcely knew at all. Their house was even more elaborate than I expected, a great, cheerful red and white Georgian Colonial mansion overlooking the bay. The lawn started at the beach and ran toward his front door for a quarter of mile, jumping over sun-dials and brick walks and burning gardens--finally when it reached the house drifting up the side in bright vines as though by the momentum of its run. The front was broken by a line of French windows, glowing now with reflected gold, and wide open to the warm windy afternoon, and Tom Buchanan in riding clothes was standing with his legs apart on the front porch.

He had changed since his New Haven years. Now he was a sturdy, straw haired man of thirty with a rather hard mouth and a supercillious manner. Two shining, arrogant eyes had established dominence over his face and gave him the appearance of always leaning aggressively forward. Not even the effeminate swank of his riding clothes could hide the enormous power of that body--he seemed to fill those glistening boots until he strained the top lacing and you could see a great pack of muscle shifting when his shoulder moved under his thin coat. It was a body capable of enormous leverage--a cruel body.

His speaking voice, a gruff husky tenor, added to the impression of fractiousness he conveyed. There was a touch of paternal contempt in it, even toward people he liked--and there were men at New Haven who had hated his guts, to speak crudely. We were in the same Senior Society and while we were never intimate I always had the impression that he approved of me and wanted me to like him with some harsh, defiant wistfulness of his own.

We talked for a few minutes on the sunny porch.

"I've got a nice place here," he said, his eyes flashing about restlessly.

Turning me around with one arm he moved a broad flat hand along the front vista, including in its sweep a sunken Italien garden, a half acre of deep pungent roses and a snub-nosed motor boat that bumped the tide off shore.

"It belonged to Demaine the oil man." He turned me around again, politely and abruptly. "We'll go inside."

We walked with insistent steps through a high hallway and into a bright rosy colored space, fragily bound into

And so it happened that on a warm windy evening I drove over to East Egg to see two old friends whom I scarcely knew at all. Their house was even more elaborate than I expected, a cheerful red-and-white Georgian Colonial mansion, overlooking the bay. The lawn started at the beach and ran toward the front door for a quarter of a mile, jumping over sun-dials and brick walls and burning gardens—finally when it reached the house drifting up the side in bright vines as though from the momentum of its run. The front was broken by a line of French windows, glowing now with reflected gold and wide open to the warm windy afternoon, and Tom Buchanan in riding clothes was standing with his legs apart on the front porch.

He had changed since his New Haven years. Now he was a sturdy straw-haired man of thirty with a rather hard mouth and a supercilious manner. Two shining arrogant eyes had established dominance over his face and gave him the appearance of always leaning aggressively forward. Not even the effeminate swank of his riding clothes could hide the enormous power of that body—he seemed to fill those glistening boots until he strained the top lacing, and you could see a great pack of muscle shifting when his shoulder moved under his thin coat. It was a body capable of enormous leverage—a cruel body.

His speaking voice, a gruff husky tenor, added to the impression of fractiousness he conveyed. There was a touch of paternal contempt in it, even toward people he liked—and there were men at New Haven who had hated his guts.

"Now, don't think my opinion on these matters is final," he seemed to say, "just because I'm stronger and more of a man than you are." We were in the same senior society, and while we were never intimate I always had the impression that he approved of me and wanted me to like him with some harsh, defiant wistfulness of his own.

We talked for a few minutes on the sunny porch.

"I've got a nice place here," he said, his eyes flashing about restlessly.

Turning me around by one arm, he moved a broad flat hand along the front vista, including in its sweep a sunken Italian garden, a half acre of deep, pungent roses, and a snub-nosed motor-boat that bumped the tide offshore.

"It belonged to Demaine, the oil man." He turned me around again, politely and abruptly. "We'll go inside."

We walked through a high hallway into a bright rosy-colored space, fragilely bound into the house by French windows at either

the house by French windows at either end. The windows were ajar and gleaming white against the fresh grass outside that seemed to grow a little way into the house. A breeze blew through the room, blew curtains in at one end and out the other like pale flags, twisting them up toward the frosted wedding cake of the cieling.--and then rippling over the wine-colored rug, making a shadow on it as wind does on the sea

The only completely stationary object in the room seemed to be a enormous couch on which two young women were buoyed up as though upon an anchored balloon. They were both in white and their dresses were rippling and fluttering as if they had just been blown back in after a short flight around the house. I must have stood for a few moments on the threshold, dazzled by the alabaster light, listening to the whip and snap of the curtains and the groan of a picture on the wall. Then there was a boom as Tom Buchanan shut the rear windows and the caught wind died out about the room and the curtains and the rugs and the two young woman ballooned slowly to the floor.

One of the two young women I had never seen before. She was extended full length at her end of the divan, completely motionless and with her chin raised a little as if she were balancing something on it which was quite likely to fall. If she saw me out of the corner of her eyes she gave no hint of it--indeed I was almost surprised into murmuring an apology for having disturbed her by coming in at all.

The other girl--it was Daisy--made an attempt to rise--she leaned forward slightly with a conscientious expression on her face--then she laughed, an absurd, charming little laugh, and I laughed too and came forward into the room.

"And so Nick just trotted down East looking for a high old time. Didn't he."

She laughed again as if she had said something very witty and held my hand for a moment, looking up into my face, promising that there was no one in the world she so much wanted to see. That was a way she had. She hinted in a murmur that the name of the balancing girl was Baker. I've heard it said that Daisy's murmur was only to make people lean toward her; an irrelevent critisism that made it no less charming.

end. The windows were ajar and gleaming white against the fresh grass outside that seemed to grow a little way into the house. A breeze blew through the room, blew curtains in at one end and out the other like pale flags, twisting them up toward the frosted wedding-cake of the ceiling, and then rippled over the wine-colored rug, making a shadow on it as wind does on the sea.

The only completely stationary object in the room was an enormous couch on which two young women were buoyed up as though upon an anchored balloon. They were both in white, and their dresses were rippling and fluttering as if they had just been blown back in after a short flight around the house. I must have stood for a few moments listening to the whip and snap of the curtains and the groan of a picture on the wall. Then there was a boom as Tom Buchanan shut the rear windows and the caught wind died out about the room, and the curtains and the rugs and the two young women ballooned slowly to the floor.

The younger of the two was a stranger to me. She was extended full length at her end of the divan, completely motionless, and with her chin raised a little, as if she were balancing something on it which was quitely likely to fall. If she saw me out of the corner of her eyes she gave no hint of it—indeed, I was almost surprised into murmuring an apology for having disturbed her by coming in.

The other girl, Daisy, made an attempt to rise—she leaned slightly forward with a conscientious expression—then she laughed, an absurd, charming little laugh, and I laughed too and came forward into the room.

"I'm p-paralyzed with happiness."

She laughed again, as if she said something very witty, and held my hand for a moment, looking up into my face, promising that there was no one in the world she so much wanted to see. That was a way she had. She hinted in a murmur that the surname of the balancing girl was Baker. (I've heard it said that Daisy's murmur was only to make people lean toward her; an irrelevant criticism that made it no less charming.)

characterization, structure, & symbolism

At any rate Miss Baker's lips fluttered, she nodded at me almost imperceptibly and then tipped her head quickly back again--for the object she was balancing had obviously tottered a little and given her something of a fright. Again a sort of apology arose to my lips. Almost any exhibition of complete self sufficiency draws a stunned tribute from me.

I looked back at my cousin who began to ask me questions in her low, thrilling voice. It was the kind of voice that the ear followed up and down as if each speech was an arrangement of notes that would never be played again. Her face was sad and lovely with bright things in it, bright eyes and a bright passionate mouth--but there was an excitement in her voice that men who had cared for her found difficult to forget: a singing compulsion, a whispered "Listen", a promise that she had done gay exciting things just a while since and that there were gay, exciting things hovering in the next hour.

I told her how I had stopped off in Chicago for two days on my way east and how a dozen people had sent her "love" through me.

"And kisses too," she cried exstaticly.

"Kisses too. The whole town is desolate. All the cars have the left rear wheel painted black as a mourning wreath and a persistent wail can be heard all night along the north shore."

"How gorgeous! Let's go back, Tom--tomorrow." Then she added, "You ought to see the baby."

"I'd like to."

"She's asleep. She's three years old. Havn't you ever seen her?"

"Never."

"Well, you ought to see her. She's--"

Tom Buchanan who had been hovering restlessly about the room stopped near me and rested his hand on my shoulder.

"What you doing, Nick?"

"I'm a bond man."

"Who with?"

I told him

"Never heard of them," he remarked decisively.

This annoyed me.

"You will," I answered shortly, "You will if you stay in the East."

At any rate, Miss Baker's lips fluttered, she nodded at me almost imperceptibly, and then quickly tipped her head back again—the object she was balancing had obviously tottered a little and given her something of a fright. Again a sort of apology arose to my lips. Almost any exhibition of complete self-sufficiency draws a stunned tribute from me.

I looked back at my cousin, who began to ask me questions in her low, thrilling voice. It was the kind of voice that the ear follows up and down, as if each speech is an arrangement of notes that will never be played again. Her face was sad and lovely with bright things in it, bright eyes and a bright passionate mouth, but there was an excitement in her voice that men who had cared for her found difficult to forget: a singing compulsion, a whispered "Listen," a promise that she had done gay, exciting things just a while since and that there were gay, exciting things hovering in the next hour.

I told her how I had stopped off in Chicago for a day on my way East, and how a dozen people had sent their love through me.

"Do they miss me?" she cried ecstatically.

"The whole town is desolate. All the cars have the left rear wheel painted black as a mourning wreath, and there's a persistent wail all night along the north shore."

"How gorgeous! Let's go back, Tom. To-morrow!" Then she added irrelevantly: "You ought to see the baby."

"I'd like to."

"She's asleep. She's three years old. Haven't you ever seen her?"

"Never."

"Well, you ought to see her. She's——"

Tom Buchanan, who had been hovering restlessly about the room, stopped and rested his hand on my shoulder.

"What you doing, Nick?"

"I'm a bond man."

"Who with?"

I told him.

"Never heard of them," he remarked decisively.

This annoyed me.

"You will," I answered shortly. "You will if you stay in the East."

"Oh, I'll stay in the East, don't you worry," he said, glancing at Daisy and then back at me as if he were alert for something more. "I'd be a God Damn fool to live anywhere else."

At this point Miss Baker said "Absolutely!" with such suddenness that I started--it was the first word she had uttered since I came into the room. Evidently it surprised her as much as it did me, for she sighed, let fall the invisible billiard cue she had been balancing and with a series of rapid, deft movements stood up into the room.

"I'm stiff," she complained, "I've been lieing on that sofa for as long as I can remember."

"Don't look at me," Daisy retorted, "I've been trying to get you to New York all afternoon.

"No thanks," said Miss Baker to the four cocktails just in from the pantry, "I'm absolutely in training.

Her host looked at scornfully.

"Yes, you are!" He took down his drink as if it were a drop in the bottom of a glass, "How <u>you</u> ever get anything done is beyond me."

I looked at Miss Baker wondering what it was that she "got done." I enjoyed looking at her. She was a slender, small-breasted girl with an erect carriage which she accentuated by throwing her body backward at the shoulders like a young cadet. Her grey sun-strained eyes glanced at me with polite reciprocal curiosity out of a wan, charming discontented face. It occurred to me now that I had seen her, or a picture of her, somewhere before.

"If you live in West Egg," she remarked contemptuously, "you know Gatsby."

"Gatsby?" demanded Daisy, "What Gatsby?"

Before I could reply that he was my neighbor dinner was announced in a solemn whisper and wedging his tense arm imperatively under mine Tom Buchanan compelled me from the room as though he were moving a checker to another square.

Slenderly, languidly, their hands set lightly on their hips the two young women preceeded us out onto a rosy-colored porch open to the sunset where four candles flickered on the dinner table in the diminished wind.

"Why <u>candles</u>?" objected Daisy frowning. She snapped them out with her fingers, "Why, in two weeks it'll be the longest day in the year." She looked at us all radiantly, "Do you always watch for the longest day of the year and then miss it? I always watch for the longest day in the year and then miss it."

“Oh, I’ll stay in the East, don’t you worry,” he said, glancing at Daisy and then back at me, as if he were alert for something more. “I’d be a God damned fool to live anywhere else.”

F. Scott Fitzgerald

At this point Miss Baker said: “Absolutely!” with such suddenness that I started—it was the first word she had uttered since I came into the room. Evidently it surprised her as much as it did me, for she yawned and with a series of rapid, deft movements stood up into the room.

“I’m stiff,” she complained, “I’ve been lying on that sofa for as long as I can remember.”

“Don’t look at me,” Daisy retorted, “I’ve been trying to get you to New York all afternoon.”

“No, thanks,” said Miss Baker to the four cocktails just in from the pantry, “I’m absolutely in training.”

Her host looked at her incredulously.

“You are!” He took down his drink as if it were a drop in the bottom of a glass. “How you ever get anything done is beyond me.”

I looked at Miss Baker, wondering what it was she “got done.” I enjoyed looking at her. She was a slender, small-breasted girl, with an erect carriage, which she accentuated by throwing her body backward at the shoulders like a young cadet. Her gray sun-strained eyes looked back at me with polite reciprocal curiosity out of a wan, charming, discontented face. It occurred to me now that I had seen her, or a picture of her, somewhere before.

“You live in West Egg,” she remarked contemptuously. “I know somebody there.”

“I don’t know a single——”

“You must know Gatsby.”

“Gatsby?” demanded Daisy. “What Gatsby?”

Before I could reply that he was my neighbor dinner was announced; wedging his tense arm imperatively under mine, Tom Buchanan compelled me from the room as though he were moving a checker to another square.

Slenderly, languidly, their hands set lightly on their hips, the two young women preceded us out onto a rosy-colored porch, open toward the sunset, where four candles flickered on the table in the diminished wind.

“Why *candles?*” objected Daisy, frowning. She snapped them out with her fingers. “In two weeks it’ll be the longest day in the year.” She looked at us all radiantly. “Do you always watch for the longest day of the year and then miss it? I always watch for the longest day in the year and then miss it.”

"We ought to plan something," yawned Miss Baker, sitting down at the table as if she were going to bed.

"All right," said Daisy, "What'll we plan?" She turned to me helplessly, "What do people plan?"

Before I could answer she fastened her eyes with an awed expression on her own little finger.

"Look," she exclaimed, "I hurt it."

We all looked--the knuckle was black and blue.

"You did it, Tom," she said accusingly, "I know you didn't mean to but you did do it. That's what I get for marrying a brute of a man, a savage, a great big hulking physical speciment of a--of a man."

"Rain tomorrow," said Miss Baker raising her eyebrows at the scalloped sky, "I'll bet you twenty-five dollars, Tom".

"I'll bet you seven-eighty," said Daisy, "that Tom owes me, the great big hulking--"

"I hate that word hulking," objected Tom crossly, "even in kidding."

"Hulking," insisted Daisy.

Sometimes she and Miss Baker talked at once, unobtrusively and with a bantering inconsequence that was never quite chatter, attaining a coolness that was like their white dresses and their impersonal eyes in the absense of all desire. They were here--and they accepted Tom and me, making only a polite pleasant effort to entertain or to be entertained. They knew already that presently dinner would be over and a little later the evening too would be over and casually put away. It was sharply different from the west where an evening was hurried from phase to phase toward its close in a continually dissapointed anticipation or else in sheer nervous dread of the moment itself in time.

"You make me feel uncivilized, Daisy," I remarked on my second glass of wine, "Can't you talk about crops or something?"

I meant nothing in particular by this remark but it was taken up in an unexpected way."

"Civilizations going to pieces," broke out Tom violently, "I've gotten to be a terrible pessimist about things. Have you ever read The Rise of the Coloured Empires by this man Goddard?"

"Why, no" I admitted, rather surprised by his tone

"We ought to plan something," yawned Miss Baker, sitting down at the table as if she were getting into bed.

"All right," said Daisy. "What'll we plan?" She turned to me helplessly: "What do people plan?"

Before I could answer her eyes fastened with an awed expression on her little finger.

"Look!" she complained; "I hurt it."

We all looked—the knuckle was black and blue.

"You did it, Tom," she said accusingly. "I know you didn't mean to, but you *did* do it. That's what I get for marrying a brute of a man, a great, big, hulking physical specimen of a——"

"I hate that word hulking," objected Tom crossly, "even in kidding."

"Hulking," insisted Daisy.

Sometimes she and Miss Baker talked at once, unobtrusively and with a bantering inconsequence that was never quite chatter, that was as cool as their white dresses and their impersonal eyes in the absence of all desire. They were here, and they accepted Tom and me, making only a polite pleasant effort to entertain or to be entertained. They knew that presently dinner would be over and a little later the evening too would be over and casually put away. It was sharply different from the West, where an evening was hurried from phase to phase toward its close, in a continually disappointed anticipation or else in sheer nervous dread of the moment itself.

"You make me feel uncivilized, Daisy," I confessed on my second glass of corky but rather impressive claret. "Can't you talk about crops or something?"

I meant nothing in particular by this remark, but it was taken up in an unexpected way.

"Civilization's going to pieces," broke out Tom violently. "I've gotten to be a terrible pessimist about things. Have you read 'The Rise of the Colored Empires' by this man Goddard?"

"Why, no," I answered, rather surprised by his tone.

characterization, structure, & symbolism

"Well, its a fine book and every body ought to read it. The idea is that if we don't look out the white race will be--will be utterly submerged. It's all scientific stuff. It's been proven.

"Tom's getting very profound," said Daisy with an expression of unthoughtful sadness, "He reads deep books with long words in them. What was that word we--"

"Well, these books are all scientific," insisted Tom, glancing at her impatiently, "This fella has worked out the whole thing. Its up to us who are the dominant race to watch out or these other races will have controll of things."

"We've got to beat them down," whispered Daisy, winking solemnly toward the fervent sun.

"You ought to live in California--" began Miss Baker but Tom interrupted her by shifting heavily in his chair.

"The idea is that we're Nordics. I am and you are and you are and--" After an infinitisimal hesitation he included Daisy with a slight nod and she winked at me again, "--and we've produced all the things that go to make civilization --oh, science and art and all that, do you see?

There was something pathetic in his concentration as if his complacency, more accute than of old, was not enough to him any more. When, almost immediately, the telephone rang inside and the butler left the porch Daisy leaned toward me, siezing upon the interruption.

"I'll tell you a family secret," she whispered entheusiasticly, "Its about the butler's nose. Do you want to hear aboat the butler's nose?"

"That's what I came over for tonight."

"Well, he wasn't always a butler. He used to be the silver polisher for some people in New York that had a silver service for two hundred people. He had to polish it from morning till night until finally it began to affect his nose--"

"Things went from bad to worse", suggested Miss Baker.

"Yes. Things went from bad to worse until finally he had to give up his position."

For a moment the last sunlight fell with romantic affection upon her glowing face, her voice compelled me forward breathlessly as I listened--then the glow faded, each light deserting her face with lingering regret like children leaving a pleasant street at dark.

"Well, it's a fine book, and everybody ought to read it. The idea is if we don't look out the white race will be—will be utterly submerged. It's all scientific stuff; it's been proved."

"Tom's getting very profound," said Daisy, with an expression of unthoughtful sadness. "He reads deep books with long words in them. What was that word we——"

"Well, these books are all scientific," insisted Tom, glancing at her impatiently. "This fellow has worked out the whole thing. It's up to us, who are the dominant race, to watch out or these other races will have control of things."

"We've got to beat them down," whispered Daisy, winking ferociously toward the fervent sun.

"You ought to live in California—" began Miss Baker, but Tom interrupted her by shifting heavily in his chair.

"This idea is that we're Nordics. I am, and you are, and you are, and—" After an infinitesimal hesitation he included Daisy with a slight nod, and she winked at me again. "—And we've produced all the things that go to make civilization—oh, science and art, and all that. Do you see?"

There was something pathetic in his concentration, as if his complacency, more acute than of old, was not enough to him any more. When, almost immediately, the telephone rang inside and the butler left the porch Daisy seized upon the momentary interruption and leaned toward me.

"I'll tell you a family secret," she whispered enthusiastically. "It's about the butler's nose. Do you want to hear about the butler's nose?"

"That's why I came over to-night."

"Well, he wasn't always a butler; he used to be the silver polisher for some people in New York that had a silver service for two hundred people. He had to polish it from morning till night, until finally it began to affect his nose——"

"Things went from bad to worse," suggested Miss Baker.

"Yes. Things went from bad to worse, until finally he had to give up his position."

For a moment the last sunshine fell with romantic affection upon her glowing face; her voice compelled me forward breathlessly as I listened—then the glow faded, each light deserting her with lingering regret, like children leaving a pleasant street at dusk.

The butler reappeared and murmured something close to Tom's ear whereapon Tom pushed back his chair and went inside without a word. Then, as if his absense quickened something within her Daisy leaned forward again, her voice glowing and singing.

"I love to see you at my table, Nick," she said, "You remind me of--of a rose, an absolute rose. Doesn't he?" She turned to Miss Baker for confirmation. "An absolute rose?"

This was untrue. I am not even faintly like a rose. She was only extemporizing now but a stirring warmth flowed from her as if her heart was trying to come out to you concealed in one of those breathless, thrilling words. Then suddenly she threw her napkin on the table and excused herself and went into the house.

Miss Baker and I exchanged a short glance consciously devoid of meaning. I was about to speak when she grew suddenly alert and said "Sh!" in warning voice. A subdued impassioned murmur was audible in the room beyond and Miss Baker leaned forward, unashamed, trying to hear. The murmur trembled on the verge of coherence, sank down, mounted excitedly and then ceased altogether.

"That's that," said Miss Baker succinctly, "Tom's got some women in New York."

"Got some woman?" I repeated blankly.

Miss Baker nodded.

"She might have the decency not to telephone at dinner-time. Don't you think?"

Almost before I had grasped her meaning there was the flutter of a dress and the crunch of leather boots and Tom and Daisy were back at table.

"It couldn't be helped", cried Daisy with tense gayiety. She sat down, glanced intently at Miss Baker and then at me and continued, "I looked outdoors for a minute and its very romantic outdoors. There's a bird on the lawn that I think must be a nightingale come over on the Cunard or White Star Line. He's singing away--" her voice sang "--Its romantic. Isn't it, Tom".

"Very romantic," he said, and looked at me--miserably, "If it's light enough after dinner I want to take you down to the stables.

The butler came back and murmured something close to Tom's ear, whereupon Tom frowned, pushed back his chair, and without a word went inside. As if his absence quickened something within her, Daisy leaned forward again, her voice glowing and singing.

"I love to see you at my table, Nick. You remind me of a—of a rose, an absolute rose. Doesn't he?" She turned to Miss Baker for confirmation: "An absolute rose?"

This was untrue. I am not even faintly like a rose. She was only extemporizing, but a stirring warmth flowed from her, as if her heart was trying to come out to you concealed in one of those breathless, thrilling words. Then suddenly she threw her napkin on the table and excused herself and went into the house.

Miss Baker and I exchanged a short glance consciously devoid of meaning. I was about to speak when she sat up alertly and said "Sh!" in a warning voice. A subdued impassioned murmur was audible in the room beyond, and Miss Baker leaned foward unashamed, trying to hear. The murmur trembled on the verge of coherence, sank down, mounted excitedly, and then ceased altogether.

"This Mr. Gatsby you spoke of is my neighbor—" I began.

"Don't talk. I want to hear what happens."

"Is something happening?" I inquired innocently.

"You mean to say you don't know?" said Miss Baker, honestly surprised. "I thought everybody knew."

"I don't."

"Why—" she said hesitantly, "Tom's got some woman in New York."

"Got some woman?" I repeated blankly.

Miss Baker nodded.

"She might have the decency not to telephone him at dinner time. Don't you think?"

Almost before I had grasped her meaning there was the flutter of a dress and the crunch of leather boots, and Tom and Daisy were back at the table.

"It couldn't be helped!" cried Daisy with tense gayety.

She sat down, glanced searchingly at Miss Baker and then at me, and continued: "I looked outdoors for a minute, and it's very romantic outdoors. There's a bird on the lawn that I think must be a nightingale come over on the Cunard or White Star Line. He's singing away—" Her voice sang: "It's romantic, isn't it, Tom?"

"Very romantic," he said, and then miserably to me: "If it's light enough after dinner, I want to take you down to the stables."

The telephone rang inside, startlingly, and as Daisy shook her head decisively at the butler the subject of the stables, in fact all subjects, vanished into the golden air. Among the broken fragments of the last five minutes at table I remember the candles being lit again, pointlessly, and I was conscious of wanting to look squarely at everyone and yet to avoid all eyes. I could not guess what Daisy and Tom were thinking but I doubt if even Miss Baker who seemed to have mastered a certain hardy skeptisism was able utterly to put this fifth guests shrill mettallic urgency out of mind. To a certain temperment the situation might have seemed intriguing--my own instinct was to telephone immediately for the police.

The horses, needless to say, were not mentioned again. Tom and Miss Baker with several feet of twilight between them strolled back into the library, as if to a vigil beside a perfectly tangible body, while with a strained, interested expression on my face I followed Daisy around a chain of connecting verandahs to the wide southern porch in front. When we were in its deep gloom we sat down side by side in a wicker settee and taking her face in her hands, as if feeling its lovely shape, Daisy's eyes moved gradually out into the darkness. She said nothing but I saw that some turbulent emotion possessed her, so I asked her a few quiet questions about her little girl.

"Listen, Nick," she broke out suddenly, "Did you ever hear what I said when my child was born?"

"No Daisy."

"Well, she was less than an hour old and and Tom was God knows where. I woke up out of the ether with an utterly abandoned feeling as if I'd been raped by a company of soldiers and left out in a field to die. I asked the nurse if it was a boy or a girl, and she said 'You have a beautiful little girl.' I can hear her now just as plainly as if she was on this porch: 'You have a beautiful little girl', she said, and so I turned my head away and swore and wept--and finally I cried right out in a loud voice: 'Well, if she's a girl all I can hope is that she's beautiful and a fool--that's the best thing a girl can be in this world, a beautiful little fool.'"

"You see I think everything's terrible anyhow," she went on in a convinced way. "Everybody thinks so--the most advanced people. And I know. I've been everywhere and seen

The telephone rang inside, startingly, and as Daisy shook her head decisively at Tom the subject of the stables, in fact all subjects, vanished into air. Among the broken fragments of the last five minutes at table I remember the candles being lit again, pointlessly, and I was conscious of wanting to look squarely at every one, and yet to avoid all eyes. I couldn't guess what Daisy and Tom were thinking, but I doubt if even Miss Baker, who seemed to have mastered a certain hardy scepticism, was able utterly to put this fifth guest's shrill metallic urgency out of mind. To a certain temperament the situation might have seemed intriguing—my own instinct was to telephone immediately for the police.

The horses, needless to say, were not mentioned again. Tom and Miss Baker, with several feet of twilight between them, strolled back into the library, as if to a vigil beside a perfectly tangible body, while, trying to look pleasantly interested and a little deaf, I followed Daisy around a chain of connecting verandas to the porch in front. In its deep gloom we sat down side by side on a wicker settee.

Daisy took her face in her hands as if feeling its lovely shape, and her eyes moved gradually out into the velvet dusk. I saw that turbulent emotions possessed her, so I asked what I thought would be some sedative questions about her little girl.

"We don't know each other very well, Nick," she said suddenly. "Even if we are cousins. You didn't come to my wedding."

"I wasn't back from the war."

"That's true." She hesitated. "Well, I've had a very bad time, Nick, and I'm pretty cynical about everything."

Evidently she had reason to be. I waited but she didn't say any more, and after a moment I returned rather feebly to the subject of her daughter.

"I suppose she talks, and—eats, and everything."

"Oh, yes." She looked at me absently. "Listen, Nick; let me tell you what I said when she was born. Would you like to hear?"

"Very much."

"It'll show you how I've gotten to feel about—things. Well, she was less than an hour old and Tom was God knows where. I woke up out of the ether with an utterly abandoned feeling, and asked the nurse right away if it was a boy or a girl. She told me it was a girl, and so I turned my head away and wept. 'All right,' I said, 'I'm glad it's a girl. And I hope she'll be a fool—that's the best thing a girl can be in this world, a beautiful little fool.'

"You see I think everything's terrible anyhow," she went on in a convinced way. "Everybody thinks so—the most advanced people. And I *know*. I've been everywhere and seen everything and done everything and done everything. Her eyes flashed around her in a defiant way, rather like Tom's and laughed with thrilling scorn, "Sophisticated--God, I'm sophisticated!"

The instant her voice broke off, ceasing to compell my attention, my belief, I felt the basic insincerity of what she had said. It made me uneasy, as though the whole evening had been a trick of some sort to exact a contributary emotion from me. I waited, and sure enough, in a moment she looked at me with an absolute smirk on her lovely face as if she had asserted her membership in a rather distinguished secret society to which she and Tom belonged.

A little later we went inside and almost immediatey Miss Bakers body asserted itself with a restless movement of her knee and a flutter of slender muscles in her brown arms. She closed the magazine, stood up, leaned backward like a West Point cadet and said she was going to bed.

"Its almost ten", she remarked inaccurately.

"Jordan's going to play in the tournament tommorrow," explained Daisy, "over at Westchester.

"Oh,--you're Jordan Baker."

I knew now why her face was familiar--its pleasing contemptuous expression had looked out at me from many "rotogravure" pictures of life at Ashville and Hot Springs and Palm Beach. I had heard some story of her too, a critical, unpleasant story, but what it was I had forgotten long ago.

everything." Her eyes flashed around her in a defiant way, rather like Tom's, and she laughed with thrilling scorn. "Sophisticated—God, I'm sophisticated!"

The instant her voice broke off, ceasing to compel my attention, my belief, I felt the basic insincerity of what she had said. It made me uneasy, as though the whole evening had been a trick of some sort to exact a contributary emotion from me. I waited, and sure enough, in a moment she looked at me with an absolute smirk on her lovely face, as if she had asserted her membership in a rather distinguished secret society to which she and Tom belonged.

Inside, the crimson room bloomed with light. Tom and Miss Baker sat at either end of the long couch and she read aloud to him from the Saturday Evening Post—the words, murmurous and uninflected, running together in a soothing tune. The lamp-light, bright on his boots and dull on the autumn-leaf yellow of her hair, glinted along the paper as she turned a page with a flutter of slender muscles in her arms.

When we came in she held us silent for a moment with a lifted hand.

"To be continued," she said, tossing the magazine on the table, "in our very next issue."

Her body asserted itself with a restless movement of her knee, and she stood up.

"Ten o'clock," she remarked, apparently finding the time on the ceiling. "Time for this good girl to go to bed."

"Jordan's going to play in the tournament tomorrow," explained Daisy, "over at Westchester."

"Oh—you're *J*ordan Baker."

I knew now why her face was familiar—its pleasing contemptuous expression had looked out at me from many rotogravure pictures of the sporting life at Asheville and Hot Springs and Palm Beach. I had heard some story of her too, a critical, unpleasant story, but what it was I had forgotten long ago.

"Good night," she said softly. "Wake me at eight, won't you."

"If you'll get up."

"I will. Good night, Mr. Carraway. See you anon."

"Of course you will," confirmed Daisy. "In fact I think I'll arrange a marriage. Come over often, Nick, and I'll sort of—oh—fling you together. You know—lock you up accidentally in linen closets and push you out to sea in a boat, and all that sort of thing——"

"Good night," called Miss Baker from the stairs. "I haven't heard a word."

When she had gone our eyes fell together gravely.

"Did you two have a little heart-to-heart talk on the veranda?" inquired Tom, looking pointedly at his wife.

"Why not?" she said.

"Don't believe everything you hear, Nick," he advised me.

I said, of course, that I had heard nothing but the situation was on my nerves to such an extent that I decided to get out as soon as it was decently possible. They came to the door with me and stood side by side in a gay square of light while I climbed into my car. Just as I started the motor Daisy called "Wait!" in a peremtory voice.

"I forgot to ask you something," she cried, "and its very important. We heard you were engaged to some girl out West."

"Yes, that's right," corroborated Tom eagerly, "We heard that you're engaged."

"Its a libel. I'm too poor."

"But we heard it," insisted Daisy, astonishing me by opening up again in a flower-like way, "We heard if from two people so it must be true--"

Of course I knew very well, as I drove away, what they were referring to. But I wasn't even vaguely engaged. The fact that people were accusing me of it was one of the reasons I had come East--you can't stop going with an old friend on account of rumors and on the other hand I had no intention of being rumored into marriage.

And yet, curiously, Daisy's and Tom's interest in my "engagement" somehow rekindled my interest in them, and two hours, made them people again; they didn't seem quite so remotely rich if they enjoyed the supposition that I was possessed by the flowery lust.

Nevertheless I was angry and confused It seemed to me that if Tom Buchanan "had some woman in New York" the thing for Daisy to do was to rush out of the house, child in arms --and not to sit on her own front porch and hope that her child would be a "beautiful little fool"

As for Tom Buchanan the fact that he had possession of some women was much less incredible than that he had been depressed by a book. Something was making him nibble at the edge of stale ideas as though not even Horses were enough for him any more.

"She's a nice girl," said Tom after a moment. "They oughtn't to let her run around the country this way."

"Who oughtn't to?" inquired Daisy coldly.

"Her family."

"Her family is one aunt about a thousand years old. Besides, Nick's going to look after her, aren't you, Nick? She's going to spend lots of week-ends out here this summer. I think the home influence will be very good for her."

Daisy and Tom looked at each other for a moment in silence.

"Is she from New York?" I asked quickly.

"From Louisville. Our white girlhood was passed together there. Our beautiful white——"

"Did you give Nick a little heart to heart talk on the veranda?" demanded Tom suddenly.

"Did I?" She looked at me. "I can't seem to remember, but I think we talked about the Nordic race. Yes, I'm sure we did. It sort of crept up on us and first thing you know——"

"Don't believe everything you hear, Nick," he advised me.

I said lightly that I had heard nothing at all, and a few minutes later I got up to go home. They came to the door with me and stood side by side in a cheerful square of light. As I started my motor Daisy peremptorily called: "Wait!

"I forgot to ask you something, and it's important. We heard you were engaged to a girl out West."

"That's right," corroborated Tom kindly. "We heard that you were engaged."

"It's a libel. I'm too poor."

"But we heard it," insisted Daisy, surprising me by opening up again in a flower-like way. "We heard it from three people, so it must be true."

Of course I knew what they were referring to, but I wasn't even vaguely engaged. The fact that gossip had published the banns was one of the reasons I had come East. You can't stop going with an old friend on account of rumors, and on the other hand I had no intention of being rumored into marriage.

Their interest rather touched me and made them less remotely rich—nevertheless, I was confused and a little disgusted as I drove away. It seemed to me that the thing for Daisy to do was to rush out of the house, child in arms—but apparently there were no such intentions in her head. As for Tom, the fact that he "had some woman in New York" was really less surprising than that he had been depressed by a book. Something was making him nibble at the edge of stale ideas as if his sturdy physical egotism no longer nourished his peremptory heart.

characterization, structure, & symbolism

But before I had driven ten minutes from their door the breeze had blown them both away. It was already deep summer on road house roofs and on dark murmurous little porches and around the garages where new red gas-pumps sat out in pools of light--and summer always promises fulfillment of my old childish desires. I wanted something definate to happen to me, something that would wear me out a little--for I suppose that the urge toward adventure is one and the same with the obscure craving of our bodies for a certain death.

When I reached my wretched lovely house at West Egg I ran the car under its shed and, feeling wide awake, walked around the house and sat down on an abandoned grass roller on the lawn. It was a loud bright night with wings beating in the trees and a persistent organ sound as the full bellows of the earth blew the frogs full of life. The shadow of a moving cat wavered across the moonight and turning my head to watch it I saw that I was not alone--fifty feet away a figure had moved out from the long shadow of my nieghbor's hedge and was standing with head thrown back, and eyes turned upward toward the silver pepper of the stars. Something in his long scrutiny and his pocketed hands and the secure position of his feet on the lawn suggested that it was Mr. Gatsby himself--perhaps come out to determine what share was his of our local heavens.

I could not see his face but I rememberd that Miss Baker had had asked me about him at dinner and I decided to speak to him. I got to my feet and was about to call out when suddenly I saw him stretch out both hands toward the sky in a curious way--as I was from him I could have sworn that he was trembling. Involuntarily I looked up. When I looked down again he was gone, and I was left to wonder whether it was really the sky he had come out to measure with the compass of those aspiring arms.

F. Scott Fitzgerald

Already it was deep summer on roadhouse roofs and in front of wayside garages, where new red gas-pumps sat out in pools of light, and when I reached my estate at West Egg I ran the car under its shed and sat for a while on an abandoned grass roller in the yard. The wind had blown off, leaving a loud, bright night, with wings beating in the trees and a persistent organ sound as the full bellows of the earth blew the frogs full of life. The silhouette of a moving cat wavered across the moonlight, and turning my head to watch it, I saw that I was not alone—fifty feet away a figure had emerged from the shadow of my neighbor's mansion and was standing with his hands in his pockets regarding the silver pepper of the stars. Something in his leisurely movements and the secure position of his feet upon the lawn suggested that it was Mr. Gatsby himself, come out to determine what share was his of our local heavens.

I decided to call to him. Miss Baker had mentioned him at dinner, and that would do for an introduction. But I didn't call to him, for he gave a sudden intimation that he was content to be alone—he stretched out his arms toward the dark water in a curious way, and, far as I was from him, I could have sworn he was trembling. Involuntarily I glanced seaward—and distinguished nothing except a single green light, minute and far away, that might have been the end of a dock. When I looked once more for Gatsby he had vanished, and I was alone again in the unquiet darkness.

characterization, structure, & symbolism

The sense of being in an unfamiliar place deepened on me and as the moon rose higher the inessential houses seemed to melt away until I was aware of the old island here that flowered once for Dutch sailors eyes--a fresh green breast of the newworld. Its vanished trees, the very trees that had made way for Gatsby's house, had once pandered in whispers to the last and greatest of all human dreams--for a transitory and enchanted moment man must have held his breath in thu presense of this continent, compelled into an aesthetic contemplation he niether understood nor desired, face to face for the last time in history with something commensurate to his capacity for wonder.

And as I sat there brooding on the old unknown world I too held my breath and waited, until I could feel the motion of America as it turned through the hours--my own blue lawn and the tall incandescent city on the water and beyond that the dark fields of the republic rolling on under the night.

Even in This Side of Paradise, *inferior in art to his later work, Fitzgerald "wrote and revised and compiled and boiled down"* ("*Who's Who: F. Scott Fitzgerald,*" The Saturday Evening Post, *September 18, 1920, p. 61*). Tender Is the Night, *composed between 1925 and 1934, went through several versions and titles. After its publication, Fitzgerald continued to labor over it, finally deciding that the story should be presented in chronological order rather than commencing with Rosemary meeting the Divers and their circle. But although he revised his work with considerable care, often making many drafts before arriving at the one he wanted, he tried to avoid polishing his prose to the point where it would lose spontaneity and vitality. In "Notes" to* The Last Tycoon, *Fitzgerald reminded himself, "Rewrite from mood. Has become stilted with rewriting. Don't look. Rewrite from mood"* (Three Novels of F. Scott Fitzgerald, *New York, 1953, p. 134*).

A good deal of labor may have preceded what the author preserved as the pencil draft of The Great Gatsby. *His Introduction to the Modern Library edition of 1934 states: "What I cut out of it both physically and emotionally would make another novel!" Kenneth Eble adds: "The difference in hand, in numbering of pages, in the paper and pencils used, suggest that much had preceded that draft"* ("*The Craft of Revision:* The Great Gatsby," American Literature, *November, 1964, p. 325*). *Of the preserved material, the middle is more heavily reworked than the beginning or the end, but even with respect to Chapter I changes occur throughout the pencil draft and in the margins of the galley proofs and the first edition.*

The single highly significant change occurring between the pencil draft version of Chapter I and the galley proof version concerns the conclusion. During the composition of the pencil draft, the paragraph involving the "Dutch sailors' eyes" and the paragraph involving "the dark fields of the republic" were transposed to the end of the entire novel, though only the paragraph involving "the dark fields of the republic" underwent important revisions. The Chapter I pencil draft version of this paragraph became the final three paragraphs of the book. After crossing out his original attempt to write the first of these three paragraphs, Fitzgerald produced them all on the final page of the pencil draft essentially as they would appear in the galley proofs and the first edition. The latter reads:

And as I sat there brooding on the old, unknown world, I thought of Gatsby's wonder when he first picked out the green light at the end of Daisy's dock. He had come a long way to this blue lawn, and his dream must have seemed so close that he could hardly fail to grasp it. He did not know that it was already behind him, somewhere back in that vast obscurity beyond the city, where the dark fields of the republic rolled on under the night.

Gatsby believed in the green light, the orgastic future that year by year recedes before us. It eluded us then, but that's no matter—tomorrow we will run faster, stretch out our arms farther. . . . And one fine morning—

So we beat on, boats against the current, borne back ceaselessly into the past.

In the Chapter I pencil draft version of the final passage, Nick identifies himself with the Dutch sailors of the preceding paragraph by virtue of sharing their feeling of awe over the American continent. In the transposed versions, however, the emphasis shifts to Gatsby, whose relationship to these sailors is made much more concrete and much more vivid than Nick's had been by the parallel the latter implicitly draws between their vision of "a fresh green breast of the new world" and Gatsby's pursuit of "the green light at the end of Daisy's dock."

Mr. Eble comments upon the surprisingly conscious genesis of the green light image:

The green light (there were originally two) came into the novel at the time of Daisy's meeting with Gatsby. "If it wasn't for the mist," he tells her, "we could see your house across the bay. You always have two green lights that burn all night at the end of your dock." Fitzgerald not only made the green light a central image of the final paragraph, but he went back to the end of the first chapter and added it there: "Involuntarily I glanced seaward—and distinguished nothing except a single green light, minute and far away, that might have been the end of a dock." ("The Craft of Revision: The Great Gatsby," p. 317)

Like other references to "green"—for example, "the 'green card' which Daisy jokes about as entitling Nick to a kiss" and "the 'long green tickets' which carried young Nick to Midwestern parties" (manuscript of Victor Doyno's forthcoming article, "Patterns in The

Great Gatsby")—the green light beckons one on. But it acquired even greater symbolic import than a "Go" signal when the author consciously juxtaposed it to "a fresh green breast of the new world." The cultural-historical analogy between Gatsby's pursuit of Daisy and the Dutch sailors' pursuit of the American continent is ironic. In the urban, industrial, post-Civil War East, where "inessential houses" have displaced "trees," "green" describes a mechanical object deceitfully masking the very opposites of virginal purity and hope. Only "beyond the city," among "the dark fields" rolling westward may transcendental dreams still be realized.

The juxtaposition of the last two paragraphs of Chapter I to the end of the novel proves Fitzgerald's awareness of the artistic need to reserve a comprehensive poetic statement about this major theme until the book's close, just as his having conceived these two paragraphs when he did proves his awareness of large issues at an early stage.

There are three significant changes between the pencil draft version of Chapter I and the galley proof version which have nothing to do with the ending but which do involve characterization. The first concerns Jordan, Tom, and Daisy, and the other two, Nick. The new passage, " 'Good night,' she said softly" through "first thing you know," treats the Jordan-Tom relationship while casting Daisy in the role of matchmaker and supplying background information about the girls.

The earlier of the changes regarding Nick—"It was lonely for a day" through "the freedom of the neighborhood"—is a new passage important for the allusion to him as "a guide, a pathfinder, an original settler." Although it concerns local geographical directions, we are to understand from it that Nick, who must seek the moral meaning of his experience, will steer us too. But not only this. "Original settler" establishes an analogy between the narrator and the founders of the country and therefore contributes to the series of parallels which make The Great Gatsby a sort of cultural-historical allegory. While some of these tend to be straightforward—for example, Nick: original settler; East-West Egg: eastern-western United States—most function ironically—for example, Gatsby: Dutch sailors; Daisy Buchanan: Daisy Miller; Dan Cody: Buffalo Bill. The ironic parallels, in particular, subtly chart the nation's decline and fall.

Later a second change regarding Nick's character—"But before I had driven" through "a certain death"—is a partly altered and partly deleted passage, noteworthy for the excision of allusions more appropriate to the romantic Jay Gatsby than to the reasonable Nick Carraway: "and summer always promises fulfillment of my old childish desires" and "for I suppose that the urge toward adventure is one and the same with the obscure craving of our bodies for a certain death." Of course, Nick becomes increasingly romantic during the telling of the story. The last two paragraphs of the novel, which were inspired by the Chapter I pencil draft version, treat the paradox of romantic time. Gatsby and idealists like Gatsby live not for the present but for the future and the past simultaneously. That the reasonable Nick Carraway has to some extent been transformed into such a person during his narration would seem apparent from the concluding reference to "us" and "we."

The reader should be apprised of four further changes recorded by the galley proofs—and hence the first edition—made some time after Fitzgerald had completed the pencil draft. Two are relatively insignificant. They involve a deletion and an addition: The sequence "Rain tomorrow" through "great big hulking" was eliminated to tighten the dialogue, and the sequence "This Mr. Gatsby" through "I don't" was inserted to make the introduction of Tom's affair and the eventual entrance of Gatsby less abrupt. Two somewhat significant changes involve fresh material: "We don't know each other very well" through "It'll show you how I've gotten to feel about—things" provides expositional data and treats Daisy's state of mind. "Inside, the crimson room bloomed with light" through "Time for this good girl to go to bed" provides physical details about Jordan and treats her relationship with Tom.

However, the transposition of the paragraph referring to the "Dutch sailors' eyes" and the one referring to "the dark fields of the republic" warrants the reader's special regard. By making the green light, which had first appeared when Daisy met Gatsby, "a central image of the final paragraph" and then adding the image to the end of Chapter I, Fitzgerald consciously created an important symbol. In so far as this symbol recurs and thus helps to unify the novel, it is a structural device. In so far as its juxtaposition to the paragraph referring to the "Dutch sailors' eyes" and the concomitant shift in emphasis from Nick to Gatsby helps to reveal the protagonist and his experience, it is a device of characterization.

VII

narrative focus

Philip Roth

Philip Roth was born in Newark, New Jersey, during 1933. He received the B.A. degree from Bucknell University and the M.A. from the University of Chicago. Harper's, The New Yorker, Esquire, Commentary, Paris Review, *and other magazines have carried his short stories. His first book,* Goodbye, Columbus *(1959), won the National Book Award for fiction (1960) as well as the Daroff Award of the Jewish Book Council of America. He has also received a Guggenheim grant and a grant from the National Institute of Arts and Letters. His latest novel is* When She Was Good *(1967).*

In 1962 Random House published Letting Go. *The dust jacket defines the central conflict of Mr. Roth's second novel: "It is with the debts and sorrows of Gabe Wallach that we are primarily concerned, with his sporadic, backhanded and finally desperate attempts to find a proper relationship between his own worldly good fortune and the misfortune of others. Gabe's behavior throughout the four-year span of this novel can be described as a kind of frenetic contest between his sympathies and his instinct for self-protection." According to the author, the most crucial technical problem posed by* Letting Go *regarded narrative focus: Through whose eyes and voice should the story be told? Naturally, this problem arose at the very outset in Chapter I, the second draft and* Published Version *of which appear below.*

LETTING GO

Chapter I

Dear Gabe,

The drugs help me bend my fingers around a pen. The whole sickness feels in my hands sometimes. I've wanted to write, but not dictating to your father. Later I don't want whispering at the bedside. I'll be panicked, breathless, have too much influence. Your father keeps leaning across my bed. He runs in after every patient and tells me what the weather is outside. He won't admit I've done him an injustice being his wife. He holds my hand fifty times a day. The injustice is done anyway. What unhappiness has been in our family springs from me. We've managed to control the surface misery. It can't be dismissed for the whole thing. It can't be blamed, the whole thing, on your father. Since I was a little girl I always wanted to be decent. Other little girls wanted to be nurses and pianists. They were less dissembling. I was clever, I picked my virtue early. The rest of my life I could push and pull at people with a clear conscience. All I want to say is I don't want to say anything. I want to give up the prerogative allowed normal dying people. I have no instructions, that's why I'm writing. Your father is coming in again. It's to him I should admit the injustice. He won't condemn me until I do first. That's the injustice. It comes of instructing. A nurse is a nurse, but decent? The pen keeps falling.

Letting Go

CHAPTER ONE

Dear Gabe,

The drugs help me bend my fingers around a pen. Sometimes the whole sickness feels located in my hands. I have wanted to write but not by dictating to your father. Later I don't want to whisper last-minute messages to him at the bedside. With all the panic and breathlessness I'll have too much influence. Now your father keeps leaning across my bed. He runs in after every patient and tells me what the weather is outside. He never once admits that I've done him an injustice being his wife. He holds my hand fifty times a day. None of this changes what has happened—the injustice is done. Whatever unhappiness has been in our family springs from me. Please don't blame it on your father however I may have encouraged you over the years. Since I was a little girl I always wanted to be Very Decent to People. Other little girls wanted to be nurses and pianists. They were less dissembling. I was clever, I picked a virtue early and hung on to it. I was always doing things for another's good. The rest of my life I could push and pull at people with a clear conscience. All I want to say now is that I don't want to say anything. I want to give up the prerogative allowed normal dying people. Why I'm writing is to say that I have no instructions.

Your father is coming in again. He's carrying three kinds of fruit juices. Gabe, it's to him I should admit all this. He won't condemn me until I do first. All through our marriage I've been improving his life for him, pushing, pulling. Oh decent decent. Dear, the pen keeps falling

Her letter had never been signed. The pen fell, and when the night nurse came on she was no longer needed. Nevertheless his father had obediently put the letter into an envelope. Gabe, when he received it had put it in a book, and now, two years later, he had loaned the book to

Her letter had never been signed. The pen fell, and when the night nurse came on duty she was no longer needed. Nevertheless my father, obedient to the last, put the letter in an envelope and without examination mailed it. I was a second lieutenant in the artillery corps at this time, stationed in an unregenerate dust bowl in Oklahoma, and my one connection with the world of feeling was not the world itself but Henry James, whom I had lately begun to read. Oklahoma nights and southwestern radio stations had thrust me into an isolation wherein my concentration was exact enough for me to attend at last to the involutions of the old master. All day I listened to the booming of cannons, and all night to the words of heroes and heroines tempting one another into a complex and often tragic fate. Early in the summer that I had been called into the Army—which was the summer after I had finished college—I had spent my last six civilian weeks touring Europe; one week was spent visiting with a friend of my mother's who lived in London, where her husband was connected with the U. S. Embassy. I remember having to hear endless incidents from my mother's childhood while sitting with her friend in a small church in Chelsea; she had taken me there to see a little-known plaque dedicated to James. It was not a particularly successful day, for the woman really liked the idea of putting on long white gloves and showing a Harvard boy around cultural nooks and crannies a good deal more than she liked the nooks and crannies. But I do remember the words engraved onto that small gray oval tablet: it was written of James that he was "lover and interpreter of the fine amenities of brave decisions."

So it happened that when I received the letter my mother had written and my father had posted, I was reading *Portrait of a Lady*, and it was into its pages that I slid the envelope and its single sheet of barely legible prose. When I returned from the funeral, and in the weeks following, I read and reread the letter so often that I weakened the binding of the book. In my grief and confusion, I promised myself that I would do no violence to human life, not to another's, and not to my own.

It was a year later that I loaned the book to Paul Herz, who looked to be a harried young man rapidly losing contact with his own feelings; he might have been hearing the boom of big guns going off all day himself. This was the fall after I had left the Army, the fall of 1953, when we were both enrolled as graduate students at the University of Iowa. Paul's costume at that time was the same day in and day out: khaki trousers threadbare around the back pocket, a white T-shirt shapeless around the arms, tennis sneakers

the darkhaired fellow in his Anglo-Saxon class. It was three in the morning and there was nothing to be done. Still his heart was pounding as though he'd been caught at something. He tried to get back to sleep. His father had called from New York again at dinner time. Their conversation, pointless on the surface, pleading beneath, must have helped to bring on the dream of his mother. Since her death he had thought of her, he had read and reread the letter, but if she appeared to him at night, up until then it had not been directly. This time he had actually seen her face. It grew gigantic before him as she cried. The pounding heart awoke him, and with open eyes he saw what might be a simple explanation for her appearance: it had to do with the letter--she had written him in sickness and confidence, he had violated the privacy of her despair. He would call the fellow tomorrow, Paul Herz was his name. Call him first thing and ask for the envelope tucked in the middle of "Portrait of a Lady." After class they had taken coffee together in the bookstore and Gabe had recommended the book; he had loaned it not even remembering the letter. If a stranger read the letter, someone who knew none of the circumstances, the facts, he would get a cockeyed idea not only of his mother but of all three of them. The morphine had been kind to her fingers, otherwise it had done none of them any good. The relief of one pain had made room for others; the misfortune was that she might easily have died without condemning herself--Everyone had been prepared to honor her like a saint.

The next morning after his class in Medieval Romances he called Herz from a campus phone booth. Mrs. Herz sounded hurried and on edge--they lived in the barracks, those gray scaly shells near the highway, and probably there was a child squalling to be diapered or fed. She said her husband had gone to class, and she was herself about to rush off. Gabe did not know her and decided to mention nothing about

and, occasionally, socks. He was forever running—it was this that brought him to my attention—and forever barely making it. The point of his briefcase could be seen edging through the classroom door just at the moment that the first unlucky student in our Anglo-Saxon class was called upon to read aloud from *Beowulf.* Leaving the library at night, I would see him streaking up the stairs after some reserve book, even while the head librarian turned the key in the lock. He would stand shivering in his T-shirt until she broke down and let him in. He was a man who evoked sympathy even if he did not come right out and ask for it; even if he *would* not ask for it. No heart could remain unmoved by the sight of that dark, kinky-haired black-eyed head racing toward the closing doors, or into them. Once, shopping for some bread and milk, I saw him nearly break several of the major bones of his body at the entrance to a downtown grocery store. The electric eye swung the door out at him just as he had turned, arms laden with packages, to watch a cop stick a ticket under the single wiper of his battered, green, double-parked Dodge.

I lived alone at the time in a small apartment near the campus, and was having troubles of my own; I was about ready to find somebody to complain to. One day in November, as Herz was darting from Anglo-Saxon, I stuck myself in his path and asked him over to the Union for a cup of coffee. He couldn't make it as he was supposed to have been somewhere else five minutes earlier, but on the parking lot, to which I accompanied him, and where he sat yanking and yanking at the throttle of his car, I managed to put in something about James, and the next time we had class together, I brought *Portrait* for him to take home and read. I awoke that night remembering that tucked in the pages of the book I had pressed upon him, somewhere between the hopes of Isabel Archer and her disappointments, was my mother's letter. I couldn't immediately get back to sleep.

The following morning, directly after Medieval Romances, I called Herz from a campus phone booth. Mrs. Herz answered sounding hurried and on edge—the family tone. She and her husband lived in one of those gray shells on the far side of the river, the married students' barracks, and I was sure that directly behind her, or beneath her, there flailed a squalling infant. Herz looked harassed enough to be the father of three or four small, mean, colicky children. Mrs. Herz, in a very few words, informed me that her husband had driven over to Cedar Rapids and that she was herself about to rush off. I decided instantly not to ask if I might come over to remove something that I had left in a book I had loaned Paul.

the book. Probably neither she nor her husband had had a chance to open it yet. Outside the booth the November morning dazzled the eye, and whatever had produced balloony images of the dead and heart palpitations at three in the morning no longer thrived. The campus trees swung in the wind, up and down, the leaves pale undersides, then blazing tops; when Mrs. Herz asked with a sudden curious brittleness if anything was the matter, Gabe realized that nothing was. He had not tipped his mother's tombstone, he had not trampled on her grave. To allow that letter out of his hands had been absentminded, not disloyal. Disloyalty, violation . . . nothing like that had been in his mind. As for the unconscious, he could not believe that he had wanted to reveal some shady side of his mother to the world. He was her son--would he let her stand condemned by a last minute confession? He had simply forgotten the letter, and that he could forget it might even be for the best. In the dark, however, what was for the best seemed sometimes for the worst. After midnight he was apt to be hard with himself, especially with his father phoning long distance once or twice a week. The old man stood being familyless all day--he had his patients' mouths to look into; alone with his avocado and lettuce dinner he broke down. When he called his voice shook. When he hung up it was as though his vibrations had passed directly into the objects of his son's room. Things moved one way, Gabe Wallach moved the other; he spilled water, dropped papers, once he sat on his reading glasses. After those calls, it would have helped to turn to someone else in his room and continue a discussion broken only by the telephone conversation. Like his father, he had never been the same person alone that he was with people; by himself his grip on reality was not so firm. Daylight, people scurrying by, had a cheering effect however, and he hung up on Mrs. Herz--rather she hung up on him--less anxious about the letter and less unsettled too by that powerful hallucination he had experienced seven hours earlier. For as he had finally pushed back into sleep, he had heard a statement spoken aloud about his mother. The tongue that spoke was dreaming, but it was his nevertheless and it had called Paula Wallach a monster. Now he stepped from the phone booth into the glassy light, and reason and a good clear memory reduced those dreamy sorded words to the faintest of echos.

Probably neither of them had had a chance at the book anyway, and I could wait and later get to Herz himself. I explained nothing whatsoever to the wife, who struck me as more rude than chagrined; besides, it was daylight and autumn and I was no longer afflicted with thoughts of the dead. The November morning was dazzling, the dead were dead.

My father had called again the night before, and I was certain now that any judgments I had made in the dark about my mother's ghost had been induced by my father's presence. Two or three evenings a week my father and I had the same phone conversation, pointless on the surface, pleading beneath. The old man stood being familyless all day, what with having his patients' mouths to look into; it was alone with his avocado and lettuce dinner that he broke down. When he called his voice shook; when he hung up—or when I did—his vibrato passed directly into the few meager objects in the room. I moved one way, my chair another; I have never sat on my reading glasses so many times in my life. I am, for good or bad, in a few ways like my father, and so have never been the same person alone that I am with people. The trouble with the phone calls, in fact, was that all the time I felt it necessary to the preservation of my life and sanity to resist the old man, I understood how it was for him sitting in that huge Victorian living room all alone. However, if I am my father's child, I am my mother's too. I cannot trace out exactly the influences, nor deal in any scientific way with the chromosomes passed on to me. I sometimes believe I know what it is I got from him and what from her, and when I hung up on Mrs. Herz that morning, without having said one word about the letter, I suppose I was using the decorum and good sense that has sifted down from the maternal line. I told myself that there was nothing really to fret about. Why would they read it anyway? And what if they did?

At five o'clock, while he sat drinking coffee and trying to memorize Anglo-Saxon verb conjugations, Mrs. Herz called him back at his apartment.

"Mr. Wallach, this is Libby Herz. You spoke to me this morning. Paul Herz's wife."

"Is your husband home?"

"His car broke down."

"I'm sorry," Gabe said.

"He blew a piston or he keeps blowing pistons . . ."

"I'll call him some other time," Gabe said.

"Yes . . . he asked me to call you," Mrs. Herz said, after a moment. "He wondered if you might have a car. He's on the highway, outside of Cedar Rapids. He needs a lift, Mr. Wallach, he asked me to call . . ."

It was an inconvenience, but even more it was a genuine excuse for putting down the OlD English Grammar. "How do I get there?" Gabe asked.

"I know the way," Mrs. Herz said in a rush. "Could you pick me up at the barracks. We live at the barracks."

"I'll be right over," Gabe said.

The day had grown dimmer and from the doorway, the first thing he saw after seeing Libby Herz herself, was his book set on the edge of the kitchen sink. There looked to be a place mark, or perhaps a letter, sticking out of it. Mrs. Herz gave him no time to check; she ran into the bedroom, then out again, whipping a raincoat around her. She yanked a kerchief from her pocket and rushed out the door, not once looking directly at him. "Paul called again," she said, "I told him we were coming."

As they drove, she stared out the car window and fidgeted with her fingers. Gabe's first impression had been of a thin, dark, intense graduate student; she had the jerky movements, the high black stockings, and the underfed look. With occasional side glances, he now refined the image. In an eager hawky way, she was goodlooking; there was a large sharp nose that sailed a little too defiantly into the wind; the black eyes seemed calm enough, but her hair, also black, was drawn back in a manner so stark and exact that at the sight of it one could begin to guess the depth and number of her anxieties. Her skin was classic and pale, and when she finally removed the kerchief, Gabe could see a small blue vein tapping at her temple; it distracted from the fragility of her complexion. In her lap she continued to twiddle with objects no one else could see.

At five o'clock I was sitting in my apartment drinking coffee and finding no pleasure whatsoever in memorizing Anglo-Saxon verb endings, when Mrs. Herz called me back.

"You spoke to me this morning," she said. "Paul Herz's wife."

"Is your husband home?"

"His car broke down."

It was the sort of news that is not news as soon as one hears it—though Mrs. Herz herself sounded surprised. "That's too bad," I said.

"He blew a piston or he keeps blowing pistons—"

"I'll call him some other time. It's not urgent."

"Well—" she said, "he asked me to call you. He wondered if you might have a car. He's on the highway outside of Cedar Rapids."

I put down the Old English grammar book. A long drive was just the inconvenience I wanted. "How do I get there?"

"Could you pick me up at the barracks?"

"I'm sure I could find it."

"I know the way. We live just at the edge of Finkbine Park—could you pick me up?" Cryptically, she added, "I'm dressed."

From the doorway the first thing I saw after seeing Libby Herz herself was my book set on the edge of the kitchen sink; I could not see what was or was not stuck between its pages. And Mrs. Herz gave me no time to check; she ran into the bedroom and then out again, her raincoat whipping around her. Then yanking a kerchief from her pocket, she rushed out the door without once looking directly at me—though she managed to let me hear her say, "Paul called again. I told him we were coming."

As we drove, her eyes stared rigidly out the car window, while beside me her limbs fidgeted in turn. My first impression of her had been clear and sharp: profession—student; inclinations—neurotic. She moved jerkily and had the high black stockings and the underfed look. She was thin, dark, intense, and I could not imagine that she had ever once gotten anything but pain from entering a room full of people. Still, in an eager hawky way she was not bad looking. Her head was carried forward on her neck, and the result was that her large sculpted nose sailed into the wind a little too defiantly—which compromised the pride of the appendage, though not its fanciness. Her eyes were a pure black, and her shiny hair, also black, was drawn off her face in a manner so stark and exact that at the sight of it one could begin guessing at the depth and number of her anxieties. The skin was classic and pale: white with a touch of blue, making it ivory—and when she pulled off her kerchief she even had a tiny purple vein tapping at her temple; it seemed to me like an affect, something willed there to remind the rest of us how delicate and fragile is a woman. My initial feeling toward her was suspicion.

After a long silence, Gabe asked, "Do you have any children?"

"No," she said, "thank goodness." She drew a deep breath: she was rushed without children.

Harvested fields, stubbled and dark, bordered the highway; Mrs. Herz looked out at all that flatness too intently. There was vigor in the way she chose to avoid his eyes. Why? She had opened the book, she had read the letter. Why else? When he found himself as self-conscious suddenly as she, he tried relaxing with the knowledge that they were strangers and no discovery she might make mattered. Her strangeness, however, her curious expectancy, made discoveries matter even more. She did not look to be a person casual about private lives, her own or others.

Darkness cut vision in two, and she turned a little from the fields. "Are you in the Workshop?" she asked.

"I thought I would be. I've decided against it," he said. "Are you?"

"Paul's the writer," she said. "I'm still getting my A.B." She turned, at last, her full face toward him. "I've been getting it for about a decade." He looked away from the highway, and with a glance as distinct, as audible almost as a camera snapping, they registered each other's features.

"Paul said you're interested in James," she said, having flushed. "My name is Libby . . ."

"I'm Gabe Wallach."

"Neither of us know anything really outside the Edmund Wilson one," she said, as though she hadn't even heard him speak. "The ghost story."

"'Turn of the Screw,'" Gabe said.

"'Portrait of a Lady' is much better."

"You've been reading it?" He spoke almost sharply, as if he'd intended the book to be loaned only to the husband. The tone startled both of them. Her fine pale skin was tinged again; the dark eyes, which lent her face the little serenity it had, now only heightened the confusion in the car.

"Aren't you the one who loaned the book?" she asked. "Aren't you from Anglo-Saxon, Paul's class?"

"Yes."

"Well, I've been reading it, yes." There was curtness, but not enough to increase self-possession much.

Nevertheless, by way of conversation I asked if she had any children.

"Oh, no," she said. The deep breath she drew was to inform me that she was rushed and harried without children. She added a few mumbled words: "Thank goodness . . . children . . . burden . . ." It was difficult to understand her because she did not bother to look at me either when speaking or sighing. I knew she was avoiding my eyes—and then I knew that she had opened the book, removed the envelope, and read my mother's letter. Since she did not strike me as a person casual about private lives, her own or others, her self-consciousness became mine too.

Darkness had dimmed my vision before either of us spoke again. "Are you in the Writers' Workshop?" she asked.

"No. Just English. Are you?"

"Paul's the writer," she said. "I'm still getting my B.A."

"I see."

"I've been getting it for about a decade." There was a frank and simple note of exasperation in her voice, and it engaged me. I looked away from the highway and she gave off staring into the countryside, and with a glance as distinct, as audible as a camera snapping, we registered each other's features.

"Paul said you're interested in James," she quickly said, flushing. Then, "I'm Libby."

"I'm Gabe Wallach—" I stopped as once again the words flew out of her.

"Neither of us know anything really outside the Edmund Wilson one—" she said, "the ghost story."

"*Turn of the Screw*," I said, a good half minute after she had not resumed talking.

"*Portrait of a Lady* is much better." She spoke these words as though to please.

"You like it?" Gabe asked as kindly as he could.

"The first scene is marvelous."

"When they're all on the lawn."

"Yes, when Isabel comes. I've been living so long in barracks, elegance has an abnormal effect on me."

"The prose?"

"The rug on the lawn. You know, how they're all sitting on chairs on that immense lawn outside the Touchett's house. Ralph and his father and Lord Warburton. James says the place was furnished like a room. There's a rug on the lawn. That appealed to me." She stopped, after speaking so extravagently, and drew on her top lip so that her nose bent a little at the bottom. When attacked by nervousness, all that was dark, her eyes and hair, came to dominate her face. "That sounds terribly private. Sometimes I miss the point, I know . . ." The little laugh she gave admitted, perhaps intentionally, to fallibilities not merely literary. "It just . . . knocked me over," she said, looking down at the floorboard.

"It knocked Isabel over," Gabe said.

"Oh," was all she answered.

In the silence that followed Gabe forgot Isabel Archer and remembered himself. A little stiffly he asked, "How far have you read?"

"Up to where she meets Osmond," Mrs. Herz answered. "I think I can see what's coming. I don't know," she added quickly, "maybe I can't . . ."

"You must have read all night."

"Almost," she said, and flushed again. With another complexion self-consciousness might have gone unrecorded; as it was, she glowed.

Once again Gabe attended only to the black road.

"Paul hasn't started the book yet," Mrs. Herz began, but then she turned, almost as if to touch him. "Mr. Wallach, there was a letter in your book."

"Yes?"

"You must have forgotten it."

"I don't remember it," he heard himself saying as he passed a slow moving car.

"Yes . . . I brought it with me." She was wearing a shabby frayed raincoat, from whose pocket she took an envelope. "It was in the book," she said and handed it across to him.

"You like it?"

"The first scene is wonderful."

"When they're all on the lawn."

"Yes," she said, "when Isabel comes. I've been living so long in barracks, elegance has an abnormal effect on me."

"The prose?"

"The rug on the lawn. You know, they're all sitting on chairs on that immense lawn outside the Touchett's house. Ralph and his father and Lord Warburton. James says the place was furnished as though it were a room. There's a rug on the lawn. I don't know, perhaps it's just across somebody's legs, one of those kind of rugs. I've read it over several times, and since you can't be sure, I like to think of it the other way, *on* the lawn. That appeals to me." She stopped, violently—and I was left listening for the next few words. I looked over and saw that she was drawing on her top lip so that her nose bent a little at the bottom. All that was dark, her eyes and hair, came to dominate her face. "That sounds terribly private," she said. "Sometimes I miss the point, I know." The little forced laugh that followed admitted to fallibilities not solely literary. I was touched by her frailty, until I wondered if perhaps I was supposed to be. "The rug," she was saying, "knocked me over anyway." Whereupon her gaze dropped to the floorboard of the car.

"It knocked Isabel over," I said.

She received the remark blankly. "Yes," she said.

I tried to remember where in the book the letter was stuck. "How far have you read?" I asked.

"Up to where she meets Osmond. I think I can see what's coming. Though," she rushed to add, "perhaps I can't. I really shouldn't say that."

"You must . . . you must have read all night," was all I finally said.

She flushed again. "Almost," she told me. "Paul hasn't started the book yet—" I was looking ahead at the road; I heard her voice stop, and then I felt her move a little toward me. I believe she touched my arm. "Mr. Wallach, there was a letter in your book."

"Was there?"

"You must have forgotten it."

The quality of her voice had altered so as to make the whole occasion much too momentous; I heard myself saying that I didn't remember any letter.

"I brought it with me," she said, and from the pocket of her shabby raincoat she took the envelope; it must have been this she had raced back into her bedroom to fetch while I had waited at the doorstep. Now she handed it to me. "It was in the book."

"Thank you." He jammed the envelope into his pocket without any examinion. With his fingers however he fumbled at it--there was no evidence either way. The flap was tucked in. Nevertheless, he drove on with only one hand on the wheel. Mrs. Herz pulled at her black stockings and stuck two fists under her knees. For two miles they said nothing.

Finally she spoke. "She marries and is miserable."

He was shocked--one hand was still in his coat pocket. After a second he looked away from the road.

"Isabel will marry Osmond and be miserable," Mrs. Herz explained uncertainly. "She's . . . she's a romantic . . . isn't she?"

He realized suddenly how unjust he was being; he tried to appear more graceful. "I guess so. She likes rugs on lawns."

"She likes rugs on lawns," Mrs. Herz said, grinning. "That's the least of it. She wants to put rugs on other people's lawns."

"Osmond?"

"Osmond. More than Osmond." She raised her hands in front of her chest and opened them out, expressively. "Everything," Mrs. Herz declared. "She wants to alter stuff that can't even be altered," she added, vehement and vague.

"She believes in change."

"Change, my God . . ." She put her hand to her forehead.

"You don't believe in change?" For the first time he was amused by her.

She took it apparently for a more momentous question than was intended. "I suppose I do," she said, staring down into her raincoat. Change, alteration (said her face) was not so much the condition of all life as it was some sad and private principle of her own. She withdrew, hands under knees again, and forgot the book. Her emotional skittering, her conversational entrances and escapes, joined together once again in a single, sharp, and offhand impression: the girl was neurotic. You saw them around graduate school all the time married or single they were all intense. He drove faster and hunted the highway for Paul Herz. An approaching car blinked on its parking lights, and the harsh gray fields went absolutely black.

"Thank you." I put the letter immediately into my own jacket pocket. Out of sight I fumbled with it, but there was no evidence either way—the flap was tucked in. Nevertheless, I drove ahead with only one hand on the wheel. Mrs. Herz pulled at her black stockings, then stuck a fist under each knee. For two miles neither of us said anything.

In the tone of one musing she finally spoke. "She marries and is miserable."

I had been musing myself, and so I misunderstood at first who exactly was the subject of her observation. My misunderstanding must have produced a very strange expression on my face, for when I turned to demand an explanation, Libby Herz seemed nearly to dissolve in her seat. "Isabel will marry Osmond," she said, "and be miserable. She's—she's a romantic . . . isn't she?" she asked shakily.

I had not meant to threaten her. I forgot my family as rapidly as I could, and tried hard to be graceful. "I guess so," I said. "She likes rugs on lawns."

"She likes rugs on lawns," Mrs. Herz said, grinning. "That's the least of it. She wants to put rugs on other peoples' lawns."

"Osmond?"

"Osmond—and more than Osmond." She raised her hands and opened them, slowly and expressively. "*Everything*," she said, drawing the word out. "She wants to alter what can't be altered."

"She believes in change."

"Change? My God!" She put her hand to her forehead.

It was the first time I was amused by her. "You don't believe in change?"

Without warning she turned momentous on me again. "I suppose I do." She stared a little tragically into her college girl's raincoat: change, alteration, was not so much the condition of all life as it was some sad and private principle of her own. The hands tugged again at the stockings, went under the knees, and she withdrew. I drove faster and hunted the highway for Paul Herz.

"Do you believe," Mrs. Herz said, "in altering that way?"

And what was she talking about now--her life, all life, James? He did not answer.

"I mean, Isabel's trouble is she wants to alter others," she said, "but a man comes along who can alter <u>her</u>, Warburton or what's his name, ramrod--"

"Caspar Goodwood."

"Caspar Goodwood--and what happens? She gets the shakes, she gets scared. She's practically frigid really. She's not much different finally from her friend, that newspaper lady. She's one of those powerful women, one of those pushers--"

Here Gabe interrupted. "I've always found her virtuous and charming."

"Charming?" Mrs. Herz said. "For marrying <u>Osmond</u>?" Incredulity rendered her helpless; she slumped down in her seat, shaking her head.

"For liking rugs on lawns," he said.

The moment after he'd spoken, it was as though he had touched her. She pushed up to a more dignified posture. After all their tension together, a compliment was a strong beam swung backwards showing up the tension for what it was. In the diminished light, alone on the highway, his very simple-sounding remark had had all the earmarks of a pass. He remembered now the seriousness with which they had looked at each other some ten miles back.

In no time at all, apparently to inform him of the depths of her loyalty to her husband, she insulted him. "Perhaps you just like pushy women. Some men do," she said. When he didn't reply she went on in a revelatory tone. "That book, for instance, is really <u>full</u> of pushy people. People pushing and pulling each other," she said, "and most often with absolutely <u>clear</u>--" She had been speaking passionately, and leaving off there she left off too late. She had said all she had to without adding "conscience" too. The letter in Gabe's pocket might have been burning through to his thigh; he felts its presence with an actual rush of heat. He looked across at her as if she would have to tell him exactly how to respond. Her chin was still high, up with her last emphatic word. She finally lowered it, and the closer her nose came to her chest, the more willing he discovered himself to forgive her her indiscretion. Now

"Well, do you believe," Mrs. Herz suddenly put in, "in altering that way? Isabel's trouble is she wants to change others, but a man comes along who can alter her, Warburton or what's his name, Ramrod—"

"Goodwood. Caspar Goodwood."

"Caspar Goodwood—and what happens? She gets the shakes, she gets scared. She's practically frigid, at least that's what it looks like a case of to me. She's not much different finally from her friend, that newspaper lady. She's one of those powerful women, one of those pushers-around of men—"

Before she went off the deep end, I interrupted and said, "I've always found her virtuous and charming."

"Charming?" Incredulity rendered her helpless. Slumping down in her seat, as though konked on the head, she said, "For marrying *Osmond?*"

"For liking rugs on lawns," I said.

It was as though I had touched her. She pushed up into a dignified posture and raised her chin. Actually I had only mildly been trying to charm her—and with the truth no less; but in the diminished light, alone on the highway, it had had for her all the earmarks of a pass. And perhaps, after all, that's what it was; I remembered the seriousness with which we had looked at each other some ten miles back.

To inform me of the depths of her loyalty to her husband, she insulted me. "Perhaps you just like pushy women. Some men do." I didn't answer, which did not stop her. Since I had asked for the truth, I was going to get all of it. "That book, as a matter of fact, is really full of people pushing and pulling at each other, and most often with absolutely clear—"

She had been speaking passionately, and leaving off there was leaving off entirely too late. There was no need for her to speak that final word of my mother's: *conscience*. I was not sure whether to be offended or humiliated or relieved; for a moment I managed to be all three. It actually seemed as though she had deliberately challenged me with my secret—and at bottom I did not know if I really minded. The worst part of certain secrets is their secrecy. There is a comfort to be derived from letting strangers in on our troubles, especially, if one is a man, strangers who happen also to be women. Perhaps offering the book to be read in the first place had been my way of offering the letter to be read as well. For I was beginning really to be exhausted with standing over my mother's memory, making sure the light didn't go out. I had never even been willing to believe that my mother had treated my father badly, until she had gone

that it was out in the open, it did not seem so crucial.

"I'm sorry," Mrs. Herz said. "It was just habit. Which is even worse . . . I really am sorry."

"That's okay."

"It's not. I had to open it. I don't know what I expected. Surprises . . ." she said, crushed by her criminality.

After a moment, Gabe said. "Anybody would have."

". . . Paul wouldn't," she said.

A tall white farmhouse with gingerbread ornament hanging from every eave and frame was faintly glowing to their right; they passed it silently and then Gabe said, "It's just an easy letter to misunderstand."

"I guess so," she said in a whisper. "I don't think . . ." but she said no more.

"'Portrait of a Lady' is an easy book to misunderstand." Having changed the subject, he found himself filled with anger. "You're too harsh with Isabel Archer."

"Perhaps I am," she confessed.

"Wait until you finish it," Gabe said.

"I will."

"She shows herself to have a lot of guts in the end." When she didn't respond, with still another apology, he wondered if perhaps she misunderstood who he'd been speaking about. "Isabel does," he said.

ahead and told me so. Much as I loved him, he had seemed to me, while she still lived, unworthy of her; it was her letter that had made me see her as unworthy of him. And that is a strange thing to have happen to you—to feel yourself, after death, turning on a person you have always cherished. I had come to feel it was true that she had not merely handled him all her life, as one had to, but that she had mishandled him . . . At least I believed this with part of my mind. I had, curiously, over a period of a year, come to distrust the woman of whom the letter spoke, all the while I continued to honor and admire the memory of the woman who could have written it. And now, when I had begun to have to handle her husband myself, the letter came accidentally back into my life, to decrease in no way my confusion as to what to do with my father's overwhelming love.

"I'm sorry," Libby Herz was saying. "It was habit. Which makes it even worse. I am sorry."

"It's okay."

"It's not. I had to open it. I'm the sort of person who does that."

Now I was irritated at the way she seemed to be glorifying herself by way of her weaknesses. "Other people do it too," I said.

"Paul doesn't." And that fact seemed to depress her most of all; she worried it while we passed a tall white farmhouse with gingerbread ornament hanging from the frame of every window and door.

After some time had passed, I felt it necessary to caution her. "It's rather an easy letter to misunderstand," I said.

"I suppose so, yes," she answered, in a whisper. "I don't think—" But she said no more. Her disturbance was private and deep, and I could not help but feel that she was behaving terribly. If she was going to feel so bad about somebody's feelings, I believed they should at least have been mine. But she seemed unable to work up sympathy for anyone but herself: *she* was still getting her B.A., after "a decade"; *she* lived in barracks, so that elegance had a special poignancy for her . . . Her own condition occupied her totally, and I knew that she could no more appreciate my mother's dilemma than she could Isabel Archer's. I was, at last, fed up with her. "*Portrait of a Lady*," I said, "is an easy book to misunderstand too. You're too harsh with Isabel Archer."

"I only meant—"

"Why don't you wait until you read it all."

"I read half—"

"She shows herself to have a lot of guts in the end," I said, again not allowing her to finish. "It's one thing marrying the wrong person for the wrong reasons; it's another sticking it out with them."

"I didn't mean to be so flip," she said, "or nosey."

"All right . . . We ought to forget it. I don't mean to appear so dramatic," he explained, however, instead of forgetting it. "It's dramatic putting letters in books . . ."

"No, it's not. Other people put letters in books," she said.

"It's dramatic being caught then!" That was that! The girl was washing everything over with sentimentality; she apologized too much, now he was doing it too.

"Mr. Wallach, I didn't show it to Paul . . . if that alleviates anything."

"We're making too much of this."

She must have agreed; when she spoke next it was only to point up ahead and say, "There he is."

On the other side of the highway, a figure in a long coat was leaning against the darkened headlamp of a car, his feet crossed, his hands in his pockets, his chin hidden in his coat. Gabe moved the car onto the shoulder at the right hand side of the road.

Libby Herz touched his arm. "Please forgive me, Mr. Wallach. I'm a snoop and I'm dumb about novels. I'm sure you're right about Isabel Archer."

"You don't sound so dumb about novels," Gabe said, and stopped the car.

Before she reached for the door handle, she turned her face toward him almost wildly. "I stayed up to read the book because . . . I was very moved by the letter," she said quickly, and then they were both out of the car.

All that had to be removed from Paul Herz's car was his briefcase stuffed with freshman themes, a flashlight, and an old Army blanket that had covered the ripped upholstery in his front seat. Then they sat waiting for an hour; at Paul's request, a wrecker had been called by a state trooper. When he finally arrived, the three moved out of Gabe's car and gathered in the dark around the damaged hood. The wrecker stuck his head through the hole where the piston had shot through.

To that she had no answer; I had not really permitted one, and perhaps she realized that I was not talking only about the book.

Crushed, she answered finally, "I didn't mean to be so flip. Or nosey."

"All right, let's forget it." Though I was myself unable to. "I don't usually leave letters in books," I said. "It was a peculiar time. I was in the Army—" I heard myself becoming, in front of this girl, as momentous about my life as she had been about her own, and I stopped talking.

"Mr. Wallach," she said, "I didn't show it to Paul, if that alleviates anything."

"We're making much too much of this. Let's do forget it."

The next time she spoke it was only to point up ahead and say, "There he is."

On the other side of the highway a figure in a long coat was leaning against the darkened headlamp of a car. I moved onto the shoulder at the right-hand side of the road just as Libby took my arm.

"Please forgive me. I'm a snoop, and I'm dumb about novels," she said. "About people."

It was supposed to have been a genuine admission, but once made I realized that it was not true; she was not so dumb finally about either.

"I'm sure you're right about everything," she said to me.

"Maybe we're both right," I answered, though not overgenerously, and turned off the motor and headlights.

Before she reached for the door handle, she turned her face toward me once again. When people have much to say to you, and hardly any time in which to say it, their eyes are sometimes like Libby Herz's were that moment; above all, they were kind. "Mr. Wallach, I stayed up to read the book because I was very moved by the letter," and then, as though we were being watched, we both jumped from the car.

All that had to be removed from Paul Herz's Dodge was a briefcase stuffed with freshman themes, a flashlight, and an old army blanket that had been used to cover the torn upholstery in the front seat. We had to sit for half an hour in my car waiting for the wrecker; Herz had asked a state trooper to call one for him. There was little conversation: Libby discovered that her husband had ripped his new coat, and Herz said that he'd caught it on the hood, and from the back seat I thought I heard his wife begin to sob. Finally the wrecker arrived and the four of us gathered solemnly in the dark around the damaged hood. A sinewy little grease monkey, the wrecker flexed his knuckles and then stuck his hand down through the hole which the flying piston had made in the engine.

"Ten dollars," he said.

Cars flashed by them, illuminating Libby Herz's face. "Ten dollars!" she said. "That's ridiculous. Paul, that's ridiculous."

"It's junk," the wrecker said to the husband.

"It's a '48," Libby said feebley.

"Lady, it's got five pistons. It's junk."

He stuck his hand down into the hood again, and Libby Herz watched for the discovery of number six. He only shrugged his shoulders.

"How much would it cost . . . to fix it?" Mrs. Herz asked the question generally, as she had to: she was being ignored all around. The wrecker folded his arms and made Gabe special witness to his exasperation. For the benefit of the man, who was not the husband, he gave off a slow hiss.

"We can't fix it," Herz said. "Please, Lib . . ."

"Paul, ten dollars. The parts alone, the heater alone--"

"Lady," the wrecker said. "It's a piece of junk--"

"Will you stop saying junk!" She kicked at the ground and walked off toward the tow truck. Under the thick iron hook that swung off the crane, she stopped; then she looked up and Gabe thought he saw her shudder. Holding her arms around her front, she climbed into the back of Gabe's car.

"She's upset," Paul Herz explained to the wrecker.

"I haven't got all night."

"Okay."

The wrecker handed Herz two five dollar bills. "Is that it?" Herz said.

"Ten dollars," he said.

"For repairs?" Libby asked.

"For the car," the wrecker replied.

Headlights flashed by on the highway, illuminating on Libby Herz's face astonishment and woe. "Ten dollars! That's ridiculous. Paul, that's ridiculous."

The wrecker addressed the husband. "It's junk."

"It's a '47," Libby said feebly.

"Lady, it's got five pistons. It's junk."

"Five?"

"It's gotta have six to go," said the wrecker.

"Still." Then she looked toward her husband. "Paul . . ."

The wrecker stuck his hand in again, and Libby turned quickly back to him as though perhaps he'd miscounted the first time. He only looked at me and shrugged his shoulders. Herz looked at none of us; I saw him shut his eyes.

"How much would it cost . . . to fix it?" Libby asked the question generally, as she had to; she was being ignored all around. The wrecker folded his arms and made me once again special witness to his exasperation. The two of us, thank God, were not married to this woman: he gave off a slow hiss for our side.

"We can't fix it," Herz said. "Please, Lib."

"Paul, ten dollars. The parts alone—the *heater* alone."

"Lady," the wrecker said, and he seemed to have summoned his patience for an explanation of engine dynamics. "Lady, it's junk," he said.

"Will you stop saying *junk!*" She was seeing through teary eyes, and talking with a full nose, and she turned her back to all of us and walked off toward the tow truck. Under the thick iron hook that swung off the crane, she stopped and blew her nose; she looked up, whether at the clear moony sky or the iron hook I didn't know, but one or the other must have made an ungenerous comment to her about her fate, for she shuddered, and holding her arms around her front like a sick woman, climbed into the back seat of my car.

Paul Herz took his hands out of his coat pockets. "She's upset," he explained.

I nodded; the wrecker said, "I haven't got all night."

Herz looked at him and then, by himself, took a little walk around his car, staring down at each of the tires as though above all else he hated losing those four old friends. When he came back to us he tried to smile at me. "Okay," he said.

The wrecker took a tight fat wad from his pocket; he flashed it a little at us college boys and peeled off two fives. He rubbed them a moment with his black fingers and handed the cash to Herz.

"Is that all?" Herz said.

The wrecker was overtaken with a sudden cheeriness. He lifted his arms in the air. "That's it, my friend."

In Gabe's car, Paul Herz sat alongside him in the front; "Thanks for being so patient," Herz said to Gabe. "I'm sorry about all this."

"It's okay."

They started back toward Iowa City, and in the rear view mirror, Gabe saw that Libby Herz had turned and was squatted on her knees.

"The thief," she said, looking out the back window.

"Libby, the car blew a piston. It's junk," her husband said without turning around.

"Ten dollars . . . The fenders alone--"

"Libby, will you please. You don't know anything about cars."

"I know about thieves."

"I've been standing there for hours. What do you expect me to do--bargain with him at eight o'clock at night?"

"It's seven and we're not millionaires!"

"You don't know anything about cars--will you please be quiet," he said, approaching exasperation.

"Why did the piston come through like that?"

"I don't know."

"What are we going to do?"

"I don't know!"

Gabe Wallach had practically hunched himself behind the wheel; he had no neck, only the emotions of an eavesdropper. The wife was impossible, she wouldn't be still. The husband's car had been raised on a hook and tugged away; his briefcase was splitting with ungraded themes; Anglo-Saxon verbs had been waiting centuries to be memorized--but she wouldn't shut up. To outrace Herz's temper, Gabe pressed his foot to the accelerator; he didn't

The grease monkey was overcome suddenly with cheeriness. He lifted his arms in the air. "That's all, professor."

We drove back to Iowa City with Paul Herz sitting alongside me in the front. As soon as we got in the car Herz had said to me, "Thanks for being so patient. I'm sorry about all this."

"It's okay."

"The thief," Libby Herz said. In the rear-view mirror I saw she was sitting on her knees looking out the back window.

Herz seemed at first to decide not to be provoked, but at last he spoke. "Libby, the car blew a piston. It's junk."

"That's what the man said," his wife answered.

"Okay," Herz said.

"Ten dollars . . . the fenders alone—"

Herz glanced my way to see if I was listening. I tried my best to attend only to the black road, but of course there were my ears to contend with. "Libby," he said, "will you please? You don't know anything about cars, honey."

"I know about thieves."

"Damn it," Herz said, turning in his seat, "nobody cheated me!"

"I didn't say he cheated you—"

"What did you expect me to do? Bargain with him for a couple of dollars in the middle of the highway? I've been standing there for over an hour!"

"We're not millionaires!"

"You don't know anything about cars. Will you please be quiet!"

"Why did the piston come through like that?" she whined.

Herz turned to the front window again; he was fingering his coat where the cuff was torn. "I don't know."

"What are we going to do?"

"I don't *know!*"

By this time I was practically hunched behind the wheel, feeling the emotions of an eavesdropper—and having the thoughts of one too. Like most people with an ear to the wall, I had taken a side: the impossible one to live with, I could see now, was clearly the wife. Her husband's car had been raised on a hook and towed away; his brief-case was splitting with ungraded themes; his new coat, which looked to me to be a pretty old coat, was torn in the sleeve; and to top things off, his Anglo-Saxon verbs, like mine, had been waiting for centuries to be memorized, and waited still. And she wouldn't let the poor guy alone. Without being too obvious about it, I pushed the accelerator into the floor, though I realized that by outracing Paul Herz's temper, and avoiding what I could of his familial difficulty,

care to be around when the whispery patience reached its end. He didnt like to think, however, that he might be racing back to another phone call. "Where were you, I've been ringing all night?" What would he answer? Did it hurt to be any kinder to the old man? All right, he would explain: there was this fellow Paul Herz and his wife and a '48 Dodge and a wrecker . . . Is that what his father wanted to hear? Gabe could explain his absence in volumes, Dr. Wallach would continue to think his son simply hadn't picked up the phone. Gabe could scoop it up on the second ring, they still had a suspicious conversation: what's the matter he hadn't been there for the first? In short, why didn't Gabe call him? In short, why had he run to Iowa when Columbia University was only two subway stops north?

"Do you think you can get another section on the campus?" Libby Herz was asking her husband.

"Who said I'm quitting Coe?" Herz said.

"How are you going to get there?"

"I'll work it out."

"Don't you have a class there tomorrow?" she asked.

"Yes."

"How are you going to get there?"

"Why don't you wait until we get home, all right?"

A silence fastened on them now that was chilling the product of hurt feelings. Paul Herz was stewing, Libby Herz might be crying. Someone crossed a limb, someone sniffed, someone tapped twice with a finger. Gabe felt pressed to speak. "You teach at Coe?" he asked Herz.

"That's where I was coming from, yes. Two sections of composition."

"I thought you taught on the campus," Gabe said.

"Just one."

"I don't understand how a piston just explodes . . . out of nowhere," Mrs. Herz said from the back seat. "What didn't we do? Didn't we put antifreze in? Wasn't there enough oil?"

At last Herz turned around. "Libby, what do you think has been knocking in the engine since Michigan? The piston's been cracking or whatever the hell it's been doing for two *years*! Let's not worry about the car, all right? It's dead. Forget it."

"I'm just upset."

"We'll work something out."

I was of course racing back to familial problems of my own. I would walk through the door, the phone would ring, I would lift it, and my father would say: "Where were you—I've been calling all night?" I could race up the stairs and crash through the apartment and catch the phone on the second ring, and he still wouldn't be satisfied: What's the matter I wasn't there for the first? In short, why hadn't I called him? In short, why had I run off to Iowa for graduate work when Columbia was only two subway stops north? I could go back to Harvard, couldn't I? At least it wasn't six million miles away!

"Can't you get another section on the campus?" Libby Herz was asking her husband.

"Honey, I'm just not quitting Coe," Herz explained.

"How are you going to get there?"

"I'll work it out."

"Don't you have a class there tomorrow?"

"Yes."

"How are you going to get there?"

"Why don't you wait until we get home, all right?"

Small sounds of brooding followed. Someone crossed a limb, someone sniffed, someone tapped for several minutes against an ash tray. I felt pressed to say something, and finally, innocuously, asked Herz if he taught at Coe College.

"That's where I was coming from." He seemed almost relieved to answer my question. "I teach two sections of composition."

"I thought you taught on the campus," I said.

"Just one section."

"I don't understand," Libby butted in, leaning forward from the back seat, "how a piston just *explodes*. Out of nowhere."

No one answered her.

"Wasn't there enough oil? It was probably the what-do-you-call-its," she said, "the tappets. Didn't the man say something once about tappets?"

It's the little questions from women about tappets that finally push men over the edge. Herz practically rose in his seat. "Libby, what do you think has been knocking in the engine since Michigan? A piston has been cracking or whatever the hell it's been doing for two years. Since Detroit. Why don't you consider us lucky—we've driven that car thousands of miles. Stop thinking of the bad—think of all the *use* we got out of it. Let's not worry about the car. I sold it. We don't have it. Forget it!"

"I'm just upset," she said.

That seemed a good enough explanation for Herz; a patient and forgiving man, he said, "We'll work something out."

"Like in Michigan . . ."

"Will you please shut up!"

Three more gas stations and two roadhouses and they were in Iowa City. With Paul Herz giving him instructions, Gabe finally reached the barracks. Most of the windows were lit; behind each of the little dwellings, two black tanks showed glistening rims. Smoke twisted out of all the metallic funnels.

"Thanks a lot," Herz said.

"Yes . . . you're welcome." Mrs. Herz stirred in the back seat.

"Have you had any dinner?" Herz asked.

"That's all right . . ." Gabe said.

"Would you care to join us?" Herz looked into the back seat; Gabe watched the smoke part from the funnels. "What are we having?" Herz asked his wife.

"I don't know."

Herz turned back to Gabe "Would you care to have some spaghetti with us?"

"I don't think I can," Gabe said; halfway to becoming a pawn in a family argument, he was more uncomfortable than ever. Herz would punish his wife by making her set an extra place. She would punish him by clamming up about the menu. "I'm expecting a phone call . . ." Gabe said.

Paul Herz tried to eradicate with a smile his rotten mood; he hardly began to succeed. "Well . . . then." He opened the door.

"We have plenty." Libby Herz had seemingly risen from twenty feet of water--she spoke with that nervous vigor of hers, a girl who'd just rediscovered air. She leaned forward with her elbow almost to Gabe's ear. "Spaghetti, yes, with garlic and oil. We'd love to have you."

Paul Herz had already swung his briefcase through the door; now he waited awkwardly, half in, half out.

"How?"

"We'll work something out, please."

"Oh *how*," she burst out, "like in Michigan?"

"Will you please *shut up!*"

Three gas stations, two roadhouses, and no words later we were in Iowa City. Paul Herz instructed me with terse lefts and mumbled rights until we turned a corner and were rewarded with a panoramic view of the settlement of barracks. Lights were on in the undersized windows and smoke curled from all the metallic funnels, and I felt a little like the enemy sneaking up on the ambushed. It might have seemed that an army was encamped here, were it not for the tricycles tipped over on the gravel lawns, and the few pieces of clothing that had been forgotten, and still hung on the lines that crisscrossed from one gray rectangle to another. When the motor of the car was slowed down, I could hear a creaking and a straining and a clanging, as though the metal sides of the barracks and the concrete foundations were slowly sabotaging themselves in the dark.

"Thanks," Herz said to me. "Right here is fine."

I heard Libby stir in the back seat. Without turning, I said, "You're welcome. And good night."

Libby was opening the back door; Herz himself had a hand on the front door handle, where for a moment he hesitated. I felt he wanted to apologize to me for what I had had to see and hear. I only smiled as a signal of my sympathy, while his wife moved wordlessly out of the car.

After a moment he asked, "Have you had dinner?"

"That's all right," I said.

"Maybe you'd like to join us. What are we having?" he asked his wife.

"I don't know."

He looked back at me and asked quickly, "Would you care to have some spaghetti with us?"

"I don't really think I can . . . I'm expecting a phone call."

He reached out then and shook my hand; I saw him try to eradicate with a smile his rotten mood. He didn't begin to succeed.

Suddenly his wife was speaking. "We have plenty—" Libby Herz seemingly had risen out of twenty feet of water. She spoke with that desperate breathlessness of hers, a girl who'd just discovered air. "Spaghetti, with garlic and oil. We'd *love* to have you."

Paul Herz had already swung his briefcase through the door, and was stuck, half-in, half-out; he looked just as shabby and defeated as a man can who has been made a fool of by his wife. I imagined that even with another, he was no less alone than I was.

narrative focus

"I don't want to inconvenience--" Gabe began.
"Oh please come," Mrs. Herz said.

If you refuse dinner from half the household refuse the other half as well. The moral?

"I don't want to inconvenience you," I said, looking at neither of them.

"It's no inconvenience," Libby Herz said. "Please come," she said. "We have plenty."

Plenty! From her mouth no word could have sounded more pathetic.

When I returned home I went directly to the phone, picked it up, and said hello.

"Hello, Gabe? Where were you?"

"I had dinner out."

"Since five in the afternoon?"

"I was out before that for something else."

"Well," he said, working at being cheerful, "you're a tough man to catch at home. I don't know why you pay rent on an apartment, you're hardly there."

"Well, I had a busy day. How are you? I didn't expect you'd call again," I said. "You called last night."

"I was thinking it was two or three nights already," he said. "What's new?"

"Nothing. How's New York?"

"I took a walk after dinner. Millie made me an early dinner. What are you doing, still eating in restaurants? They overcook vegetables, I'll tell you that."

"I had dinner with friends."

"Look, when is your vacation again? I've got a calendar right in front of me."

"Christmas."

"I thought Thanksgiving."

"I don't get off then," I said. "Only Thanksgiving Day. I'm really busy with work, you know."

"You have dinner with friends, maybe you can have dinner with your father sometimes."

"It isn't just dinner with you," I said firmly, trying to keep separate my emotions and the facts. "It's all the traveling. It wouldn't be worth it coming all the way East for one or two days."

"Worth it." He simply repeated my words; then, having made his point, went on. "It's not my fault you went a million miles away," he reminded me. "There's NYU, there's Columbia, there's City College. I could name them all night."

"Don't," I said. "Please."

"Do you think I call up to be insulted?"

Drawing morals was no easier than conjugating anomalous verbs, u-declension. He set down the Anglo-Saxon grammar, but could not forget Paul Herz's silence. Why had Herz ignored him? Because he'd accepted Libby's invitation and refused is own? Maybe Herz's spirit still lurked down beneath his hood, mourning the sixth piston. A tall thin fellow with liquidy brown eyes and a smashed nose, Herz had the stunned air of a prizefighter who's just murdered his opponent. He stared at his hands with a blank face. The blowup Gabe hadn't looked forward to could have been, for a spectator, no more gruelling to witness. Mrs. Herz had to do all the talking, and she'd said too much. Gabe's tongue was still unravelling from the tinny tasting V-8 juice when she began to pour out the Herz family history; by the Bartlett pears he knew everything. It was apparently an even exchange, Herz Chronicle for Wallach Correspondence. Well, the debt was paid. He took his coffee in two gulps, mumbled about the phone call he was expecting, and fled.

"I'm sorry. I don't mean to insult you. But these phone calls, these phone calls are driving me nuts."

"Well, I'm sorry," he said, after a pause. "I don't mean to drive you nuts. I just thought a father had a right to call his son when he wanted to. Five minutes a couple times a week . . ."

"You're right," I said.

"Gabe—Gabe, I sit around here and I look at that orange sofa and I think of your mother. And I look at that Moroccan rug and I think of her. What am I supposed to do, get rid of all this furniture? We had it thirty years."

"I understand."

"Why don't you fly in Thanksgiving? I'll send you a check, get a ticket, come home for a little while. Millie will make a regular Thanksgiving dinner. We'll have Dr. Gruber here. We'll go down to the Penn-Cornell game. How does that strike you?"

"Why don't we wait until Christmas. It's only a few weeks later, and I'll have plenty of time—"

"But Thanksgiving is *traditional!*" he exploded. "What's the matter with you?" he said, and I heard him trying not to cry at the other end.

"I know it's traditional," I said. "I only get the day off. Just Thanksgiving Day. It's just not enough time. But Christmas I'll be home for two weeks."

"Your mother's been gone *sixty*-two weeks!" His unreason was nothing to the shaking in his voice. Yet there were no longer any patient explanations for me to make. Here it was November, 1953, the funeral had been in September of 1952, and still he was spinning down and around, deeper in his morbid sea. When I had been released from the Army early in August I had only suspicions about what it would be like; but three weeks with a drowning roommate had been all that I could bear. I could not help him out with his loneliness: I could not prop him up, counsel him, direct him, run him. I could not be Anna Wallach. I had finally to tell him (it had been a cold and nasty scene) that I was not his wife or his mother, but his son. A son, he said, a son *exactly!* What he wanted to know was if all sons run off, leaving fathers to sink forever by themselves.

I gave him several seconds now to get control. "Why don't you call Dr. Gruber?" I asked. "Why don't you go to the theater with him? See a show, go skating at Rockefeller Plaza—"

"Gruber? Gruber's happy. He had a wife he hated. I sit around with him all night and all he does is grin. It's worse than being alone, being with Gruber. I went skating with him last week. All he does, Gabe, all afternoon, is little figure eights, and all the time, smiling. What kind of man is that?"

Hours had passed, it was the dreary side of midnight, and his father hadn't called. Maybe he had; if so, it was a painful way to avoid him, dining with these Herz's. But what else--when they did speak he was cold and short and hated himself later. It was all out of hand--here it was 1953, the funeral had been in the spring of '51, and still his father spun down and around and deeper in his morbid sea. Gabe had come from the Army aware of responsibilities, anxious to help, but three weeks at home and he saw how his roommate was drowning; to share any longer that Central Park West apartment would be to sink himself, wrapped, weighted, in his father's loneliness. He told Dr. Wallach he must fly off to Iowa. No, NYU wouldn't do--nothing but Iowa, where they had a Writer's Workshop. Once there he enrolled for a straight Ph.D. program in English; he said nothing for the time being about the change. He would finish his degree, get a teaching job . . . and his father? He knew what Dr. Wallach didn't--Gabe across the table at breakfast was not the answer. Gabe could not prop him up, counsel him--he could not be Paula Wallach, he was a son. A son . . . exactly. Do sons run off leaving fathers to sink by themselves forever?

He was not laughing, but at least the worst was over; he was willing to tease himself.

"Dad," I said, "I don't know what to tell you."

"That's funny," he said softly, "because I know just what to tell you."

"I don't think I'd be a help." I felt myself losing control.

"I think you would. Look, what's wrong with going back to Harvard? At least I'll expect you Thanksgiving, huh?"

I knew he was wrong; everything in my experience told me he was wrong, and yet I said, "I'll see about Thanksgiving. I can't promise."

"I never asked for promises, Gabe. Just try. Just meet me halfway. I'll send you a check for the plane."

"Why don't you hold it off until I see—"

"It's only a check."

"I've got two checks I haven't even cashed yet."

"Cash them. You want to foul up my bank statements?" he asked gaily.

"I just don't need all that money, that's all. I've got the G.I. Bill. I've got Mother's money—"

"Will it kill you to cash them?" he asked. "I send them off, it makes me feel good. Will it kill you if I can balance up my account at the end of the month?"

"No."

"You cash those checks. Is that too big a favor to ask?"

I said no again, with as little conviction this time as before.

"And I'll see you Thanksgiving," he said.

"Please, Dad—please stop pushing me—about Thanksgiving—"

"Who's pushing? Let's get it straight, are you coming Thanksgiving or aren't you? You want me to have Millie buy a turkey or not?"

"I don't really see how I can make it, truly."

"You have time for other things, to eat dinner out—you have time to visit people—"

"That was involved. I was doing somebody a favor."

"Well, that's all I'm asking for."

"Please, stop pleading!"

"Don't shout at me!"

"Well, don't *beg* me!"

"Tell me, tell me, how else does one get through to you?"

"By making decent demands, that's how."

"I don't want to push your generosity too far."

"It's not even generosity we're dealing with."

narrative focus

It had almost been as though the chattering Mrs. Herz knew his predicament and set out to top it. She and her husband had the problem in reverse and it was much worse. Their families had run out on <u>them.</u> Jew wed Gentile and two wounds opened, one in Brooklyn, one in Queens, that

"No, you're right. It's supposed to be love."

"I don't think I deserve all this," I said.

"Nobody told you to run away."

"I didn't run."

"Iowa. Why not Canada! That's farther."

"That's closer," I said, but he wouldn't laugh. "I don't think either of us wants to have these kind of conversations. I don't think this is how either of us feels. Let's relax."

"Gabe, I'm sitting here with a calendar in front of me. I count days. I know how many days between now and Thanksgiving, between now and Christmas, from now to *Easter*. Maybe I'm going nuts, I don't know."

"You're just lonely."

"Yeah," he said, "some just."

"Please," I said, "I do understand. I'll do my best."

"All right, all right." He sounded suddenly very tired.

"You're feeling all right, aren't you?"

He laughed. "Terrific."

"Maybe you should go to sleep."

"It's all right, I'm watching a little television. Why aren't you in bed? It's midnight where you are. It's like wearing two watches; whenever I think what time it is here, I think what time it is there. What are *you* doing so late?"

"I'm going to study some Anglo-Saxon."

"That would impress your mother," he said, wisecracking. "It doesn't impress me."

"It doesn't impress me either. It bores hell out of me."

"Then," he began, "I don't know why you do it—"

"Let's go to sleep," I said.

"Okay, okay," he said, and when he yawned it was as though we were in the same room. "Take it easy, boy."

"Good night."

"See you Thanksgiving," he said, and hung up before I could answer.

When I finally got to bed that night, I found it impossible to get any solace from feeling sorry for myself. The irritation I generally felt toward my father—for things like hanging up as calculatingly as he had—I now felt for myself. Fresh from their drafty little house, I could not help comparing my condition with the Herzes': what I had learned at dinner was that all that my father would bless me with, the Herzes of Brooklyn and the DeWitts of Queens withheld from their struggling offspring. Once Jew had wed Gentile wounds were opened—in Brooklyn, in Queens—that were unhealable. And

were unhealable. Even conversion made matters worse; switching loyalties apparently proved you really had none. Libby read six thick books on the plight and festivals of the Jews, she met weekly with a thoughtful rabbi in Ann Arbor--finally there was a laying on of hands, she was a daughter of Ruth . . . and in Brooklyn no one was much moved; they listened to Paul's explanation, then they hung up. A shiksa was a shiksa. Knowing the dates of the Temple's destruction didn't change her blood any.

The DeWitt's, mother and father of Ruth Elishabeh Herz, were not notified. A priest and a two nuns already graced Mrs. DeWitt's side of the family; no Jew was needed to round things out. They hadn't needed one, why two?

No love then, no words or money flowed between the boroughs of New York and that particular barrack where the young couple had set up their bricks and boards. Gifts and feeling had disappeared over the years, and each with untimely exactness. They had married near the end of Paul's senior year at Bucknell (Libby was a junior), and the phone calls were hysterical from Brooklyn, stern from Queens. Still they were phone calls; someone had done some dialling. They went on to Ann Arbor, Paul for his M.A., Libby still for her B.A., and though the phone was silent, occasionally there was a check for twenty-five dollars to be paid to the order of Libby DeWitt. Checks in one's maiden name are not the stuff to build a marriage on, especially occasional checks. The Herz's quit school and moved three suitcases and a typewriter into a housekeeping room in Detroit so as to accrue; they sold bricks, boards, and books. "And then the money stopped," Libby had explained. "Paul worked in the Buick plant, hinging trunks. I was a waitress. And my father, he wrote us a little note to say that he had obligations to a daughter in school, not to Jewish housewives in Detroit. We saved what we could--which turned out to be about half what we'd planned--" her husband, who might have been dead, now raised his head and glared; she stopped, then started, apparently having skipped a little history--"and we came to Iowa. Now we don't hear from them at all. They're my parents, I suppose I like them for some things, but mostly I despise them."

Paul Herz had already looked down and so did not see what it had cost his wife to say the last.

all that Paul and Libby could do to make matters better had apparently only made them worse. Conversion, for instance, had been a fiasco. "Switching loyalties," Libby Herz had said, "somehow proved to them I didn't have any to begin with. I read six thick books on the plights and flights of the Jews, I met with this cerebral rabbi in Ann Arbor once a week, and finally there was a laying on of hands. I was a daughter of Ruth, the rabbi told me. In Brooklyn," she said, pouring me a second glassful of tinny-tasting tomato juice, "no one was much moved by the news. Paul called and they hung up. I might be Ruth's daughter—that didn't make me theirs. A shikse once," she said, drinking a tomato juice toast to herself, "a shikse for all time." As for *her* parents, they hadn't even been notified. Over the spaghetti I learned that a priest and two nuns already graced Mrs. DeWitt's side of the family; no Jew was needed to round things out.

The two families, it seemed, had chosen to withdraw help just when it was needed most. The young couple had been married at Cornell, sometime near the end of Paul's senior year and Libby's junior year. Apparently, in the weeks afterward, there followed some very stern phone calls from Queens. "Still," as Libby said, "they were phone calls. Someone at least did some dialing." When they went on to Ann Arbor, Paul for his M.A., Libby still for her B.A., the phone had gone dead. Only occasionally was there a check for twenty-five dollars, and that was to be paid to the order of Elizabeth DeWitt. The Herzes quit school and moved three suitcases and a typewriter into a housekeeping room in Detroit in order to accrue some capital. "And then," Libby explained, ladling out the Bartlett pears, "the money stopped. Paul worked in an automobile plant, hinging trunks, and I was a waitress. And my father wrote us a little note to say that he had obligations to a daughter in school, but none to Jewish housewives in Detroit. We saved what we could, which turned out to be about half what we'd planned—" At this point a fierce look from her husband caught her up short; when she started in again it was clear that she had passed over a little of their history. "And we came to Iowa. Now we don't hear from them at all," she told me. "They're my parents; I suppose I like them for some things—but mostly I despise them."

Paul Herz had already looked down into his pears and so did not see what it had cost his wife to speak those last words. And that was too bad, for she had said them for his benefit. Having doubtless realized how much she had irritated him by chronicling so thoroughly their bad luck, she had tried to square things with him by denouncing those people who had once fed and clothed her, and

"And now," she began drearily, "the car--"

Here Gabe left. She had squared the debt; he would forget she had read his mail. He could not forget the confessions themselves, however, as they'd left him feeling guilty--a fifty dollar check was still in his pocket; money, love, words, he had a superfluity of each. Returning a check to New York was like not picking up the phone, a cruelty; leaving them uncashed complicated bank statements; complaint was misunderstood. Besides he hadn't the control; he opened his mouth for one grievance, the rest followed. He reminded his father he was on the G.I. Bill--that made no difference. "It won't," his father said, believing the fact incontestable, "kill you."

But Libby Herz knew none of this; she chronicled their life with no evil motive Gabe could see. Her indiscretion wasn't moral, she just talked too much. Still he could not dismiss her. Desparate, nervous, vigorous, she made you listen; an emotional acrobat, skittering on her toes across high wires, she made you watch. In her presence one had almost the impulse to reach out and yank her to safety.

probably loved her too. Whatever had befallen them—she had decided to make clear at the very end—had not been the fault of her husband, but of those despised parents in the East.

I finished my dessert and went off to the bathroom where I stood looking in the mirror for a long time, hoping that when I returned to the table the both of them would be better able to face me as a guest again. Paul Herz may have smiled from time to time during dinner, but I knew he was not happy with his wife's performance. So I took my time, but coming out of the bathroom I was probably more stealthy than I had intended. I had given them no signal —I neither flushed the toilet, nor did I slam the door, the last only to spare the beaverboard interior of the house, which looked as though a little too much force might well bring down the works. From the hallway I was able to see into the living room, where the two Herzes were standing beside the dining table. Paul's arms were around his wife's waist, and his chin rested on her black hair. I stood with my hand on the bathroom door, unable to move one way or the other; I saw what Libby could not: her husband's face. His eyes were closed like a man in prayer. I heard him say, "*Please* don't complain. All you've done all night is complain." Earlier Libby had changed into a black full skirt, and now her hands were held close up against it; her head was bowed and no part of her touched her husband that could be prevented from touching him. "I'm not complaining," she said. "Every time I tell a story you think I'm complaining." Herz took his hands from her. "Well, you *were* complaining." I did not know what might come next and did not want to know; at the risk of unhinging the whole place, I laid my shoulder into the door and came clomping down the hallway, a man with shoes and ears entirely too large for himself. For our separate reasons, we were all uncomfortable saying good night.

From this I had come home to hear myself indicted for spitting on parental benevolence. Here was I (I had been reminded) with all that these Herzes were without. When my mother died, in fact, she had left to me all that her family had left to her, which, if not a fortune, was enough to spare me from calamity for the rest of my life; on top of this there was my father and his checks. Phone calls. Love. Money. It did not seem very manly of me to be suffering over my abundance, and I began to wonder, as I went to sleep that night, how I would perform if I were Paul Herz.

Paul Herz's overcoat could have been handed down from a beggar, it had that much class. A big, brown tent, it enveloped him; for all anyone knew, within he might be living a separate life. When he walked, no knees were to be seen anywhere. Cloth shuffled and he moved three feet closer to wherever he was going. Standing still and seated he had more dignity. Swimming brown eyes, good dark skin, and hair that rose in tenacious kinky ridges off a marked brow gave him a grim and cocky air; with his dark brown shirt and frayed green tie he looked finally to be a dissatisfied civil servant, a product of some nineteenth century Russian imagination. In class he inhabited not the room but just his own chair. Where the others recited their Beowulf hesitantly, skittering on syntax like a pack of amateur mountain climbers, Herz delivered Old English so that the blackboards shook; the vowels were from Brooklyn, the force for meadhalls. Finished, he slid his books in a crumpley tan briefcase--egg salad smelled somewhere at its bottom--and head down, left the room, silent as the North Pole. The separate life lived under the coat was dead serious.

Now, the morning after their dinner together, the coat swung beside Gabe Wallach. He had asked Herz to have coffee with him after class; he could not, however, bring himself to make his offer. The idea had come to him upon waking--at either end of sleep he had his most startling visions; puzzled with riddles in the dark, he was visited with solutions at dawn. The discomfort was to find that the problems you'd solved were the other fellow's. He had troubles of his own, why not face them? But his own dissatisfaction he couldn't pin down. Everything he did, work, sleep, everything, pumped up melancholy. For days he'd been trying to attach it all to his dead mother or gloomy father, or both. But that was blotting out the sun with his hand. Behind the hand the sun still glowed.

"Paul," he said, and when Herz's head turned in that thick dark collar, Gabe offered him the use of his car on those afternoons he had to teach at Coe. Then he found himself expectant, as though having cheered Herz, Herz should cheer him.

"That's awfully nice of you," Herz said, and he fastened on him a look whose force and penetration sent Gabe's eyes to the treetops. The gaze had pushed past gratitude to a place he couldn't recognize right off.

The following morning, out in the sunlight, I got a good look at Herz's new coat. It could have been handed down from a beggar; it had, I'm afraid, that much class. A big brown tent, it enveloped him; for all anyone knew, within it he might be living a separate life. When he walked no knees were to be seen anywhere. Cloth shuffled and he moved three feet closer to wherever he was going. Standing still and seated he picked up more dignity. Swimming brown eyes, good dark skin, and hair that rose in tenacious kinky ridges off a marked brow gave him a grim and cocky air. On the first of November he had had to give up on the T-shirt; now in a dark brown shirt and a frayed green tie he had the look about him of a dissatisfied civil servant, a product of some nineteenth-century Russian imagination. In class he inhabited not the room but just his own chair. Where the others skittered on the syntax of their *Beowulf* like a pack of amateur mountain climbers, Herz, when asked to recite aloud, delivered Old English so that the blackboards shook; the vowels were from Brooklyn, but the force was strictly for meadhalls. Finished, he slid his books into a crumpling tan briefcase—the smell of egg salad wafted up from its bottom—and head down, left the room, silent as the North Pole. The separate life lived under the new coat was dead serious.

The morning after our evening together, this same coat—whose cuff I noticed had already been sewn into one piece again—was swinging to and fro beside me. No words came from its owner, which made speech somewhat difficult for me. Upon arising I had thought of how I might be able to help Herz alleviate one of his problems; now his reticence made me hesitate to say what was on my mind. I had the feeling that he was nettled at me for having been witness to all that had happened the night before. If I were to make my suggestion, it would probably seem to him that I was prying into his affairs.

I asked him how Libby was and he replied with the shortest of answers: fine. I invited him to the Union for coffee, but by the time we reached the stairs I couldn't think of anything more to say that wouldn't really have been beside the point—so I went ahead and offered him my car to drive up to Cedar Rapids on the afternoons he taught there.

He turned and fastened on me a look whose penetration sent my own eyes up to the treetops for a moment. "That's very nice of you," he said, and in his voice, as in his gaze, there was something more than gratitude. Later I realized that what he'd been searching for was my motive.

"I hardly use it," Gabe said. A motive, it seemed, was owed Herz; he could only add, "Hardly ever in the afternoon. I'm usually at the library."

"I appreciate the offer."

"It's no inconvenience."

"My wife and I had a talk. We're changing our plans."

"You're not leaving?"

"We're working something out."

Herz preceded him into the thronging student union where they stood in line before the coffee machine; face to back they said nothing. Then face to face again, and still nothing. Gabe was too confused for anger. Had he insulted Herz? It was a car he offered, a couple afternoons a week, not a substitute overcoat. Why was the fellow so curt? Hadn't Gabe given him a lift? Why so secretive about the future?

Herz drank from his steamy cup, volunteering no more information. For someone whose clothing made such a strenuous appeal, it seemed unfair of him not to discuss his condition out loud; but inside the coat life was not just serious, it was mysterious. So where did Libby Herz figure in? Was she allowed within the shabby garment? If so, was she happy there? Gabe could continue to question only himself. Each of the young men finished his coffee, each stuffed his cup into the receptacle, and neither added to the general hum in the smoky room. They left, and at the bottom of the stone stairs Herz extended a hand and Gabe shook it: well, so much for the Herz's. Herz didn't need a ride anymore. They separated.

Gabe walked slowly to the library, slightly dejected. The truth was that the home of a married couple--even that chilly barren living room--might have been pleasant to visit from time to time. His loneliness wasn't helping his melancholy any, and perhaps (since he would not lay off searching for that motive owed Herz) it was to attach the Herz's to him, to put them firmly in his debt, that he had offered the car. That was harsh reasoning, but there'd been harshness in Herz's taciturnity; though it was actually Herz who in a way had used him as a convenience, Gabe felt accused. Surely though he would forget it--he would find other people. Till then he had actually been putting _off_ friendships and connections--he might have to pack and fly to a pining father at any moment. Now though he was ready--

"I don't need it in the afternoon," I said. "I'm usually at the library."

"I appreciate the offer," he said.

Thinking that perhaps he could not accept until I assured him that the arrangement would inconvenience me in no way, I added, "I live close enough to the library to walk—"

"Yes, but you see, my wife and I had a talk."

"Oh, yes?"

"We're changing our plans."

He smiled; but there was in his manner something stiff and withdrawn, particularly when he had referred to Libby as "my wife." I asked him, after a moment's silence, if perhaps they had decided to leave Iowa. I said that I hoped they had not.

"We've just worked something out," he answered, and started down the stairs. I followed, too confused as yet to believe that I was simply being rebuffed. While we drank our coffee there came a moment (at least for me) when I felt that one or the other of us could have said, "Look, all I meant..." and so on. But neither of us felt called upon to be the one to say it. After all, it was only a car I was offering him a few afternoons a week, not a new overcoat. Why so curt?

I waited, but he volunteered no further information. For someone whose clothing made such a strenuous appeal, it was a little silly of him, I thought, not to admit to his neediness out loud. Not that I expected him to come begging; I simply did not care for my offer to be written off as patronizing... unless of course he really did have a new plan, which made my car unnecessary. Perhaps it was prying of me, but I thought I had a right to an explanation somewhat more detailed than the one with which he had shut me up.

I never got it. Outside the Union he was abrupt but by no means discourteous; he extended a hand, I shook it, and we said goodbye. But as I walked off I said to myself, So much for Mrs. Herz and her silent husband. And though we had an acquaintanceship of only some twenty-four hours, and not a particularly gracious one at that, I was saddened. Whether Herz was more proud than wise was beside the point for me; I had awakened that morning positively elated that I could come to his aid. Denying my help, he'd managed to deny me my elation as well.

Finally I discovered myself piqued with him. However he chose to increase his discomfort, I realized, he chose to increase Libby Herz's discomfort as well. Clearly, she had not the talent for misery that he had. Were she to go out after a new coat, she would not come back, I was sure, with such a wailing piece of goods. It seemed to me that Herz actually found pleasure in saying to the world: Woe

and strangely enough it was Libby Herz who had helped make him ready by freeing him, as much as she was ble, from the East. That too had been an early morning discovery: Libby had said that she was moved by his mother's message, and saying that, she'd made his mother human again. His mother and himself, he'd come to think, had been unkind to Dr. Wallach--she by manipulation, he by desertion. But that wasn't so; his poor father, that emotional volcano, had nearly smothered both. Finally it was not immoral, it was natural that both had had to search out ways to live with him. For Gabe it was living without him. Freed, however, adrift in the world again, he had made his first mistake. He had moved to the wrong people. One didn't want friends, the other couldn't be moved toward alone: she was someone else's wife. That gaze of Herz's, the look that had appeared to question the very generosity it was supposed to appreciate, seemed suddenly to have a classic, simple explanation. Well, Herz shouldn't worry. His wife had fed Gabe spaghetti--that hardly made him correspondent. He was quite willing to stay the hell out of their sorrows and bother neither of them again. There was, in fact, a pretty girl from California sitting beside him in Bibliography; he would invite her for a drink that night. She, it was true, was plainer than Libby Herz, and she had not read the deathbed note; but it was also true that she was not married to the inscrutable, ungracious Mr. Herz.

* * * * * * * * *

is me. There was a scale moving inside me, and as my irritation with Herz grew weightier, my sympathy rose for his wife. The remark she had made late in the afternoon of the day before sounded clear once again in my ear.

The stresses and strains of the previous day had allowed me to forget that this girl, whose husband wouldn't sit behind the wheel of my car, had said to me that she had been moved by my mother's words; doubtless, too, by my mother's circumstance. And by my own? I wanted all at once to sit down with Libby Herz and explain to her why it was that my poor father had to be manipulated by the people with whom he shared his life. I wanted to explain why I had had to desert him. And for my explanation I would not have minded receiving the balm of sympathy. Which might have been the reason—might it not?—for Paul Herz finding it necessary to turn down my offer. When there's trouble at home, why encourage a sympathy-hunting young man to hang around? One can never tell—if there happens to be a sympathy-hunting young wife at the other end—just how the balm may find expression. That deep gaze Herz had given me then was explained: he hadn't been looking for a motive, he'd come up with one. Perhaps he did not see what Libby might give to me quite so clearly as he saw what he thought I could give to Libby, and what she might accept. But that had been enough to force him to rule me out as a friend or aid. And it was enough, I decided, to persuade me to rule myself out. We would each have to work out the problems of family life within the confines of the family in which the problem had arisen. I only hoped for Herz's wife that she would come through her tribulations with her energy and her complexion undamaged. Both, I discovered, had touched me more than I had thought.

We come now to an interlude about which there is not too much that need be explained. The girl's name was Marjorie Howells and she was in revolt against Kenosha, Wisconsin. For several months she had been sitting beside me in Bibliography, and the morning that I was rejected by Paul Herz, I happened to run into her in the library. I was feeling at the time somewhat superfluous—and here was this girl, very pretty, albeit a little overhealthy. I did not know, when I asked her to have a beer with me that night, that she was in revolt against Kenosha, Wisconsin; I only believed that few complications could thrive behind such a perfect set of teeth. We had many beers, it turned out, and after a while she was looking across at me with flames flashing in her eyes, and asking me how it felt to be a Jew in America. I asked her how it felt to be a Protestant in

America—and she told me. It was very dry and very typical. Jews, she explained, were different. Marge's father, a white-haired investor in Chicago, of whom she showed me a rather intimidating photograph (high tariff written all over his face)—her father thought Jews were different too, but Margie thought they were different from the way her father thought they were different. When I told her that in 1948 my own father had been chairman of an organization called New York City Professional Men for Wallace, I only fed the furnace. It wound up that I could not say anything that did not produce in her a larger and larger passion for me and my background: even the fact that the living room of my family's apartment looked out over Central Park seemed to impress her disproportionately. Halvah and Harvard and Henry Wallace—I suppose I cut an exotic figure. We wound up back in my apartment with no lights on and my sense of reality—as happens in the dark—out the window. It was all as typical as Protestantism: I held the girl and kissed her and soon enough the two of us were revolting against Kenosha as though Caligula himself was city manager. Margie had spent four years at Northwestern and later in the night we got in our licks against that bourgeois institution too. When we spoke again I teased her about her image of me—me, a delicious specimen of Hebraic, Marxist exotica—which was not exactly my image of myself. But by then teasing was only another endearment.

Margie said, "I'd like to stay with you."

"You can stay," I said.

"Can I?"

"Yes."

"Shouldn't we go back and get some things?"

"I have eggs and orange juice," I assured her.

"I meant stay," she said. "Really stay."

I spoke then not only for Kenosha but for all small towns everywhere."Marge, we hardly know each other."

"We can be happy as kings," she said, very sweetly.

"What do you need to get?"

"Do you have Breck shampoo?"

"No."

"I want to get my Breck and my Olivetti. I have an electric frying pan," she said, a little breathlessly.

"I have gas," I pointed out.

"Electric cooks perfect eggs," she told me. "Oh I want to eat so many breakfasts here."

So we drove to Margie's room and she packed a suitcase full of skirts and underwear, and in a large cardboard carton which I

took from the shelf of her closet, I began to lay her frying pan and her Olivetti and her steam iron and her Breck and her *Oxford Book of Seventeenth-Century* Verse. And all the time I bent over the carton I wondered what I was doing. Some things—carrying George Herbert into a sinful union! Not till I felt fully the absurdity of what I was about did I realize how clutchy I had become of late: when I had seen Paul Herz in class, I had rushed to give him a book; when Libby called for a lift, I had dropped my studies and run right over. That very morning I had tried virtually to graft the Herzes to me by loaning them my car. That was an anxious way to interpret a simple act of kindness, but with all the evidence, with Marge Howell's soapy smell moving back and forth only a foot behind me, what else could I think about myself? I had not realized that I had been missing my father as much as he had been missing me.

She put her arms around me, this sweet empty-headed girl, and from behind me kissed my neck. With wryness, which never protected anyone from anything for very long, I said, "Oh, Margie, I am your Trotsky, your Einstein, your Moses Maimonides." And that foe of Luther and the Middle West asked, "Was that his last name?"

Was it a feeble joke or didn't she know? Either way, I continued to lose confidence in myself.

Mindlessly, mindlessly, mindlessly—pushing our shopping cart through the market, and late in the afternoon sipping cocoa in bed, and every few nights watching Marge let down her whirly blond hair to be washed. I would be sitting on the edge of the tub translating *Beowulf* to her while she leaned across the sink wearing her half slip and raising luxurious bubbles on her scalp. With her hair combed out straight, the wet strands just touching her back, she would turn to me with a look of perfect well-being and satisfaction. "And yet I don't feel I have to marry you. Isn't that something? I didn't think I could feel so liberated." There were nights when it was charming, but there were other nights too, and then the girl at the sink and I on the tub seemed no more facts of this life than those impossibilities, Hrothgar and Grendel, whose words and deeds I had just been trying to comprehend.

Margie soon came down with the grippe and was very hard to deal with. In bed she took to wearing my pajamas, and posing in them. She wanted to hear about all the girls I had made love to, and then I could hear about all the boys who had wanted to make love to her. She would not sleep with the lights out, and finally when she did sleep and I was alone, I had to face the fact that she was not much different sick from what she was well: the strain was simply

narrative focus

Late one afternoon in December he met Libby Herz in the supermarket. Rounding a corner near the meat department, their carts collided.

"Hello," she said.

"Hello, how are you?"

"Better," she said. "How are you?"

"I'm okay. Were you sick?"

"I had a fever. It's gone." She answered, cheerily, as if she was herself unaware that signs of her illness, the fever, were still in her face; directly beneath the eyes however she had suffered--she looked scribbled on with a pencil. A crease extended too from the edges of her nostrils to the edges of her mouth, barely visible, but still a mark on the skin.

"How's your husband?" he asked.

"Fine . . . Come see us some night."

"I've been very busy . . ."

"I want to thank you," she said, "for the car offer. That was really very nice." A strand of hair was swept away from the side of her head; she brushed it with her hand and then pulled everything tighter, through the rubber band at the back.

"I'm sorry you couldn't use it," Gabe said.

"Thank you anyway."

She left off with the rubber band and rearranged some items in the cart. Her black hair was in order again--yanked back from her forehead, it was a declaration of openness: what shows below is mine. With her dark eyes retreating a little into her skull, what did show below was mostly nose--it leaped from the center of her face with arrogance and shame. When she stood still finally she had nothing more to say; Gabe did not know whether to continue to stare into her oleomargarine or push on with his cart.

"How do you get those groceries home?" he finally asked.

"Walk," she said, shrugging.

purer, that was all. On the third day of her illness I was at last able to tear myself away from her by way of the necessities of shopping. Leaving our casino game, I drove to the supermarket under threatening winter skies. I knew that when Margie was fully recovered, strong and bouncy, we would have to arrange a parting; I was no gray-haired Chicago investor, no left-wing Jewish intellectual, and I could not continue to serve as either, or both. Nevertheless, because I was at the time as weak in the face of loneliness as in the face of pleasure, I shopped for two for the week, buying in the drug section of the market four bottles of Breck and three jars of the dainty underarm deodorant she used, and later the chocolate drink she was so fond of. Then as I was rounding an aisle by the meat department, I saw Libby Herz pushing a cart toward my own. I ducked away, but a few minutes later we collided in front of Detergents.

"Hi," she said.

"Why, hello—how are you?"

"Better. How are you?"

"I'm fine. What's the matter?" I asked. "Were you sick? Or are you just feeling generally better?"

"I had a fever."

"There's one going around."

"It's gone now," she answered cheerily; too cheerily, for looking at her I saw the after-effects of illness still in her face.

"How's your husband?"

"He's fine."

We both did not know where to go from there. She must have heard, as I did, that I had not called Paul Paul.

"You must come see us some night," Libby suggested.

"I've been very busy."

A strand of hair that was swept away from the side of her head suddenly engaged her; she brushed it with her hand, and pulled everything tighter through the rubber band at the back. "I want to thank you," she said, "for the car offer. That was very nice. Paul told me."

"I'm sorry he couldn't use it."

With her hair out of the way, she began fiddling with the items in her cart; she had a great deal of oleo but no Breck. "Thank you anyway," she said, and we both looked off at the shelves of Tide and Rinso.

"How do you get all those groceries home now?" I asked.

She shrugged. "Walk."

"It's far."

"Not that far."

"Why don't you wait? I'll drive you there."

Before she answered, she looked into his cart. It was true that he had more groceries than one person might need. In front of Libby Herz he felt embarassed; only three weeks earlier he had been available for meals out, alone. In seeking connections he had moved too fast The girl from Bibliography had turned out to be only a little less plain than he'd imagined, still he had allowed himself the pleasure of drifting mindlessly toward her. Neither he nor Barbara were serious--they were more vocal than necessary about that--but the strain of their being constantly casual and constantly together, made him feel less than he was. He seemed to set out after people with sentiment having little to do with it; where sentiment existed, he ran. But that was necessity--take the girl standing before him . . .

"I'll wait just out in front," Libby said.

In the car he put his bundles out of sight on the back seat; her package sat between them. He asked how school was.

"I'm not in school anymore. I quit a few days after we saw you."

"I didn't know."

"I'm working in the registrar's office," she said. He turned a corner and she spoke again. "I finished your book. You don't mind if we keep it, do you? Paul hasn't gotten around to it yet. He's just starting to get some time."

"That's all right."

"Isabel has a lot of courage in the end. You were right. Too much almost . . ." she said, hesitantly. "Going back to Osmond, I mean . . ."

"It does resemble stubbornness," Gabe said.

She apparently did not know what side he was on.

"Why don't you wait—" I found myself looking at a crease that extended from the edges of her nostrils to the edges of her mouth, barely visible, but still a mark on the skin. "Maybe you shouldn't walk . . ."

"Oh but I'm fine."

"I can drive you. I'm almost finished."

When she looked to see how finished I was, I realized that it was clear from my cartful that I was feeding and deodorizing more than one. It was also clear—to me—that the other person was not one toward whom I had a great deal of feeling. It was beginning to seem that toward those for whom I felt no strong sentiment, I gravitated; where sentiment existed, I ran. There was my father; there was even the girl before me. With her, of course, circumstances had combined with judgment to hold me back. But no circumstances had forced me, really, into a liaison with Margie Howells, whose sickroom behavior informed me that even if I had not developed feelings, I had at any rate initiated obligations. Standing there with Libby Herz, I found myself feeling rather shabby.

"Do let me drive you," I said.

"I'll wait just outside."

In the car I put my bundles out of sight on the back seat. I propped up Libby's bag in front, between us, and asked her how school was.

"I'm not in school any more."

"I didn't know that," I said.

"I decided to quit a couple of weeks ago. A few days after we saw you, I guess."

"I suppose it's less hectic."

She shrugged her shoulders again, and I saw that somehow I was making her nervous. "I'm working in the registrar's office," she said. "You're right, it is less hectic. I mean generally." And rather than explain, she raced ahead. "I finished your book. You don't mind if we keep it for a while, do you? Paul hasn't gotten around to it yet. He's just starting to get some time."

"That's all right."

"Isabel *has* a lot of courage in the end," she said. "You were right. Going back to Osmond, I mean. I don't know—I think some people might think it was stubbornness. Do you think it was?"

I thought she thought it was, so I said, yes, in a way it probably was. However, I said, stubbornness might be the other side of courage.

"That's very hard to figure out," she answered. "When you're being stubborn and when you're being courageous. I mean, if you

"Maybe . . . yes . . . Why don't you come to visit us?"

"Well. . ."

"Don't judge either of us by that night, please don't. We were . . . preoccupied."

"Actually I've been very busy." He realized too late how involved he made himself sound--yet he was involved, there was a carton full of evidence in the back seat. That he had initiated obligations without feeling was a private distinction To say he was busy was practically the truth. Somehow Libby Herz's presence made the truth seem more tiresome and indecent than it had until then.

"Paul did appreciate your offering the car," she said. "It just wasn't a solution for us. I hope you didn't think he was ungrateful. He's just very . . . private. He's very sweet," she said, blushing lightly. "I know he can look rude-"

"No, no, I didn't think him rude at all."

"We're much better off now, really. I thought it was awfully kind of you, considering what we'd been the night before. I realize I must have complained all night." The fact had apparently been pointed out to her by another; she gave a forced laugh. "Paul was just overworked. It's not so bad, truly."

"Yes . . ." he said, without looking at her. "Doesn't he teach at Coe anymore?"

"It was just too much, and I don't mind working," she said. "He couldn't write, he was up every night marking papers. He was too upset. We'll finish one education at a time. I think tempers are better all around." She stopped abruptly.

were alone—but there are other people . . ." The conversation seemed suddenly to depress her. Whenever we talked principle it always wound up seeming as though we were talking about her. I could tell when she spoke next that she had told herself to stop brooding.

"Why don't you come visit us?" she asked.

I did not answer.

"Don't judge us by that night," Libby said. "Please don't. We, both of us, were preoccupied."

"It's not that," I said. "Actually I've just been busy."

"Paul . . ." she began slowly, "did appreciate your offering the car." She looked out the side window as she spoke, and I was reminded vividly of our first interview. "It simply wasn't a solution for us. I hope you didn't think he was ungrateful. He did appreciate the ride. He appreciated it very much. He's—very private. He's sweet, you know"—she toppled one word on the next—"and, I know, I know he can look a little rude, to strangers—"

"No, no. I didn't think him rude at all."

"We're much better off now, really. I thought it was awfully kind of you, considering what we'd been the night before. I realize," she said in a voice too loud for a two-door sedan, "that I must have complained all night."

"Oh no. I just thought you were telling some stories."

What I said confused me, and confused Libby too. Her voice was hardly natural when she said, "Paul was just overworked. It's not nearly so bad as I must have made it seem."

"Doesn't he teach at Coe any more?" I asked.

"Well, he does—but he won't be, starting next semester. It's too much. And I don't mind working. Really, it's sort of a nice change. There's a bus, he found out, that goes up to Cedar Rapids and he's finishing out the semester taking that. It shoots a lot of his day—but that's okay anyway because he can read on it—and oh, I know it sounds involved, but now in fact it's less involved than it was. Before he couldn't write, and he was up every night marking papers, and he was too upset. We'll finish one education at a time. I think tempers are better all around."

"I'm glad everything is going well."

"Oh yes. You must come to see us."

"I will."

"I'm sure Paul would like it."

Then why the hell hadn't he asked me himself? I saw him three times a week, and got from him only a hello and goodbye . . . But his life had only just changed, I told myself, and perhaps it was true that as his several frustrations dropped away, he would come to feel less defensive about me.

Gabe said, "Well, I will come--"

"I'm sure Paul would like it. Come tonight."

"I don't think I can make it tonight."

". . . You're certainly welcome to bring somebody," she said.

"Maybe some other night. Right now it's . . ." but he finished by saying, "Maybe after Christmas." He turned the car up toward the barracks.

"Paul will return the book soon. I've changed some opinions since last time."

"We'll have to talk about it."

"I do want to. Bring somebody if you like," she added quickly. "I think Paul would like that," and she stepped out of the car, and smiled, not too happily, back at the driver.

"I will come," I said.

"Come tonight."

"I don't think I can make it tonight."

As we headed up toward the barracks, Libby said, "You're certainly welcome to bring somebody with you, if you like."

"Maybe some other night." Obviously I could not tell her that at the moment there was a sick girl home in my bed. "After Christmas," I said, hoping that by then there would be no girl in my bed at all.

"Paul will return the book soon," Libby said. She pointed up to the gray hut that was theirs. "Right here. There are a lot of things to talk about, about Isabel's character."

"There are, I know."

"I'd like to talk about them," she said. "And do, really, bring anyone you like. I think Paul would like you to bring someone." When I looked at her pulling the bundle from the car, she tried to avoid my eyes. I knew she did not want me to suggest that I carry the bundle for her.

Aside from a forty-page story that served as the original version of Chapter I, Letting Go evolved into its published form through three preliminary drafts. The first and third of these are difficult to read because numerous changes pertaining to the second draft and the Published Version were superimposed upon them. Draft #2 has been reproduced above. While less marred by corrections than Draft #1, it illustrates the writing problem under consideration as well as Draft #1 does. That problem concerns Mr. Roth's choice of storyteller. His novel, which was narrated during the first two versions from the point of view of "he," shifted at the beginning of the third to the point of view of "I." First person remains the predominant narrative focus in the Published Version, predominant being a necessary qualification since the author varies his basic approach there with passages related through the eyes—if not the voices—of characters other than Gabe Wallach.

Mr. Roth has explained why he altered the narrative focus of Letting Go between the second and third drafts. As "he," the protagonist seemed stiff and boring and away from the center of the novel. Using this technique, Mr. Roth was unable to evaluate him or to get at Paul and Libby Herz satisfactorily. But when Gabe Wallach could talk about his problems and those of his friends, such dilemmas were resolved, the talk itself forming a part of the meaning of their lives. And by changing to first person in Chapter I, Mr. Roth was able to create a technical contrast of considerable import. It now became possible for the protagonist to revert back to "he" during the last 150 pages, an appropriate maneuver considering that Wallach, who has had all the choices, has grown as powerless as the others, who must save him.

Perhaps a brief analysis of the same passage from the second draft and the Published Version will make the essential differences between third and first person narration clearer. The second contains this description of Libby Herz:

As they drove she stared out the car window, and fidgeted with her fingers. Gabe's first impression had been of a thin, dark, intense graduate student; she had the jerky movements, the high black stockings, and the underfed look. With occasional side glances, he now refined the image. In an eager hawky way, she was goodlooking; there was a large sharp nose *that sailed a little too defiantly into the wind; the black eyes seemed calm enough, but her hair, also black, was drawn back in a manner so stark and exact that at the sight of it one could begin to guess the depth and number of her anxieties. Her skin was classic and pale, and when she finally removed the kerchief, Gabe could see a small blue vein tapping at her temple; it distracted from the fragility of her complexion. In her lap she continued to twiddle with objects no one else could see.*

In the Published Version this description reads:

As we drove, her eyes stared rigidly out the car window, while beside me her limbs fidgeted in turn. My first impression of her had been clear and sharp: profession—student; inclinations—neurotic. She moved jerkily and had the high black stockings and the underfed look. She was thin, dark, intense, and I could not imagine that she had ever once gotten anything but pain from entering a room full of people. Still, in an eager hawky way she was not bad looking. Her head was carried forward on her neck, and the result was that her large sculpted nose sailed into the wind a little too defiantly—which compromised the pride of the appendage, though not its fanciness. Her eyes were a pure black, and her shiny hair, also black, was drawn off her face in a manner so stark and exact that at the sight of it one could begin guessing at the depth and number of her anxieties. The skin was classic and pale: white with a touch of blue, making it ivory—and when she pulled off her kerchief she even had a tiny purple vein tapping at her temple; it seemed to me like an affect, something willed there to remind the rest of us how delicate and fragile is a woman. My initial feeling toward her was suspicion.

Of these two descriptions, the second has the greater air of immediacy (plus the veracity which comes with a well-defined "I" witness). We are aware—if only unconsciously—that in the first version a mediator is standing between the characters and us. This mediator, the all-knowing author, refers to the protagonist as "Gabe" or "he," which forces us to see him from a distance. In the second version, however, no such screen intervenes. There the reader experiences a direct relationship with the protagonist. And although both versions call Libby Herz "she," the second brings us slightly closer to her than the first by virtue of our increased proximity to the scene. Other differences become equally apparent. Mr. Roth indicates that Libby is being observed through Gabe's eyes in the first version—"he now refined the image"—but the impressions of the protagonist and those of the author may seem to blend. This dilemma cannot arise in the second version where we are certain of getting only the protagonist's views. Which fact has significance, for besides rendering a unique picture of Libby Herz, these views tell us much about Gabe Wallach.

narrative focus

The shift from third to first person narration is not the sole important divergence between the second draft of Letting Go, *Chapter I and the Published Version. Among additional variances, the reader's attention should be directed toward at least two. In the third draft—and consequently in the Published Version—the long telephone sequence involving Gabe and his father makes its appearance and the "interlude" involving Gabe and Marjorie Howells (Barbara) becomes greatly expanded.*

VIII

verse-drama into novel

Robert Penn Warren, who was born on April 24, 1905, completed his formal education at Oxford as a Rhodes Scholar. Currently Professor of English at Yale, he has taught in several American universities and has received the Hon.D.Litt. from several others. Mr. Warren is a member of the American Academy of Arts and Letters and the American Philosophical Society. Many honors have been given him: Houghton Mifflin fellowship, 1931; Guggenheim fellowship, 1939, 1947; Shelley Memorial Award, 1942; Chair of Poetry, Library of Congress, 1944–45; Meltzer Award, 1949; Sidney Hillman Award, 1957. He has won the Pulitzer Prize twice: in 1947 for All the King's Men *(1946) and in 1958 for* Promises: Poems 1954–1956 *(1957). The latter also earned the Millay Prize and the National Book Award.*

Besides Promises, *Mr. Warren has published a number of volumes of verse, among them the long narrative poem,* Brother to Dragons *(1953) and* You, Emperors, and Others: Poems 1957–1960 *(1960), and besides* All the King's Men, *a number of distinguished novels, among them* Night Rider *(1939),* At Heaven's Gate *(1943),* World Enough and Time *(1950),* Band of Angels *(1955),* The Cave *(1959),* Wilderness *(1961), and* Flood *(1964). His nonfictional works include* Segregation: The Inner Conflict in the South *(1956) and* The Legacy of the Civil War *(1961).*

Robert Penn Warren

All the King's Men was originally the still unpublished verse-drama, "Proud Flesh," then a novel, then a play, and then an Academy Award-winning motion picture. Perhaps the most crucial differences between the verse-drama and the novel arose from the evolution of one of the verse-drama's minor characters, "Jack, a reporter, and boyhood friend of Dr. Keith Amos," into the novel's first person narrator, Jack Burden. The two scenes of "Proud Flesh" during which Jack speaks have been reproduced below. Juxtaposed to the earlier—Willie's assassination—is the identical passage in All the King's Men. Juxtaposed to the later—the verse-drama's climax—is the very dissimilar climax of the novel.

A third pair of juxtaposed scenes from "Proud Flesh" and All the King's Men—their respective renditions of the governor's (Talos'-Stark's) offer to make the doctor (Amos-Stanton) director of the new hospital—follows these in order to demonstrate the novel's greater realism and discursiveness.

Though all three pairs illustrate very well other differences between dramatic and fictional technique, these differences are discussed only in relation to the excerpt involving Willie's assassination.

PROUD FLESH

Act III, Scene iii

(A man approaches from the opposite end of the corridor, somewhat shabbily and loosely dressed, with a sheaf of papers stuck in the side pocket of his coat and his hat stuck jauntily on the back of his head. He carries a rain-coat. He is one of the reporters who appeared in I:iii. His name is Jack and he is a boyhood friend of Dr. Amos.)

JACK. Well, I'll be damned if it ain't Keith! Damned if I've seen you in a generation. How you been?

AMOS. (His face lights up for a moment.) Fine, Jack! How are you making it? -- (He puts out his hand to his friend, who takes it and at the same time seizes Dr. Amos' shoulder and playfully shakes him.) -- How you making it?

JACK. Oh, I'm getting along. Dishing out the dirt for the gentle reader. Covering the special session. -- But you -- I always knew you'd be a big-shot someday!

AMOS. Not exactly.

JACK. Come on, come on! I read about you in the papers.

AMOS. Well --

JACK. Sure, I read the papers. When I ain't working for 'em. Yeah, old big-shot director of the Medical Center. Yeah, folks say you put that bug in the Big Boss' ear. He got an idea that time, all right. Yeah, I used to say all he needed was somebody to tell him how to heave his strength.

AMOS. I didn't.

JACK. But, boy, he's sure heaving it tonight. He's God's gift to us reporters, for a fact. Well -- (He steals a glance at his wrist watch.) -- I got to shove. I got to be back in half an hour. But say, why don't you come out with me some time? Come out and r'ar round with the

published novel (excerpt)

Robert Penn Warren

All The King's Men

CHAPTER NINE

boys, huh? We used to have some pretty good times, you and me, a thousand years ago when we were kids.

AMOS. I'd like to, but I'm --

JACK. Busy. Sure, you're busy. But you ought to knock off some night. Give me a ring. You used to be human before you were twelve years old. Well -- (He seizes Dr. Amos' hand, and shakes it abruptly.) -- I'll be seeing you --

(As Jack is about to go, Dr. Amos, not releasing the handclasp, reaches out with his other hand and takes Jack by the arm, preventing him from going.)

AMOS. Wait -- I --

JACK. Huh? -- Sure -- (Uneasily.) -- What is it?

AMOS. (Slowly releasing his friend.) Nothing.

JACK. (Puzzled.) Well -- so long!

(He hurries away and Dr. Amos stares after him.)

AMOS. Try to remember, try, if there is time
To remember, all our uninvolved delight,
All arbored afternoons and the sun's slow slant,
And how thin was the shout across the long water,
Before --

(He pauses.)

But the tooth is now set through the thick rind.

(The reporter has disappeared. From the right, beyond the Chorus, Governor Talos enters, flanked on each side by a highway patrolman. The patrolmen carry sub-machine guns. The nearer patrolman is Al Suggs. Dr. Amos, at first, does not seem to be aware of the presence of the group, nor does the Governor notice him. Then, seeing the Governor, Amos stiffens. The Governor sees him, and lifts one hand in a salute.)

TALOS. Hello, doc.

AMOS. Hello.

TALOS. What you been do --

(As the Governor speaks, Dr. Amos takes one step forward, almost deliberately, then, jerking a pistol from the side pocket of his coat, leaps toward the Governor and fires twice. Almost simultaneously with the last report, there is a burst from the machine guns. Dr. Amos, with arms outstretched spins several times, as though suspended on a string, and then, as though the string has been snipped, collapses heavily to the floor. Meanwhile, Governor Talos has stood motionless, with his hands laid across his chest

We came out into the great lobby, under the dome, where there was a blaze of light over the statues which stood with statesmanlike dignity on pedestals to mark the quarters of the place, and over the people who moved about in the area. We walked along the east wall, toward the inset where the elevators were. Just as we approached the statue of General Moffat (a great Indian fighter, a successful land speculator, the first governor of the state), I noticed a figure leaning against the pedestal.

It was Adam Stanton. I saw that his clothes were soaked and that mud and filth were slopped up his trousers half to the knees. I understood the abandoned car. He had walked away from it, in the rain.

Just as I saw him, he looked in our direction. But his eyes were on the Boss, not me. "Adam," I said, "Adam!"

He took a step toward us, but still did not look at me.

Then the Boss veered toward Adam, and thrust out his hand in preparation for a handshake. "Howdy-do, Doctor," he began, holding out his hand.

For an instant Adam stood there immobile, as though about to refuse to shake the hand of the man approaching him. Then he put out his hand, and as he did so I felt a surge of relief and thought: *He's shaking hands with him, he's all right now, he's all right.*

Then I saw what was in his hand, and even as I recognized the object, but before the significance of the recognition had time to form itself in my mind and nerves, I saw the two little spurts of pale-orange flame from the muzzle of the weapon.

I did not hear the report, for it was lost and merged with the other more positive staccato series of reports, on my left. With his right arm still extended Adam reeled back a step, swung his reproachful and haggard gaze upon me and fixed it, even as a second burst of firing came and he spun to the floor.

In the astonishing silence, I rushed toward Adam as he fell. Then I heard somewhere in the lobby a woman begin screaming, then a great rush of feet and babble of voices. Adam was bleeding heavily. He was stitched across the chest. The chest was all knocked in. He was already dead.

I looked up to see Sugar-Boy standing there with the smoking automatic in his hand, and off to the right, near the elevator, a highway patrolman with a pistol in his hand.

I didn't see the Boss. And thought: *He didn't hit him.*

and upper abdomen, an expression of puzzled and introspective concern on his face. Then he staggers slightly. The body of Dr. Amos has scarcely struck the floor before Al Suggs, dropping his weapon, swings toward the Governor to support him.)

AL. Boss, Boss! He's done shot you!

TALOS. (Very soberly and detachedly.) Yes -- he shot me--Al.

(The Governor's knees sag, and Al Suggs prevents him from falling.)

AL. Boss, Boss! Does it hurt much, Boss?

(Governor Talos' head falls forward on his chest. People are running toward the spot. The other patrolman is standing over the body of Dr. Amos, with the machine gun trained upon it, as though waiting for any sign of vitality.)

AL. Boss, Boss! Does it hurt?

But I was wrong. Even as I thought that and looked around, Sugar-Boy dropped his automatic clattering to the marble, and uttering some strangled, animal-like sound, rushed back beyond the statue of Governor Moffat.

I laid Adam's head back on the marble and went beyond the statue. I had to shove the people back now, they were crowding so. Somebody was yelling, "Stand back, stand back, give him air!" But they kept crowding up, running to the spot from all over the lobby and from the corridors.

When I broke through, I saw the Boss sitting on the floor, breathing heavily, staring straight ahead. He had both hands pressed to his body, low on the chest and toward the center. I could see no sign that he was hit. Then I saw a very little ooze of blood between two of the fingers, just a little.

Sugar-Boy was leaning above him, weeping and sputtering, trying to speak. He finally managed to get out the words: "D-d-d-d-does it hur-hur-hur-hurt much, Boss—does it hur-hur-hur-hurt?"

*unpublished play
(excerpt)*

PROUD FLESH

Act III, Scene iv

(There is applause from the Chorus. During the remarks of the Chorus Leader, the light has gradually been diffused over the stage, revealing the waiting room outside of an operating room. There are benches along the rear wall, and a door in the middle. Toward the left, there is a table on which magazines are piled, and the table is flanked by two chairs. Above one of the benches hangs a printed sign: No loud conversation -- Please. Clara Talos is seated, very rigid in her posture, on the bench at the left, under the sign. Anne Amos enters, and seats herself on the other bench, very quietly, while the Chorus Leader still speaks. In a moment Sue Parsons comes in, hesitantly, looking about her, then moves to the extreme end of the bench on which Anne Amos is seated. Just in the middle of the applause from the Chorus, Commissioner Harper enters, followed by Jack, the reporter; they take the chairs by the table.)

JACK. (Leaning toward the Commissioner, and speaking in a loud whisper.) Thanks for getting me in.

TINY. Sure, I'm always glad to do anything for you boys.

JACK. That's a fact, Commissioner, you always co-operate.

TINY. That's what I always want to do, co-operate.

(Jack picks up one of the magazines from the table and begins to thumb through it.)

CHORUS. There is no dismay. No voice. Dubiety,
Gust-screamer, rides like a gull the drowsy swell,
Latched beak on bosom, tidy. And no mouth mews
Like a kitten at night, lost in the terrible grass.
And you --
You should try to attend to the wintry palm at the window:

published novel
(excerpt)

Robert Penn
Warren

All The King's Men

CHAPTER TEN

But I still had the money, and so I am spending it to live on while I write the book I began years ago, the life of Cass Mastern, whom once I could not understand but whom, perhaps, I now may come to understand. I suppose that there is some humor in the fact that while I write about Cass Mastern I live in the house of Judge Irwin and eat bread bought with his money. For Judge Irwin and Cass Mastern do not resemble each other very closely. (If Judge Irwin resembles any Mastern it is Gilbert, the granite-headed brother of Cass.) But I do not find the humor in this situation very funny. The situation is too much like the world in which we live from birth to death, and the humor of it grows stale from repetition. Besides, Judge Irwin was my father and he was good to me and, in a way, he was a man and I loved him.

Its old blades rattle thinly and only as,
Nocturnal and despised, some recollection.
Tomorrow its blades will gleam in the sun, like tin.
Tomorrow is always a new day, and the different, undiffident faces.

CHORUS LEADER. It is difficult to name the year of the dispensation.

(During the speech of the Chorus, the spot has again been focussed upon the Chorus, very gradually. At the end, from the right, between the Chorus and the audience, appears a wheeled stretcher, pushed by a negro, who wears the white costume of a hospital orderly. On the stretcher a figure lies, draped with a sheet except for the face. It is the face of Governor Talos. He appears to be asleep, or drugged. The rubber soles of the orderly's shoes make no sound, but the wheels of the stretcher squeak a little as it moves in a slow, ceremonial pace. As it passes the Chorus, the surgeons descend and form a ritualistic procession behind the orderly. The stretcher moves slowly across the stage, the blue spot remaining upon it. Just as the stretcher disappears, the light is again diffused over the stage.

Jack is still looking idly at his magazine. Commissioner Harper is examining his nails, toying at them with a pearl-handled knife and polishing them gently on his trousers. Anne Amos, after a moment of obvious hesitation, moves across the room and sits on the bench beside Clara Talos, but at a little distance from her. It is not long before, with a quick, decisive moment, she reaches out to lay her hand on the hands of the other woman, which are folded on the lap. Sue Parsons seems to be sunk in herself.

The door at the rear opens, and a nurse appears.)

NURSE. (Softly.) Mrs. Talos! Please.

CLARA. Yes?

(The nurse beckons to her. She rises and goes to the door. The nurse steps forward and aside. A surgeon appears at the door, his robe disordered and stained. He speaks to Mrs. Talos, but his words are not audible. The nurse steps to her side, and makes as to support her,

When the old man is dead and the book is finished, I shall let the First and Third National Bank take the house and I don't care who lives here afterward, for from that day it will be nothing to me but a well-arranged pile of brick and lumber. Anne and I shall never live here again, not in the house or at the Landing. (She doesn't want to live here any more than I do. She has let her place go to the Children's Home she was interested in and I imagine it will become a kind of sanatorium. She's not very complacent about having done that. With Adam dead the place was not a joy but a torture to her, and the gift of the house was finally her gift to the ghost of Adam, a poor gift humbly offered, like the handful of wheat or a painted pot in the tomb, to comfort the ghost and send it on its way so that it would trouble the living no longer.)

but this does not seem necessary. Then, slowly, with the nurse beside her, Clara Talos moves toward the left, and disappears. Anne Amos follows her, apparently trying to overtake her. The Commissioner and Jack watch the women curiously.)

TINY. Well, I'll be durned!

JACK. Me, too.

(Sue Parsons rises, and moves, slowly, toward the exit at the left. After she has passed the table, the Commissioner gestures to her, and calls in an excited whisper.)

TINY. Sue! Hey, Sue!

(Sue Parsons turns toward him with a white and convulsed face, and apparently tries to speak. But no word comes. She, too, goes out. Meanwhile, Jack has extracted from the side pocket of his coat a pencil and a pad of paper. He turns to the Commissioner.)

JACK. Well, Commissioner, I'd appreciate it if you can make a statement. You know, something -- some expression.

TINY. (After a moment in which he stares out over the heads of the audience as into space.) You know -- you know, there ain't much for a man to say. Just this. I don't know what us boys is gonna do, now the Big Boss is gone.

JACK. Thanks, Commissioner.

So by the summer of this year, 1939, we shall have left Burden's Landing. We shall come back, no doubt, to walk down the Row and watch young people on the tennis courts by the clump of mimosas and walk down the beach by the bay, where the diving floats lift gently in the sun, and on out to the pine grove, where the needles thick on the ground will deaden the football so that we shall move among trees as soundlessly as smoke. But that will be a long time from now, and soon now we shall go out of the house and go into the convulsion of the world, out of history into history and the awful responsibility of Time.

Robert Penn Warren

unpublished play
(excerpt)

PROUD FLESH

Act I, Scene ii

AMOS. I'm Dr. Amos.

TALOS. (Nodding.) I picked you for him. -- (He moves toward Dr. Amos, who stands his ground, his hands hanging loosely at his sides, even after Governor Talos has extended his hand.) -- Yep, I picked you for him. -- (He approaches, grinning, his hand outstretched, and after hesitation, Dr. Amos shakes hands. The Governor, releasing the handclasp, grins again.) -- See, boy, it wasn't nearly as bad as you figured on. -- (As Dr. Amos steals a glance at his own hand, Governor Talos regards him amusedly.) -- If you can stick around a minute, Dr. Amos, there's something I'd like to say to you.

(The group of doctors are going out at the left. Sue Parsons has already disappeared at the right. But Tiny is propped back in one of the chairs at the table, with the unlighted cigar in his mouth. The Governor discovers him.)

TALOS. Beat it,Tiny!

(Tiny rises slowly, and for an instant a shade of confusion and resentment appears on his face before being supplanted by an unconvincing somewhat apologetic grin. The grin is directed at Dr. Amos, and seems to imply a tolerant apology for the Governor's lack of decorum.)

TALOS. Get the lead out, Tiny! I want to talk to the doc, here. You'll find some pictures to look at in my office.

TINY. (Moving toward the right, rapidly now.) So long, Boss. -- (He wags his head at Dr. Amos.) -- I'll be seeing you. -- (He goes out.)

published novel (excerpt)

Robert Penn Warren

All The King's Men

CHAPTER SIX

For a half moment, while Sugar-Boy was easing in, and I was shutting the door, Adam and the Boss simply took each other in, without a word. Then I turned and said, "Governor Stark, this is Dr. Stanton."

The Boss took a step forward and put out his right hand. Perhaps I imagined it, but I thought I noticed a shade of hesitation before Adam took it. And the Boss must have noticed it, too, for when Adam did put out his hand, the Boss, in the middle of the shake, before any other word had been spoken, grinned suddenly, and said, "See, boy, it's not as bad as you thought, it won't kill you."

Then, by God, Adam grinned, too.

Then I said, "And this is Mr. O'Shean," and Sugar-Boy lurched forward and put out one of his stubby arms with a hand hanging on the end of it like a stuffed glove, and twisted his face and began, "I'm pl-pl-pl-pl—"

"I'm glad to know you," Adam said. Then I saw his glance pick up the bulge under Sugar-Boy's left armpit. He turned to the Boss. "So this is one of your gunmen I've heard about?" he said, definitely not grinning now.

"Hell," the Boss said, "Sugar-Boy just carries that for fun. Sugar-Boy is just a pal. Ain't anybody can drive a car like Sugar-Boy."

Sugar-Boy was looking at him like a dog you've just scratched on the head.

Adam stood there, and didn't reply. For a second I thought the deal was about to blow up. Then Adam said, very formally, "Won't you gentlemen have seats?"

We did.

Sugar-Boy sneaked one of his lumps of sugar out of the side pocket of his coat, put it into his mouth, and began to suck it, with his fey Irish cheeks drawn in and his eyes blurred with bliss.

AMOS. Well?

TALOS. Well, boy, what do you think of it?

AMOS. I think that the people of the State will get some good out of it. More than from some other recent public works. And you will get your publicity and your votes. And the crooks will get their graft.

TALOS. (Studying the doctor's face.) Dr. Amos, I want you to be director. -- (As Dr. Amos seems to be collecting himself for a reply, the Governor raises his hand sharply and commandingly.) -- Listen here, you're going to say, no. Just think about it a minute.

AMOS. Think?

TALOS. I know what you are thinking. You think I would interfere with you. Listen here: I might fire you, boy, but I wouldn't interfere with you. And when I fired you it would be for incompetence. -- (His voice sinks to a harsh whisper.) -- You got that straight?

AMOS. (Detachedly.) Yes.

TALOS. And listen here, I know what your political opinions are, and I'm not trying to buy you off. Boy, if you think so, you flatter yourself. I can run this State. _Shoot_ your mouth off. So long as you do your job, I don't give a toot.

AMOS. I see.

TALOS. (A little more expansively.) Well, the kind I do give a toot about when they start shooting off their mouth and trying to turn on the heat -- well, I know more'n one way to skin a cat. Take the late Governor of this State, where is he now? _He's not Governor._ He couldn't be elected sergeant-at-arms in an institution for the feeble-minded. -- (He hesitates, grinning.) -- He'll be peddling fish to niggers before I'm through. And Senator Crosby, where is he?

AMOS. He's dead. He shot himself. You know that.

Adam waited, sitting straight up in his chair.

The Boss, leaning back in one of the overstuffed wrecks, didn't seem to be in any hurry. But he finally said, "Well, Doc, what do you think of it?"

"Of what?" Adam demanded.

"Of my hospital?"

"I think it will do the people of the state some good," he said. Then added, "And get you some votes."

"You can forget about the vote side of it," the Boss said. "There are lots of ways to get votes, son."

"So I understand," Adam said. Then he handed the Boss another big chunk of silence to admire.

The Boss admired it awhile, then said, "Yeah, it'll do some good. But not too much unless you take over."

"I won't stand any interference," Adam said, and bit the sentence off.

"Don't worry," the Boss laughed. "I might fire you, boy, but I won't interfere."

"If that is a threat," Adam said, and the pale-blue blaze flickered up in his eyes, "you have wasted your time by coming here. You know my opinions of this administration. They have been no secret. And they will be no secret in the future. You understand that?"

"Doc," the Boss said, "Doc, you just don't understand politics. I'll be frank with you. I could run this state and ten more like it with you howling on every street corner like a hound with a sore tail. No offense. But you just don't understand."

"I understand some things," Adam said grimly, and the jaw set.

"And some you don't, just like I don't, but one thing I understand and you don't is what makes the mare go. I can make the mare go. And one more thing, now we are taking down our hair—" The Boss suddenly stopped, cocked his head, leered at Adam, then demanded, "Or are we?"

"You said there was one more thing," Adam replied, ignoring the question, sitting straight in his chair.

"Yeah, one more thing. But look here, Doc—you know Hugh Miller?"

"Yes," Adam said, "yes, I know him."

"Well, he was in with me—yeah, Attorney General—and he resigned. And you know why?" But he went on without waiting for the answer. "He resigned because he wanted to keep his little hands clean. He wanted the bricks but he just didn't know somebody has to paddle in the mud to make 'em. He was like somebody that just loves beefsteak but just can't bear to go to a slaughter pen because

TALOS. Sure, dead as a door nail! But he ought never taken that cut on building those municipal docks twenty years ago when he was a bright young man just getting a start. And then to sign his name to things! -- (He shakes his head commiseratingly.) -- Twenty years, but you know -- the Good Book says a man's sins will find him out. If he signs his name to things. A man ought to live so that when his summons comes to join the innumerable caravan that throngs the silent halls -- (He stops, leering amiably, and slaps Dr. Amos on the shoulder. He suddenly becomes serious.) -- About that hospital, you directing it, I want to know pretty quick.

there are some bad, rough men down there who aren't animal lovers and who ought to be reported to the S.P.C.A. Well, he resigned."

I watched Adam's face. It was white and stony, as though carved out of some slick stone. He was like a man braced to hear what the jury foreman was going to say. Or what the doctor was going to say. Adam must have seen a lot of faces like that in his time. He must have had to look into them and tell them what he had to tell.

"Yeah," the Boss said, "he resigned. He was one of those guys wants everything and wants everything two ways at once. You know the kind, Doc?"

He flicked a look over at Adam, like a man flicking a fly over by the willows in the trout stream. But there wasn't any strike.

"Yeah, old Hugh—he never learned that you can't have everything. That you can have mightly little. And you never have anything you don't make. Just because he inherited a little money and the name Miller he thought you could have everything. Yeah, and he wanted the one last damned thing you can't inherit. And you know what it is?" He stared at Adam's face.

"What?" Adam said, after a long pause.

"Goodness. Yeah, just plain, simple goodness. Well you can't inherit that from anybody. You got to make it, Doc. If you want it. And you got to make it out of badness. Badness. And you know why, Doc?" He raised his bulk up in the broken-down wreck of an overstuffed chair he was in, and leaned forward, his hands on his knees, his elbows cocked out, his head out-thrust and the hair coming down to his eyes, and stared into Adam's face. "Out of badness," he repeated. "And you know why? Because there isn't anything else to make it out of." Then, sinking back into the wreck, he asked softly, "Did you know that, Doc?"

Adam didn't say a word.

Then the Boss asked, softer still, almost whispering, "Did you know that, Doc?"

Adam wet his lips and said, "There is one question I should like to ask you. It is this. If, as you say, there is only the bad to start with, and the good must be made from the bad, then how do you ever know what the good is? How do you even recognize the good? Assuming you have made it from the bad. Answer me that."

"Easy, Doc, easy," the Boss said.

"Well, answer it."

"You just make it up as you go along."

"Make up what?"

But don't answer off-hand. Hang around a minute or two and think about it. -- (He looks at his watch, a heavy, old-fashioned instrument.) -- Damn it, I've got to get the lead out! Sue'll be pawing the earth in there. She'll be giving the stenographers heart failure. See you in a minute. -- (He bolts away, to the right, turning once to wave as he goes.)-- So long!

"The good," the Boss said, "What the hell else are we talking about. Good with a capital G."

"So you make it up as you go along?" Adam repeated gently.

"What the hell else you think folks been doing for a million years, Doc? When your great-great-grandpappy climbed down out of the tree, he didn't have any more notion of good or bad, or right and wrong, than the hoot owl that stayed up in the tree. Well, he climbed down and he began to make Good up as he went along. He made up what he needed to do business, Doc. And what he made up and got everybody to mirate on as good and right was always just a couple of jumps behind what he needed to do business on. That's why things change, Doc. Because what folks claim is right is always just a couple of jumps short of what they need to do business. Now an individual, one fellow, he will stop doing business because he's got a notion of what is right, and he is a hero. But folks in general, which is society, Doc, is never going to stop doing business. Society is just going to cook up a new notion of what is right. Society is sure not ever going to commit suicide. At least, not that way and of a purpose. And that is a fact. Now ain't it?"

"It is?" Adam said.

"You're damned right it is, Doc. And right is a lid you put on something and some of the things under the lid look just like some of the things not under the lid, and there never was any notion of what was right if you put it down on folks in general that a lot of them didn't start squalling because they just couldn't do any human business under that kind of right. Hell, look at when folks couldn't get a divorce. Look at all the good women got beat and the good men got nagged and couldn't do any human damned thing about it. Then, all of a sudden, a divorce got to be right. What next, you don't know. Nor me. But I do know this." He stopped, leaned forward again, the elbows again cocked out.

"What?" Adam demanded.

"This. I'm not denying there's got to be a notion of right to get business done, but by God, any particular notion at any particular time will sooner or later get to be just like a stopper put tight in a bottle of water and thrown in a hot stove the way we kids used to do at school to hear the bang. The steam that blows the bottle and scares the teacher to wet her drawers is just the human business that is going to get done, and it will blow anything you put it in if you seal it tight, but you put it in the right place and let it get out in a certain way and it will run a freight engine." He sank back again into the chair, his eyelids sagging now, but the eyes watchful, and the hair down over his forehead like an ambush.

AMOS. (Slowly, looking after the Governor.)
Has hands and feet, and face, and the face smiles.
I do not see the human reality, but the face smiles.
And I would have scarcely thought so, but I have seen
Sun glint the rotten water under the tangle.
But I'll not smile, or sup it, lap it, take it in,
For I think I know how the mire is black beneath it,
Velvet, and heaves, and in dark utters the bubble.
It is black, and it has no name but his vanity --
It has no name --
And the bubble bursts on the black surface.
It has no name --

Adam got up suddenly, and walked across the room. He stopped in front of the dead fireplace, with old ashes still in it, and some half-burned paper, though spring was on us, and there hadn't been any fire for a time. The window was up, and the night air came into the room, with a smell different from the diaper-and-cabbage smell, a smell of damp grass and the leaves hanging down from the arched trees in the dark, a smell that definitely did not belong there in that room. And all of a sudden I remembered once how into a room where I was sitting one night, a big pale apple-green moth, big as a bullbat and soft and silent as a dream—a Luna moth, the name is, and it is a wonderful name—came flying in. Somebody had left the screen door open, and the moth drifted in over the tables and chairs like a big pale-green, silky, live leaf, drifting and dancing along without any word under the electric light where a Luna moth certainly did not belong. The night air coming into the room now was like that.

Adam leaned an elbow on the wooden mantelpiece where you could write your name in the dust and the books were stacked and the old, dregs-crusted coffee cup sat. He stood there as though he were all by himself.

The Boss was watching him.

"Yeah," the Boss said, watchful, "it will run a freight engine and—"

But Adam broke in, "What are you trying to convince me of?" You don't have to convince me of anything. I've told you I'd take the job. That's all!" He glared at the bulky man in the big chair, and said, "That's all! And my reasons are my own."

The Boss gave a slow smile, shifted his weight in the chair, and said, "Yeah, your reasons are your own, Doc. But I just thought you might want to know something about mine. Since we're going to do business together."

"I am going to run the hospital," Adam said, and added with curling lip, "If you call that doing business together."

The Boss laughed out loud. Then he got up from the chair. "Doc," he said, "just don't you worry. I'll keep your little mitts clean. I'll keep you clean all over, Doc. I'll put you in that beautiful, antiseptic, sterile, six-million-dollar hospital, and wrap you in cellophane, untouched by human hands." He stepped to Adam, and slapped him on the shoulder. "Don't you worry, Doc," he said.

"I can take care of myself," Adam affirmed, and looked down at the hand on his shoulder.

"Sure you can, Doc," the Boss said. He removed his hand from the shoulder. Then his tone changed, suddenly businesslike and calm. "You will no doubt want to see all the plans which have been drawn

up. They are subject to your revision after you consult with the architects. Mr. Todd, of Todd and Waters, will come to see you about it. And you can start picking your staff. It is all your baby."

He turned away and picked up his hat from the piano top. He swung back toward Adam and gave him a summarizing look, from top to toe and back. "You're a great boy, Doc," he said, "and don't let 'em tell you different."

Then he wheeled to the door, and went out before Adam could say a word. If there was any word he had to say.

Robert Penn Warren has commented upon the genesis of his finest novel's narrator:

In the 1930's I lived in Louisiana. Until September 1935, when he was assassinated by a young physician, Huey Long was the scarcely challenged master of that state. In that atmosphere, punctuated by gun fire in the Capitol, the story that was to become All the King's Men *began to take shape.*

The first form—like this, the last—was a play, a verse play called Proud Flesh. *I began work on it in Louisiana, worked on it in Italy, in an olive grove overlooking Lake Garda, in the summer of 1938, and finished it in the winter of 1939–40, in Rome, to the music of military boot-heels on the cobbles. So the shadow of a European as well as a home-grown American dictatorship lies over the composition. I say "shadow," for my Willie Stark is no more like Huey Long than he is like Mussolini. He is, I hope, himself, and more humanly acceptable, I hope, than either.*

My play is, indeed, about power, its genesis and the temptations it carries for both leader and follower; but I wanted my story to be personal rather than political. I wanted the issues to come to crisis in personal terms. I wanted to indicate some interplay, as it were, between the public, political story and the private, ethical one: a mirror held up to a mirror.

To return to the old play Proud Flesh. *I finished a draft and laid it aside. Picking it up three years later I decided to start all over again with a novel. Decisions of this kind rarely come with perfect clarity, but I suppose that what I wanted was the "follower" to go with my "leader" —a follower whose modern frustrations and aimlessness would, in a complicated ambivalence, be set in relation to the will of the leader. So Jack Burden, who had been glimpsed before as only a nameless newspaper man in the last Act of* Proud Flesh, *entered as narrator and chorus.*

After the publication of the novel All the King's Men, *Eric Bentley read the old play, liked it, and arranged for a production at the theater of the University of Minnesota. Shortly afterwards, Irwin Piscator, then living in America, became interested and offered to produce and direct the play. By the time preliminary work had begun on this production I had discovered that* Proud Flesh *was a very different thing from* All the King's Men *and that I should like to keep Jack Burden in the important role he holds in the novel.* (Quoted from the typescript of the introductory note for the Italian translation of the play, All the King's Men. Robert Penn Warren Papers, Yale University Library.)

With the metamorphosis of Jack Burden from "nameless newspaper man" to "narrator and chorus," the issues of Mr. Warren's story do "come to crisis in personal terms." This character—the "real hero" of All the King's Men as Nick Carraway is of The Great Gatsby—develops emotionally and intellectually through his "ambivalent" relationship to the "ostensible hero," Willie Stark. Thanks to Willie's practical views regarding the political world which enabled him to act, Jack discovers in the oddly analogous world of sexual behavior that "purity" does not exist or matter, that if the terms "good" and "bad" are at all relevant, then "good" grows out of "bad." From a disillusioned idealist and consequently a cynic, he becomes a realist; having learned to face the complexities of the past, he can function today and tomorrow.

Jack's new role affects the plot and the characters of the novel too. Many events and people present in Proud Flesh recur with modifications or elaborations in All the King's Men: for instance, Willie Talos' intention to build a hospital and to appoint Dr. Keith Amos its director; Tiny Harper's (Duffy's) efforts to get Gummy Satterfield (Larson) the contract, and Max Tully's (Hubert Coffee's) attempt to bribe Dr. Amos, who resigns; Anne Amos' (Stanton's) interest in a children's home, her affair with Willie, whom her brother murders; Willie's relation to Al Suggs (Sugar-Boy) and Sue Parsons (Sadie Burke), his decision to return to Clara (Lucy), her attitude toward their son, the football player, bon vivant, and, finally, corpse. But when Jack becomes Jack Burden, when the reporter becomes the narrator and chorus (formerly a group of surgeons), several important episodes and figures merely suggested or not mentioned at all appear: for example, Jack's involvement as boy and man with the Stanton children; their father, the deceased ex-governor; his father, Judge Irwin; his mother and her various husbands.

In an introduction to All the King's Men for Time Magazine, Mr. Warren said that his novel was "more realistic, discursive, and documentary in spirit" than "Proud Flesh" had been:

> How directly did I try to transpose into fiction Huey P. Long and the tone of this world? The question answers itself in a single fact. The first version of my story was a verse drama—and the actual writing began, in 1938, in the shade of an olive tree by a wheat field near Perugia. In other words, if you are sitting under an olive tree in Umbria and are writing a verse drama, the chances are that you are concerned more with the myth than with the facts, more with the symbolic than with the actual. And so it was. It could not, after all, have been otherwise, for in the

strict, literal sense I had no idea what the now deceased Huey P. Long had been. What I knew was the "Huey" of the myth, and that was what I had taken with me to Mussolini's Italy, where the bully-boys wore black shirts and gave a funny salute.

I had had no way of knowing what went on in the privacy of the heart of Senator Long. Now I could only hope, ambitiously, to know something of the heart of the Governor Talos of my play Proud Flesh. *For Talos was the first avatar of my Willie Stark, and the fact that I drew that name from the "iron groom" who, in murderous blankness, serves Justice in Spenser's* Faerie Queen *should indicate something of the line of "thought and feeling" that led up to that version and persisted, with modulations, into the novel.*

But Talos was to become Stark, and Proud Flesh *was to become* All the King's Men. *Many things, some merely technical, led to this transformation, but one may have some bearing on the question of the ratio of fact and fiction. In 1942 I left Louisiana for good, and when in 1943 I began the version that is more realistic, discursive, and documentary in spirit (though not in fact) than the play, I was doing so after I had definitely left Louisiana and the world in which the story had its roots. By now that literal, factual world was only a memory, and therefore was ready to be absorbed freely into the act of imagination. (Quoted from the typescript, Robert Penn Warren Papers, Yale University Library.)*

The material involving Willie's assassination contains good illustrations of two other important differences between dramatic and fictional technique.

One of these concerns time, the action of a play occurring in the present even though treating past events and the action of a story usually occurring in the past even though treating present events. Thus, the play, which is an enacting, focuses on the experience of its design, while the story, which is most frequently a recounting, focuses on the design of its experience. "Proud Flesh" renders Willie's assassination immediately through movement and speech, as, for instance, during the confrontation and interchange between Jack and Amos. But *All The King's Men*, when not borrowing the scenic method from the drama (i.e., the Chapter VI excerpt), renders the same event through a picture of movement and a transcription of speech, as, for instance, during Jack's account of Sugar-Boy's response to the Boss's wound. That Mr. Warren remained essentially a novelist while composing the play is suggested by the extent and length of his stage directions, whose audience are readers rather than spectators. The conversion of "Proud Flesh" into *All the King's Men* enabled him to make us aware of the work's design or recounting process, which, considering the significance of the narrator, is especially pertinent and effective.

Another important difference between dramatic and fictional technique concerns their respective use of language. Considered from the angle of its intended end as something to be performed, the play must rely solely upon dialogue, while the story may juxtapose dialogue and narration. This gives the story several advantages over the play, one being stylistic. In "Proud Flesh" the linguistic version of the assassination scene consists of three lines that should be compared to the sequence in the novel beginning "Howdy-do, Doctor" and ending "from the muzzle of the weapon":

TALOS. Hello, doc.
AMOS. Hello.
TALOS. What you been do——

It could be argued that the enactment of the assassination communicates more power than a prose description or that stage directions serve a purpose similar to the purpose of narration, but neither of these contentions would mitigate the story's stylistic advantage. Enactment is nonlinguistic and stage directions—generally practical and perfunctory—stand outside the play as performance. What the latter achieves through action, scenery, costumes, properties, etc., the story achieves through description. This the author knew, and in his effort to transcend the limitations of dialogue—what people would actually say in a situation presented visually—he turned to the language of verse. But Mr. Warren caught neither the "poetic" richness nor the introspection of All the King's Men by composing passages like:

> Try to remember, try, if there is time
> To remember, all our uninvolved delight,
> All arbored afternoons and the sun's slow slant,
> And how this was the shout across the long water,
> Before—
> But the tooth is now set through the thick rind.

Although he was to become a fine poet, these passages seem incongruous and therefore artificial and sentimental in the context of "Proud Flesh."

IX

story into novel

John Hawkes

John Hawkes, who was born in Stamford, Connecticut, during 1925, is a graduate of Harvard College. Currently Associate Professor of English at Brown University, he has taught at many other schools. In 1962 Mr. Hawkes received a Guggenheim grant and a National Institute of Arts and Letters Award; during 1964–65 a Ford Foundation fellowship enabled him to study with a professional theater company. His books include The Cannibal (1949), Charivari (short novel, New Directions 11 anthology, 1949), The Beetle Leg (1951), The Goose on the Grave and The Owl (two short novels, 1954), The Lime Twig (1961), and Second Skin (1964).

Mr. Hawkes "remembered that I had published a piece called The Nearest Cemetary in the San Francisco Review Annual (1963) and realized that this piece is actually the preliminary vision out of which my last novel Second Skin was generated." "The Nearest Cemetery" —"a microcosmic version of a good portion of the book"—appears below with excerpts from the two chapters of Second Skin most directly affected by it.

The Nearest Cemetery

Scene of narration: a small state penitentiary in New England.
Characters:

THE PRINCESS: summer visitor to Bloody Clam Shell Island; unhappy wife of a New York meat packer; woman of beauty; victim of the local barber.

MILDRED: The barber's wife.

CAPTAIN RED: lobsterman in his fiftieth year; first lover of the Princess.

BLUD: lighthouse keeper; Mildred's brother; second lover of the Princess.

JOMO: off-island gas station attendant and vicious small-town sport; third lover of the Princess.

THE BARBER: narrator; fourth and final lover of the Princess. He loved her from afar and killed her.

I remember the day—blue, puffy white, orange—and that I was smiling until we passed a hot dog stand and a shingled church with windows as bright and painful as some of my own dreams. In the darkness my eyes began to heal. But the car was twisting over a torn-up section of the road or pushing between the pines or darkening the corner of a plowed field, and I couldn't smile. I remember the smell of upholstery and gasoline and vomit and the sound of the Marshal talking to himself the whole way. He looked like Vinny who wore a poppy in his cap. Suddenly I blinked and through the window I saw Blud's lighthouse standing in a plot of dry yellow sod, Blud's lighthouse by the side of the road and rising up from dead ground and sand instead of the bright wet rocks that always looked as if they had been freshly painted with black tar. But it was a hot dog stand. Another hot dog stand and closed for the season.

We drove through Jomo City and there, in the door of the trailer, was Jomo's mother husking an early ear of corn. A heap of pop bottle caps was sparkling out of the tall grass at her feet, and

Jomo's mother made me think of Mildred, except my Mildred lives in an unpainted clapboard house on Bloody Clam Shell Island instead of in Jomo City in a trailer with flat tires and propped on concrete blocks in the tall grass. The old woman did not look away and did not wave, though she recognized the car and shadow that fell within twenty feet of her and swallowed the three gasoline pumps —two were dry—and even though she knew I was the only passenger that day. But between the trailer and the pumps was an overturned rowboat with a hole ripped in the bottom and, before the dust settled and we passed once more into the damp pines, a small dog thrust his head and paws out of the hole in the rowboat and barked as he might at a great crow flying across the woman's head. There was sun in the dog's mouth, sun reflecting from the bottle caps and from the antennas Jomo had rigged on the trailer's roof.

The Princess always stopped in Jomo City to fuel her car. The old woman worked the pump while Jomo brought bottles of orange pop for the Princess and her little boy, Jomo whose brown arms bare to the shoulder were washed with gasoline and whose hair is still a wavy cap of pitch, Jomo who sometimes let the little boy shoot at the rowboat with an old .22 calibre rifle hung inside over the trailer door, or at a piece of window glass propped against a stump while the Princess leaned out of the white Cadillac and laughed and smelled the salt in the air. Princess always brought Jomo's mother a bottle of perfume from New York and next Saturday at three o'clock, when the old woman comes in with the rest, Jomo and Captain Red and Blud and I will smell the odor of that perfume again and think, each in turn, of culvert or open sea or the town hall or the Princess coming down the rocks like a little plume fluttering in the sun or the pinging of the rifle and the smash of glass (all of us will remember that the Princess had a mouth the color of the orange pop Jomo gave her in the cold wet bottles he wiped with his undershirt)—and all because of a few drops of scent daubed behind the ears of an old woman who sits heavily on her trailer steps in weeds and wears a corset, Jomo says, which she repaired with pieces of a black inner tube.

Like an island. In the first sunset that prison was an island without rock or spume or salt, an island without buried barns and sea air pollinated and apples that fall from fractured boughs to rot on the shore line with the periwinkles—island almost the size of Bloody Clam but with gongs and siren instead of buoys and twenty-eight miles inland from the sea. So that day I only went from one island, Bloody Clam, to another island lying in a white valley across which move not boats, orange and black, but a few muddy dump trucks and, occasionally, the Marshal's car.

Each of us has his Venus—four men and four women who are either mothers or wives—Venus at least in memory. And if there is no seaspray here, no Crooked Finger Rock, there is at least the wind, though wind over watch towers and down lengths of walls makes other sounds, whether moan or sough or shriek, than it does through the wormholes in unpainted clapboard or when it is bending the tops of pines that ring the burning town dump of a little island town. With the wind, on which I smell the blood of fish, and with masonry and with fixed perimeter that is nonetheless fluid rather than geometric, the walls buttressed against open fields, road and village in a circumference vaguely but not perfectly circular, the prison is in itself an island (and time is the calm, or time the hurricane) but further it brings to mind the lighthouse because of the white painted stone, the metal underfoot thick with coatings of gray heavily-leaded paint, lighthouse because of the narrow walks and odors of fresh paint and oil and half-inch sheets of glass blinding, at sunset, high above our heads and behind bars. Island of men; lighthouse large enough to contain so many men each with his own Venus (though in memory; though only some approximation of her who charmed, each to her liking. Blud and me and Jomo and the Captain) and each with denim pants and coat and face like that of the keeper and the kept combined, since in his tower at dusk the lighthouse keeper shows his enchantment in his white stubbled jaw and eye that looks and looks nowhere except down the three-mile path of his silent light toward a sea from which no ship may rise and approach because of the very nature of that eye's desire, the very nature of that light's dangerous beam. It is the lure that warns away the catch.

My shop is empty on Bloody Clam, empty and boarded up, and the hair will grow long on Bloody Clam Shell Island. But here I keep most of the heads of hair cut short, and every day I shave the allotted number of white jaws and cheeks the texture of a field of lice. Among so many men, week by week, I wait until it is their turn and they come to me; and I smile, knowing that first this neck and ear and hairless scalp—it is forever speckled red and white with sunburn and bears a scar—and this temple-pulse of the oldest man of them all belong to the captain of the *Peter Poor*. And next I find that I am lathering the swollen cheek of Blud, my own brother-in-law. (Isn't he like Mildred? Mildred to a tit?) Jomo still has his curls, the blue-green hair sticky with pine sap. Then one day I notice my hands are becoming sticky. And I turn the chair and my razor shapes those sideburns—they are the color of trees in gloom, the color of water at high tide—and I remember the black T-shirt with the sleeves cut off at the tight shoulder seams, and I remember the bleached purple baseball cap he wore high and tight and perfectly horizontal on the living hair. A faded baseball cap he wore for Princess. And I reach for the hot towel and on the end of my finger see the little red line as bright and delicate as something you might see wriggling in the eyepiece of a microscope. I stop for a minute and suck it clean. Then with the towel in my hand I see again that he has a chin, rounded to a point and firm and white as a duck's egg, and that he has a mouth unmistakable and two lips bowed and dry and faintly red and capable of moistening or smile. He has all this, the hair and chin and lip. He had them for Princess. Carefully I brush on the powder and sometimes, holding the talcum flask in one hand and, in the other, the silver shears—sometimes I wonder if all those features won't suddenly disappear when I wipe off the powder. There is no talking in this barber shop; I talk with none of them. But I know their heads, their hair, I know what they did. And each of them knows me. And our eyes meet in the glass.

They—these three—were waiting for me when I arrived. I knew that despite the identical denim pants and shirts and coats and despite these numbers of men, they would find me, or I them. I knew that they were waiting and, in shoe factory or corner of the yard or high on a catwalk, would be standing or walking slowly or gesturing together out of their common dream. And now I wait for them. There is no talking in the barber shop, or in the yard or factory; no talking here, except for a single half-hour after dinner at noon and yet during all the hours measured by the moving shadow of a tilting shotgun's barrel and on through the dark hours when the men lie on their backs asleep or smoking—during all this time the forbidden word goes around from tier to tier, from one end of our state's island to the other. Only a joke (about Johnny in the privy, about the old white horse) or a plan to steal knives (I listen in such cases but never reply). But whatever word it is, it goes around among us like temper shooting down a row of quickening hands or the laugh that only we can see on faces expressionless and cold. Talking is against the rules and you have to be able to read the tongue still thrust into a cheek or hear the drag of the foot or the sound hissing from between two front teeth. No talking here. And yet for most of them, for me, there has been no talking all their lives (or mine). At least there is no talking on Bloody Clam Shell Island, very little requiring actual speech or anything more than the slow ceremonial of the dumb, the daily slow hustling of the island's dumb. But honor and piety or desire and stealth create different silences, and the child learns to hold out his cup, the waitress to set down the plate, a man his money. The child learns to get from the cemetery to the barber shop without a word, from the wild still competition and gainless amusement of the single bowling alley to the salt and blood and danger of the fish-bait bench without a word. The man has already learned his silences. Through habit. Through years of practice. Through contempt or love or inability or weeks and months of long days when the wind is too high to talk, the sea too rough.

The wordless life. The lifting of his chin for a fight, the tossing of his head for a kiss. And everything is in the lift of an eye, a hitching of the hips, the tossing of his head after a bottle of beer drunk under the herring boat docks in the mud at low tide or the way spring daisies appear wordlessly bound into a bun of hair. One sentence will sell boats, nets, house and land; one sentence will serve for a whole night and get a child. Nobody talks more than that. But everybody knows. Like Johnny in the privy or the white horse. There are six hundred and fifty people on Bloody Clam and three thousand convicts here. And none of them are talkers. They never were.

But the Princess talked. Each summer from the moment her yacht first came flashing into the green harbor and she stood on the bow in sunglasses and silk trousers cut like a man's and waved, with her little boy propped in a deck chair behind her and the husband buried away in the pilot house, until the day she left (always last to board the white boat with the crew and child and husband looking up at her and waiting to cast off) the Princess talked—talked all over the island—and on a clear day it would be the only voice to hear, the foreign tongue and fairy tale accent coming down from the hill in a lilting continuum we knew was words (so many she might have been reading aloud or singing aloud the pages of a book) and someone rolling a cigarette or someone holding a knife with a hand slimy and silvery would hear that voice and listen, not stopping the fingers or staying the hand, but listen and nod perhaps if there was anyone else nearby. But the Princess would be too far away for the old men to hear and they would go on looking at their feet or sleeping with their backs dusty and humped in the sun. Sleeping, not knowing what they missed.

I lie on my back just waiting to hear it all again, just listening. Because the ear is already packed with sound like the hollow tree or the dog's skull in the dump or the coffin Vinny carries out of town in his garbage truck. Every object—length of wood, weight of bone—and every place already contains its fill of sound and the ear is its own coffin, its own little reverberating casket that hears everything it was ever meant to hear at any moment of the night and even though sometimes you want to sleep and so lie there holding it beneath your trembling hand. Your ear. The barber's ear.

The ear is the coffin that can't be closed or nailed or buried—it is forever warped with so much sound—and through the snoring and scraping of the old men in the sun I hear the girlish floating of words rounded in peculiar tingling accent (*Good morning, boys*) or among the picking of the rats in the dark Town Hall I hear it again (*Poor Blud, poor Blud*) and through the rumble of the captain pulling on his boots, fishing for the patched rubber, feeling about and then jamming in a foot like a cannonball puffing into a mountain of used car tires I hear it still clear and round and insistent at five o'clock in the morning (*Take me out on the water with you, Red*) and sometimes I can make out what she said to Jomo and sometimes I can't, and then (despite the singing of the larches and the rote of the sea and the wind and the clattering of Vinny's truck outside) she talks just to me.

So the mind lies between the echoing coffins of the ears—a barber's ears—and you try to calm it in the midst of all that roar and whisper while a shadow falls through the bars and sweeps your chest. But then I raise my hands; I hold one ear; I hold both of them; I press with my palms. Because then it is not Mildred's voice I hear —not the voice, though I hear it often enough—but rather Mildred playing steadily on the church organ, Mildred pumping her feet, Mildred pushing the keys and Mildred making the reeds and seagulls shriek. And in each of Mildred's chords is the heavy harmony of the Lord and bass voice of Mildred's other brother who died from drink. And I cannot bear to listen. The barber cannot bear to listen to Mildred pumping and marching with the Lord at the town's church organ. The Lord and Mildred deafen me. They make me think of lying dead and naked beside the body of the shipwrecked woman on Crooked Finger Rock at the height of the gale.

Short as the watch that ends the night is what I hear, and *Time, like an ever-rolling stream, Bears all its sons away* is what I hear, the phrases filling the mind with their monotony and fear, and *They fly, forgotten, as a dream Dies at the opening of day*—all of it this booming, this beating of hymn on slick shingles and empty beach, and the Lord and Mildred are bearing me away to the Rock. Singing. Bearing off the naked barber to the heart of the hymn that is the gate, carrying me away at the center, easily, while the plankton spurts aloft into the dark of the storm, and I fly, fly, while Vinny cranks his truck in the wind and Mildred sings with the lost brother.

The barber. But even the barber has his tongue and toes and fingers, his hidden hair. The barber too has his lungs of twisted and dampened paper, his ears in which the islands float, his eyes that gleam, his sensitivity to skin, his touch. And sometimes I think I am all water. Hair and water. What the crack leaps upon, leaping to deform the image further, is nothing and my shop is on Bloody Clam Shell Island—closed, safely boarded up—while I am here.

John Hawkes

Second Skin

"THE GENTLE ISLAND"

And wet, rubbery, exuberant, I emerged into a clearing and stopped short, opened my eyes wide. I saw only a listing hand-made jetty and a fisherman's hut with boarded-up windows, a staved-in dory and a tin chimney that gave off a thin stream of smoke. But beside the dory—gray ribs, rusted oarlock—there was a boy's bicycle propped upside down with its front wheel missing and a clot of black seaweed caught in the sprocket. And though there were days and days to pass before I met the boy—his name was Bub—and met also his fishing father and no-good brother—Captain Red and Jomo—still I felt that I knew the place and had seen that bicycle racing in my own dreams. I could only stop and stare at the useless bicycle and at two squat gasoline pumps pimpled with the droppings of departed gulls and wet with the cold mist, those two pumps once bearing the insignia of some mainland oil company but standing now before the hut and sagging jetty as ludicrous signs of the bold and careless enterprise of that outpost beside the sea. I knew intuitively that I had stumbled upon the crafty makeshift world of another widower. But how could I know that Captain Red's boat, the *Peter Poor*, lay invisible and waiting only fifty yards from shore in its dark anchorage? How could I know that we, Cassandra and I, would sail away for our sickening afternoon on that very boat, the *Peter Poor*, how know about the violence of that sea or about the old man's naked passion? But if I had known, if I had seen it all in my glimpse of Jomo's pumps and Bub's useless bicycle and the old man's smoke, would I have faltered, turned back, fled in some other direction? No. I think not. Surely I would have been too proud, too innocent, too trusting to turn back in another direction.

So I was careful to make no noise, careful not to disturb this first intact and impoverished and somehow illicit vision of the widower's overgrown outstation in the collapsing dawn, and staring at bleached slabs of porous wood and rusted nailheads I restrained my impulse to cup hands against the wind and cry out a cheery hello. And I merely waved to no one at all, expecting no wave in return, and gathered my rubber skirts and swept down the path to the beach.

Overhead the dawn was beginning to possess the sky, squadrons of gray geese lumbered through the blackness, and I was walking on pebbles, balancing and rolling forward on the ocean's cast-up marbles, or wet and cold was struggling across stray balustrades of shale. At my shoulder was the hump of the shore itself—tree roots, hollows of pubic moss, dead violets—underfoot the beach—tricky curvatures of stone, slush of ground shells, waterspouts, sudden clefts and crevices, pools that reflected bright eyes, big smile, foolish hat. Far in the distance I could see the cold white thumb of the condemned lighthouse.

But time, the white monster, had already gripped this edge of the island in two bright claws, had already begun to haul itself out of an ugly sea, and the undeniable day was upon me. I slipped, the coat blew wide, and for some reason I fell back and found myself staring up at a gray sky, gray scudding clouds, a thick papable reality of air in which only the barometer and a few weak signals of distress could survive. An inhuman daytime sky. And directly overhead I saw the bird, the gray-brown hungry body and crescent wings. He was hovering and I could see the irritable way he fended off the wind and maintained his position and I knew that he would return again and again to this same spot. And against the chopping and spilling of the black water I saw the lighthouse. It was not safely in the distance as I had thought, but was upon me. Black missing tooth for a door, faint sea-discolorations rising the height of the white tower, broken glass in its empty head, a bit of white cloth caught up in the broken glass and waving, the whole condemned weight of it was there within shouting distance despite the wind and sea. I could even make out the tufts of high grass bent and beating against its base, and even through the black doorless entrance way I could feel the rank skin-prickling texture of the darkness packed inside that forbidden white tower, and must have known even then that I could not escape the lighthouse, could do nothing to prevent my having at last to enter that wind-whistling place and having to feel my way to the topmost iron rung of its abandoned stair.

Hovering bird, hollow head of the lighthouse, a sudden strip of white sand between myself and the mud-colored base rock of the lighthouse, little sharp black boulders spaced together closely and evenly in the sand, and then as white as a starfish and inert, naked, caught amongst the boulders, I saw a woman lying midway between myself and the high rock. Vision from the widow's photography magazine. Woman who might have leapt from the lighthouse or rolled up only moments before on the tide. She was there, out there, triangulated by the hard cold points of the day, and it was she, not I, who was drawing down the eye of the bird and even while the thought came to me—princess, poor princess and her tower—I looked up at the bird, still hovering, and then turned to the strip of beach and ran forward. But I stopped. Stopped, shuddered, shut my eyes. Because of the voice.

"So here you are!"

It was deep, low, husky, strong, the melodic tough voice of the woman who always sounds like a woman, yet talks like a man. It was close to me, deep and tempting and jocular, and I thought I could feel that enormous mouth pressed tight to my ear. It sounded like a big throat, shrewd powerful mind, heart as big as a barrel. And I was right, so terribly right. Except for the heart. Her black heart.

"My God. What are you doing down there?"

Somehow I opened my eyes, looked over my shoulder and raised my eyes from bright pink heart-shaped shell to bunches of weed to jutting hump of the shore to rising tall figure of the woman standing wind-blown on the edge above me. Looked and fought for breath.

Slacks. Canary yellow slacks. Soft thick canary yellow slacks tight at the ankles, cut off with a cleaver at the bare white ankles, and binding the long thighs, binding and so tight on the hips—yellow smooth complicated block of flesh and bone—that she could force only the tips of her long fingers into the slits of the thin-lipped and slanted pockets. Slacks and square white jaw and great nest of black hair strapped in an emerald kerchief. Great white turtle-neck sweater and trussed white bosom, white breast begging for shields. Shoulders curving and muscular, unbowed. But yellow, yellow from the waist down, the tall easy stance of a woman proud of her stomach—lovely specimen of broad flat stomach bound and yellow and undulating down the front of the slacks—and staring at me with legs apart and elbows bent and eyes like great dark pits of recognition in the bony face. A strand of the black hair came loose and there was a long thick silver streak in it.

"Water's about twenty degrees," she said, and I heard the deep voice, saw the mountain of frosty breath, the toss of the hair. "You look like a damn seal. People shoot seals around here." And with one canary stride she was gone.

"Wait," I called, "wait a minute!" But she was gone. And of course when I looked again there was no bird in the sky and no poor white dead thing lying between myself and the blind tower on the rock. So I flung myself up the hump of the shore, knelt for a moment and carefully ran my fingers over the earth where she had stood—the footprints were real, real enough the shape of her large naked foot in the crushed frozen grass—and bewildered, cold, I sped off across those empty fields as best I could; cold and sweating, I found my way back to the sleeping house.

John Hawkes

Second Skin

"DRAG RACE ON THE BEACH"

Red sun in the morning, sailor's warning. I knew that much. And hadn't I sworn off the sea? After my one thousand days and nights on the *Starfish* hadn't I sworn off the sea forever? There was my mistrust of the nautical life, the suspicion of my tendency toward seasickness, the uneasiness I had come to feel in the presence of small boats whether in or out of the water. My sympathy for all the young sun-tanned and shrapnel-shredded sailors in deep southern seas would never die, but I was done with the water, the uncomfortable drift of a destructive ocean, done trying to make myself acceptable to the Old Man of the Sea. So what drew me to the *Peter Poor?* How to explain that dawn in March which was an eastern blood bath, in the first place, and full of wind? Why did I interrupt our Mah Jongg games or my friendly fights with the black Labradors? Having recovered from the indignities of that crippling December dance, and having spent three frozen months in the calm inside the gale—trying a little of the Old Grand-Dad myself now, not much, but just a little, and building the fires, drying the dishes, dragging Pixie down the cow paths on a miniature creaky sled with turned-up wooden runners—why, having watched the snow at the window and having kept my mouth shut during all those Sunday dinners and having learned to sleep at last on those hard cold nights, why, suddenly, did I trot right down to the dock with Cassandra and submit myself to the *Peter Poor* which was a fishing boat and didn't even have a head?

"Go on, Skip, don't spoil the fun. It's a good way to see the island. And Skip," clicking the needles, giving the log in the fireplace a shove with her bare toes, "it's just what Candy needs. My God, Skip, how could you refuse?"

And toying with the East Wind, watching her: "What about you, Miranda?" I said, "it's not like you to miss a good time?"

And throwing back her head and twinkling the light in her glass and laughing, "No, no, I've already been out sailing with the boys. Besides, every girl deserves to be the only woman on the *Peter Poor* just once in her life."

But Cassandra only looked at me and took my hand.

So it was on a red dawn in the month of March that I succumbed to the idea of Crooked Finger Rock and sunken ships and a nice rough ghostly cruise around the black island, succumbed and gave Cassandra the one chance in her life to be the only woman on the *Peter Poor*. And it was in the month of May that I raced down the beach for my life in Miranda's hot rod, in May, the month of my daughter's death. And in June that we got out of there, Pixie and I, June when I packed our flight bag and hurried out of that old white clapboard house and carried poor Pixie off to Gertrude's cousin in New Jersey. Four months. Four short months. A brimming spring. And of course I know now that there was a chance for Cassandra up to the very moment she swung her foot gaily over the rail of the *Peter Poor* and stood with her hair blowing and her skirt blowing on the cluttered deck of that water-logged tub of Red's. But there was no chance really for Cassandra after that. No chance at all. The second of the four seasons sucked her under, the sea was cruel. March, then May, then June, and the last fragments, the last high lights, last thoughts, the time of my life.

Red sun in morning, sailor's warning. That's it. And the dawn was lying out there on its side and bleeding to death while I fidgeted outside Cassandra's door—accomplice, father, friend, traveling companion, yes, old chaperon, but lover and destroyer too—and while Miranda waltzed around the dark kitchen in her kimono and tried to fix an early breakfast for Pixie. Dawn bleeding from half a dozen wounds in its side and the wind blowing and my old bird fighting its slow way across the sky.

"Hurry up, Cassandra," I called through the closed door, blowing on cold fingers, stuffing a fat brown paper sack—lunch for two—under my arm and watching the bird, "you'll have to hurry a little, Cassandra, if the Captain is going to make the dawn tide." Even upstairs in the cold dark house I could feel the tide rising, feel the flood tide reaching its time and turning, brimming, waiting to sweep everything away. But there was no need to hurry. I should have known. I should have known that Red had been waiting seven months already for this tide, this dawn, this day at sea, and that he would have waited forever as long as he had any hopes at all of hearing her heels clicking on the deck of the *Peter Poor*, that he would have let the *Peter Poor* list forever in the green mud for the mere sight of Cassandra coming down his weedy path at six o'clock in the morning, would have sailed the *Peter Poor* onto rocks, shoals, reefs, ledges, anywhere at all and under any conditions if he could once persuade Cassandra to climb aboard. No hurry. And yet perhaps I was aware of his bald-headed, wind-burned, down-East, inarticuate seagoing licentious patience after all, and fidgeted, marked the stages of the dawn out of the intuitive resources of my destructive sympathy. God knows. But she appeared to me then, unsmiling—unsmiling since the blustery high school dance when I had done my best to tell her everything, make her understand—and wearing a little pale blue silk kerchief tied under her chin.

"I thought you were going to wear slacks, Cassandra," I said. "Slacks are more appropriate to a boat, you know. Much more appropriate than a full skirt, Cassandra. But of course it's too late now anyway."

We went downstairs together—shadows and little playful drafts on the stairs, and if it wasn't a big prize bow for a high school dance then it a was big billowing rust-colored skirt for a windy day—and in the kitchen she hugged Miranda and kissed Pixie's forehead. Then hot coffee, standing up, and then another hug, another kiss, and then good-by.

"While we're gone, Miranda," I said, "don't fool around with the nipples or do anything harmful to the child. OK, Miranda?"

"My God, Skip, you've got a sore memory, haven't you? But everything's forgiven, Skip. Don't worry."

The wind, the red sun, and I tried to take her arm under the chestnut tree, but she walked on ahead of me with the kerchief tilted back and her two small white hands pressed down flat against the tiny round abdomen of the orange skirt which lunged and kicked and whirled in woolen fury. The hard thin mature white legs were bare, I could see that, and I tried to come abreast of her again on the empty road.

"That skirt's going to give you trouble, Cassandra," I said, just as all at once she turned off the road and began to run lightly down the weedy path with the skirt whipping and fumbling about her legs and the tight kerchief changing color in the dawn light.

"Wait, Cassandra, wait for me," I called. I wondered what figure of unhappiness it was that I could see plainly enough in the stiffness of the slender shoulders and forlorn abandonment of the little swathed head. Her feet were describing those sad uncomfortable circles of the young female who runs off with wet eyes or uncommunicative smile or tiny cry clutched, held, in the naked throat, and I wanted to stop her, wanted to walk awhile with my arm about her shoulder and her hand in my hand. But it was no use.

"Jomo, good morning," I heard her say in her best voice, and I saw it all, Cassandra still lightly running and Jomo looking at her from where he was crouched at the gasoline pump and Red watching her from the bow of the *Peter Poor* and Bub buttoning his pants near the overturned skiff and grinning into the wind and watching her. So I put on the steam then and caught up with her.

And leaning over the tin can with the hose in the hole and peering up at me from under the bill of the baseball cap and shielding his mouth with his hand: "How's Papa?" Jomo said, and spit through his teeth.

"OK, Jomo," I said, "I'm OK, thanks." And softly and under my breath, "Viva la Salerno, Jomo," I said to myself.

"A little winded, ain't you?"

"Well, yes, Jomo, I've been running."

But he was returning the nozzle to the pump, spitting between his teeth again, catching the wire handle of the tin can in his hook and lifting it, holding the tin can out to Bub: "Here, Bub, take this fuel to the Captain. On the double. Tide's full."

I thought of offering Bub a hand and then thought better of it. So I stood on the end of Red's jetty—mere crumbling slatted catwalk covered with mollusks and broken pots and splashes of old flaking paint—and watched Cassandra balance herself down the plank to the *Peter Poor*, watched Red take her hand, her elbow, brace one massive palm in the curve of the little sloping rib cage until she had swung her foot, boarded the boat, and I watched Bub lug the gasoline down the plank black with oil and tar and the dawn tide, and wished that he would slip, that he would take a plunge, tin and all. But Bub was steady that morning with chicken feathers sticking to the seat of his pants and the wind in his hair.

And helping her around the anchor and leading her aft: "Sea's rough," I heard Red say, "hope you like a rough sea."

And Cassandra: "I'm a good sailor, Red—Captain Red—really."

John Hawkes

Second Skin

"DRAG RACE ON THE BEACH"

"Hold on, Cassandra," I shouted out of the window, "it won't be long!" I smelled the night, the salt, the armies of mussels and clams ground under our wheels and the dense smoke of our high-octane fuel. And the excitement touched the backs of my hands, told me the time was near, and I wondered how he could have been foolish enough to trap himself here on Dog's Head beach, how foolish enough to underestimate my courage, the strength of my love. I was half a radiator length ahead of him and Miranda might have touched that black-lacquered car had she held out her hand.

"Now!" I shouted, "Now!" and swung down on the wheel and smelled the rank sizzling cremation of the brake bands as we stopped short of the moonlit choppy waters—half-spin in the sand but safe, dry, coming to a sudden and miraculous standstill—while the black car went pitching in. It pitched headlong into the rising tide and rocked, floundered, stalled. Smacked one of the rocks.

I fumbled for the ignition and fought the door, using fist, shoulder, heels of both palms. "Get your hook ready," I cried, "I'm coming after you!" And once more I was running until I too hit the shock of the cold water and suddenly found myself knee-deep in it but running in slow motion, still running toward the half-submerged black-lacquered hot rod wrecked on this bitter shore. Already it was bound in kelp, already the cold waters were wallowing above the crankcase, already the thick white salt was sealing up forever those twin silver carburetors which Jomo had buffed, polished, installed, adjusted beside the battered gas pump in front of Red's shack. Half-sunken now, wet and black and pointing out to sea in the moonlight.

"Game's up, Jomo, don't try anything. . . ."

And my two hands went under water and gripped the door handle. My soggy foot was raised high and thrust flat against the side of the car. And then I pulled and there was the suck of the yielding door, the black flood and, baseball cap and all, I dragged him out by the arm and shook him, wrestled with him, until I slipped and we both went under.

And then up again and, "You!" I cried, "It's you!" and I threw him off his feet again and lunged into the car just as Miranda began laughing her breasty deep Old Grand-Dad laugh at the edge of the beach. I lunged into the car and reached out my hand and stopped, because it was not Cassandra. Because it was nothing. Nobody at all. A mere device, a laundry bag for a torso, something white rolled up for a head. Oh, it was Bub all right, Bub wearing Jomo's cap and driving Jomo's car. Bub's trick. Bub's decoy. And it had worked. Oh, it had worked all right, and while I was risking my neck in Miranda's blue and white and orange hot rod and making my foolish laps on Dog's Head beach or standing hip-deep in the biting black waters of the Atlantic, my Cassandra was lying after all in the arms I had tried to save her from, and falling, fading, swooning, going fast.

So I plunged both hands down and collared Bub, held him, dragged the streaming and spitting and frothy face up close to mine. He had a nosebleed and a little finger-thick abrasion on his upper lip and terror on the narrow sea-white boyish face beneath the dripping duck bill of the baseball cap.

"Where is she," I said. "Where's Cassandra?"

And choked and high-pitched and faint but still querulous, still mean: "Him and her is at the lighthouse. Been up there to the lighthouse since sundown. You old fool. . . ."

So for the first and only time in all my lifelong experience with treachery, deception and Death in his nakedness or in his several disguises, I gave way at last to my impulse and put Tremlow's teaching to the test, allowed myself the small brutal pleasure of drawing blood and forcing flesh on flesh, inflicting pain. Yes, I stood in the choppy and freezing darkness of that black water and contemplated the precise spot where I would punch the child. Because I had gone too far. And Bub had gone too far. The long duck bill of the cap, the cruel tone of his island voice and the saliva awash on his thin white face and even the faint suggestion of tender sideburns creeping down the skin in front of each malformed ear, by all this I was moved, not justified but merely moved, to hit Bub then and there in the face with all my strength.

"Hold still," I muttered, and took a better grip with my left hand, "hold still if you know what's good for you," I said and, keeping my eyes on the little bloody beak in the center of his white face I pulled back my arm and made a fist and drove it as hard as I could into Bub's nose. I held him close for a moment and then pushed him away, let him go, left him rolling over in the cold black water where he could fend for himself.

I left him, rinsed my fist, staggered up into the moonlight and shouted, "No, no, Miranda, wait!" Once more I broke into my sloshing dogtrot on Dog's Head beach, because Miranda was in the hot rod and shifting, throwing the blue and white and orange demon into gear, and waving, driving away. So I was alone once more and desperate and running as fast as I could toward the lighthouse. What heavy steps I took in the sand, how deep those footprints that trailed behind me as I took my slow-motion way down that desolate beach toward the lighthouse.

Slow-motion, yes, and a slogging and painful trot, but after a while I could see that the abandoned white tower of Dog's Head lighthouse was coming down the beach to meet me, was moving, black cliff and all, in my direction. And crab grass, pools of slime, the rusted flukes of a lost anchor, and then the rotted wooden stairs up the side of the cliff and a bright empty Orange Crush bottle gleaming on the tenth step and then the railing gave way under my hand on the head of the cliff and the wind caught hold of me and the lighthouse went up and up above my craning head. The lighthouse. The enormous over-grown moonlit base of it. The tower that had fought the storms, the odor of high waves in the empty doorway, the terrible height of the unlighted eye—I wanted nothing more than to turn my back on it and flee.

But I cupped my hands and raised my mouth aloft and shouted: "Cassandra? In the name of God, Cassandra, are you there?"

No answer, of course. Still no word for her father. Only the brittle feet of the luminous crabs, the cough and lap and barest moan of the slick black tide rising now at the bottom of the cliff and working loose the periwinkles, wearing away the stone, only the darkness inside the tower and, outside, the moonlight and the heavy unfaithful wind that was beating me across the shoulders, making my trousers luff. But of course she was there, of course she was. And had she climbed the circular iron staircase knowing she would never set foot on it again? Or, as in the case of my poor father, was I myself the unwitting tinder that started the blaze? Could she really have intended to spend the last six or eight hours of her life with Jomo in Dog's Head light? My own Cassandra? My proud and fastidious Cassandra? I thought she had. Even as I approached the black doorless opening in the base of the tower I was quite certain that she had planned it all, had intended it all, knowing that I would come and call to her and force myself to climb that tower, climb every one of those iron steps on my hands and knees, and for nothing, all for nothing. Even as I thrust one foot into the darkness of Dog's Head light I knew that I could not possibly be in time.

In the previously quoted letter of September 22, 1965, Mr. Hawkes also commented: "The Nearest Cemetary is a compression of 20–30 handwritten pages prepared in the summer of 1960. Second Skin was written in 1962–63 and really could not have been written without the earlier microcosmic effort and the intervening two years of thought. . . . It seems to me there would be much to say about the various transformation evident between the original version and the book (the metamorphosis of the island barber as first-person narrator into Skipper as narrator, the transformations of various characters, the expansion of certain metaphors, ideas, etc. what has been retained and what omitted, the transformation of the plot itself—these all seem to the point)."

"The Nearest Cemetery" and Second Skin both employ first-person narration, but while the barber's story approximates the interior monologue, Skipper's resembles the dramatic monologue (with interspersed dialogue). The barber—totally unconscious of an audience—often moves forward associatively, as when the Princess' talk gives rise to a discussion of "the ear," which gives rise to certain things she said, which give rise to Mildred at the organ, which gives rise to the barber's impressionistic view of himself. Conversely, Skipper—highly conscious of an audience—organizes his main action spatially, beginning at "Chinatown" and ending at "our wandering island."

Although Second Skin does not borrow the associational method of "The Nearest Cemetery," it does borrow the earlier version's technique of juxtaposing past and present. In both, the present grows out of the past and is developed in considerable detail. However, the story's past—indefinite except for the day the marshal drove the barber to prison—has far less complexity and specificity than the novel's. The latter comprises several periods fitted neatly into an elaborate chronology.

That the tone of the two fictions strikes the reader as very different may be attributed partly to the dissimilarities between interior and dramatic monologues. "The Nearest Cemetery" is a reverie, Second Skin an explanation; consequently, the interpretative problem of the first centers on what has been excluded while that of the second on what has been included. The author, who otherwise remains hidden, prefaces "The Nearest Cemetery" with a cast of characters, thus providing many particulars not contained among the barber's thoughts when we overhear them. But Mr. Hawkes, standing just behind and judging Skipper, provides irony to help us understand Second Skin. This establishes another and greater tonal difference between it and the earlier version which is straightforward.

Yet even after we have assimilated such information supplied by the cast of characters as "He loved her from afar and killed her," much must be inferred about "The Nearest Cemetery," whose vagueness typifies preliminary drafts. Did Mildred's obsession with the Lord and a deceased brother cause the barber to turn to the Princess? Was it a combination of his Puritanism and her promiscuity that motivated the murder? Why are the three actual lovers—Captain Red, Blud, and Jomo—also incarcerated?

The perplexities of Second Skin arise less from the material which has been omitted than from a misreading of the material which has been presented. If its narrator is taken at his word, he assumes the aspect of victim-hero surviving despite the world's malice. But this view completely ignores the author's bitter-comic irony: the discrepancies between what the character says and does. Skipper tells us that he is a courageous fellow, yet he always acts tardily and ineffectively. Skipper claims that Woman, in the person of the mannish Miranda who detests his impotence, is the archenemy, yet he drives both his wife (Gertrude) and daughter (Cassandra) to suicide. And while the bearer of the Good Conduct Medal considers himself to be the latter's paternal protector, his incestuous desires become subtly manifested through the vicarious pleasure he experiences when other men seduce her.

Perhaps the novel's most pervasive symbolism concerns death. Before committing suicide, the narrator's father was a mortician; afterward, Skipper—"one of those little black seeds of death"—suffers hallucinations over the demise of his mother and his wife during which he imagines a muffled chauffeur wearing goggles. There are numerous additional allusions to death, but the dominant metaphor is the cemetery.

This symbolic setting derives from the earlier version whose title would seem to refer to Bloody Clam Shell Island, the burial place of the barber's past. As with the mode of narration, the tone of the narrative, and the character of the narrator, it becomes more complex and specific in Second Skin. Skipper visits four cemeteries, each having sexual associations. At Gertrude's grave, he leaves his sword; at Cassandra's, the jar containing the fetus. At the high school dance, Bubbles, a "little girl guide" toward whom Skipper feels amorously attracted, leads him outside to a romantic rendezvous with Miranda, but when he approaches the cemetery—where children are buried and members of the senior class make love—he is pelted by snowballs. Finally, the book closes at the graveyard on the wandering island. Here Skipper and his followers celebrate the Night of All Saints.

To understand Second Skin's death symbolism the reader must understand what has shaped the psyche of the narrator. The reason behind the barber's conduct remains shadowy; not so with Skipper's. At the very outset, he calls himself "the child-accomplice" in his father's suicide, and we learn later that the action he took to prevent "the shot" which "killed everything" may have hastened it. Victim of a traumatic experience, Skipper becomes an indirect victimizer. He forswears reality, refusing to examine inner or outer motives and refusing to act even upon the things he cannot avoid knowing. Ego gives way to egotism, the man to the mask. As a result, Skipper never grows up, a circumstance made plain through his love life. He pursues little girls because he fears women, not realizing that sexual inadequacy, like impotence in general, is synonymous with sterility and death. At the end of the novel's action and the height of its irony, Skipper feels triumphant over death, but we know better. He may be a leader, yet his followers are illiterate Negroes. He may be a creator, yet only as an artificial inseminator on an island where steers try to impregnate cows and cows other cows. Skipper may be a master, yet the mistress is an adolescent female. Responding to the question, "Who do you think it looks like, Kate? Sonny or me?" she says of the baby, "Him look like the fella in the grave."

"The Nearest Cemetery" contributed several characters besides the narrator to Second Skin. Of these, its Princess is the most significant, for she inspired the novel's two principal women, Miranda and Cassandra. Like the first, whom Skipper thinks of as a princess, the Princess of the story wears slacks; like the second, she has a small child; and like both, this "unhappy wife," this "woman of beauty" flirts and sleeps with the barber's male acquaintances. That he loves her "from afar," then kills her reveals much about the later version since it is a conscious enactment of Skipper's unconscious attitude toward his daughter.

Captain Red, Jomo, and Blud are not related in "The Nearest Cemetery" but become members of a single family in Second Skin. No longer the barber's brother-in-law or the lighthouse keeper or the Princess' lover, Blud appears there as the boy Bub. Captain Red remains the bald, middle-aged master of the Peter Poor, while Jomo—who has acquired an artificial hand—continues to be characterized by his baseball cap and his "black hair plastered down with pine sap." Jomo's mother is displaced by Captain Red's mother and the barber's wife gives her name to Skipper's mother. Because "The Nearest Cemetery" influenced only "The Gentle Island" portions of the novel directly, the story does not have many of the novel's other important figures.

By the same token, however, Bloody Clam Shell Island served as model for the setting of these portions. Its church, lighthouse, clapboard house, gasoline pumps, orange pop, Crooked Finger Rock, and overturned rowboat are among the properties which Second Skin borrowed.

afterword

Even if it were theoretically possible, this book could not have included examples of all the problems authors face when creating fiction, because the content has been governed by what the contributors submitted. Fortunately these submissions cover a comparatively wide range of considerations and fall into a rather neat pattern that proceeds from smaller to larger difficulties. But the apprentice must never lose sight of the fact that the possible variations upon both the included problems and others are infinite.

Chapters I and II treat language changes, the first showing how Miss Welty converted "From the Unknown" into the more compact, more vivid "Where Is the Voice Coming From?" and the second how Miss Boyle developed progressively more individual, elaborate, and complex characters in "The Ballet of Central Park." Chapter III explains why James Jones expanded the role of O'Brien in Chapter II of The Pistol. Chapters IV, V, and VI also deal with characterization, but while Chapter IV relates characterization to structure alone, Chapters V and VI relate it, respectively, to structure-setting and structure-symbolism. Chapter VII is devoted to the question of narrative focus in Philip Roth's Letting Go. And finally the two concluding chapters focus on the transformation of genres, VIII discussing the evolution of a verse-drama and IX the evolution of a story into a novel.

As should be apparent from the headings, this book demonstrates that fictional elements are as inextricable and interdependent as variations upon writing problems are infinite. All of the chapters reflect this, though the two groups IV-V-VI and VIII-IX do so most forcefully.

To a large extent through subtler presentation of character, Mr. Malamud's "Idiots First" manifests a tighter organization than "A Long Ticket for Isaac," and to a large extent the dramatic ending that resulted makes the characters of the published story richer. The structural difference between the two second-draft climaxes of One Day's Matamoros episode enabled Wright Morris to deepen his protagonist's makeup, while the fresh details of place accompanying the structural difference reinforce Cowie's situation and state of mind. During the construction of The Great Gatsby, F. Scott Fitzgerald devised the symbol of the green light. Because this symbol recurs and thus adds to the unity of the novel, it is a structural tool. Because the green light was juxtaposed to "Dutch sailors' eyes" with a new emphasis on Gatsby and thus reveals his nature and his experience, it is a tool of characterization.

But perhaps even more impressive examples of the inextricability and interdependence of fictional elements occur in Chapters VIII and IX, for the metamorphosis from one genre to another inevitably affects several aspects of imaginative composition. The most crucial discrepancy between "Proud Flesh" and All the King's Men and between "The Nearest Cemetery" and Second Skin concerns narrative focus. When Jack became Jack Burden, there was an enormous impact upon the plot and characters of Mr. Warren's tale, just as when the barber became the Skipper there was an enormous impact upon the structure and tone of Mr. Hawkes's tale. The evolution of verse-drama into novel provided greater realism and range of language. The evolution of story into novel provided greater complexity with regard to the past and to the setting.

It is hoped that the sequence of problems which constitutes this book will benefit the classroom instructor by giving him an opportunity to teach process over product. His students should profit from exploring authorial dilemmas both similar to their own and of a more sophisticated kind. In addition, they should come to realize what the instructor already knows: How much conscious, painstaking labor creative rewriting entails.

glossary

dramatic monologue

An old poetic form associated in recent literary history with Robert Browning, who used it frequently. The author presents an individual talking at a crucial time in order to reveal that individual's character to others. Although a novel rather than a poem, Second Skin *by John Hawkes may loosely be termed a dramatic monologue because its protagonist reveals his innermost nature to us, the auditors, through what he says about people and events.*

imagery

A complex term, which, according to its literary application, stands for verbal representations of sense experience. When images recur, as do those of "heat" in Miss Welty's "Where Is the Voice Coming From?" *and those of "green" in Scott Fitzgerald's* The Great Gatsby, *they are called "iterative." Often imagery signifies the language of metaphor and simile.*

interior monologue

A distinction should be made between interior monologues that seem to render the flow of a character's thoughts and feelings more or less directly and those that give evidence of the author's presence as a controlling factor. An example of the first is Mr. Hawkes's "The Nearest Cemetery," whose narrator moves from one subject to another with apparent freedom, and of the second, "Where Is the Voice Coming From?" Although Miss Welty nowhere intrudes upon the latter, we sense her hand there selecting and organizing the material.

irony

A manner of speech in which literal meanings are the opposite of intended meanings. For instance, Daisy Buchanan and Dan Cody of The Great Gatsby embody qualities antithetical to those their namesakes, Daisy Miller and Buffalo Bill, traditionally represent. That irony is sometimes difficult and subtle may be illustrated by its employment in Second Skin, where only highly intelligent readers will perceive the discrepancies between what Skipper says and what he does. This usage resembles "dramatic irony" or knowledge shared by the audience but withheld from the actors of a play.

narrative focus or point of view

The angle from which a story is told. There are several possible perspectives and combinations of perspectives, but most fiction is either the "omniscient" point of view wherein the author becomes the all-knowing narrator or the "first person" point of view wherein one of the characters becomes the narrator. Sometimes the omniscient narrator moves from character to character freely and sometimes he relates the events through the eyes of a so-called "central intelligence." Sometimes the first person narrator functions as the protagonist and sometimes merely as a concerned observer. "The Ballet of Central Park," The Pistol, "A Long Ticket for Isaac" and One Day employ the omniscient technique, while "Where Is the Voice Coming From?" The Great Gatsby, Letting Go, All the King's Men and Second Skin employ the first person technique. Letting Go demonstrates the importance and complexity of narrative focus. For reasons already given, Mr. Roth shifted at the beginning of his third draft from "He" to "I" and then varied this approach with passages related through the eyes of characters other than Sabe Walloch.

scenic method

Every work of fiction combines "panoramas" or representations of the general and "scenes" or representations of particular moments. The "scenic method," which fiction has borrowed from the drama, and which, consequently, emphasizes "showing" as opposed to "telling," is well illustrated by the Chapter VI excerpt from Robert Penn Warren's All the King's Men, where Jack Burden introduces Dr.

Stanton and Governor Stark. Their confrontation incorporates many elements associated with dramatic art, among them the enactment of a tense situation and the revelation of character through dialogue.

setting or place

The "natural" setting of a literary work is the locale where the action occurs, while the "social" setting includes the emotional and intellectual environment of the characters. Thus the bus horn and the burro's braying are elements of the natural setting of One Day *and the references to "the Matamoros law" and "the next of kin" elements of the social setting. Bloody Clam Shell Island—"the nearest cemetery"—is a "symbolic" setting because it stands as the burial place of the barber's past.*

structure

Overall organization, which, in a narrative, centers upon the plot or the sequence of events. If a story's action proceeds basically in terms of movement from place to place, as does "A Long Ticket for Isaac," *its structure may be termed "spatial."*

symbol

Something that stands for something else—often a material object used to represent the immaterial. An example would be the green light in The Great Gatsby. *It exists both as an actual electrical fixture and as an ironic emblem of enticement and hope.*

appendix

William Styron was born in Newport News, Virginia, during 1925. After serving three years with the United States Marine Corps, he completed his studies at Duke University. Lie Down in Darkness, Mr. Styron's first novel, was published during 1951 and earned for the author the Prix de Rome of the American Academy of Arts and Letters. Two years later his novella, The Long March, appeared, followed in 1960 by Set This House on Fire, and The Confessions of Nat Turner in 1967.

Reproduced below are the holograph and published versions of Chapter I of The Long March. An analysis of Mr. Styron's method of revision and of the revisions themselves should reveal much about the creative process in fiction writing.

facsimile of a draft

holograph

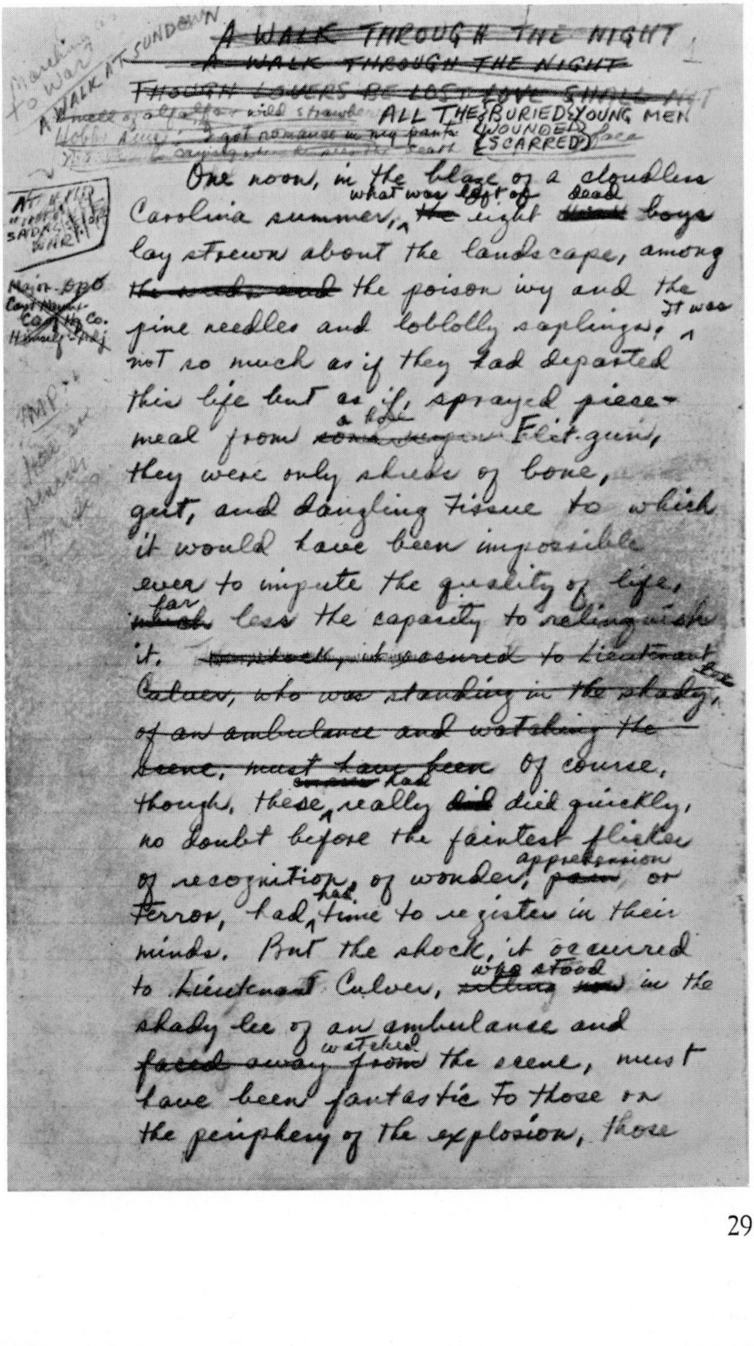
~~A WALK THROUGH THE NIGHT~~

~~A WALK THROUGH THE NIGHT~~

~~THOUGH LOVERS BE LOST LOVE SHALL NOT~~

A WALK AT SUNDOWN

Marching to War

ALL THE BURIED / WOUNDED / SCARRED YOUNG MEN

One noon, in the blaze of a cloudless Carolina summer, what was left of eight ~~dead~~ boys lay strewn about the landscape, among ~~the weeds and~~ the poison ivy and the pine needles and loblolly saplings. It was not so much as if they had departed this life but as if sprayed piecemeal from a hose ~~some weapon~~ Flit-gun; they were only shreds of bone, gut, and dangling tissue to which it would have been impossible ever to impute the quality of life, far ~~much~~ less the capacity to relinquish it. ~~... it occurred to Lieutenant Culver, who was standing in the shady lee of an ambulance and watching the scene, must have been~~ Of course, though, these had really ~~did~~ died quickly, no doubt before the faintest flicker of recognition, of wonder, apprehension ~~pain~~ or terror, had time to register in their minds. But the shock, it occurred to ~~Lieutenant~~ Culver, who stood ~~sitting now~~ in the shady lee of an ambulance and watched ~~faced away from~~ the scene, must have been fantastic to those on the periphery of the explosion, those

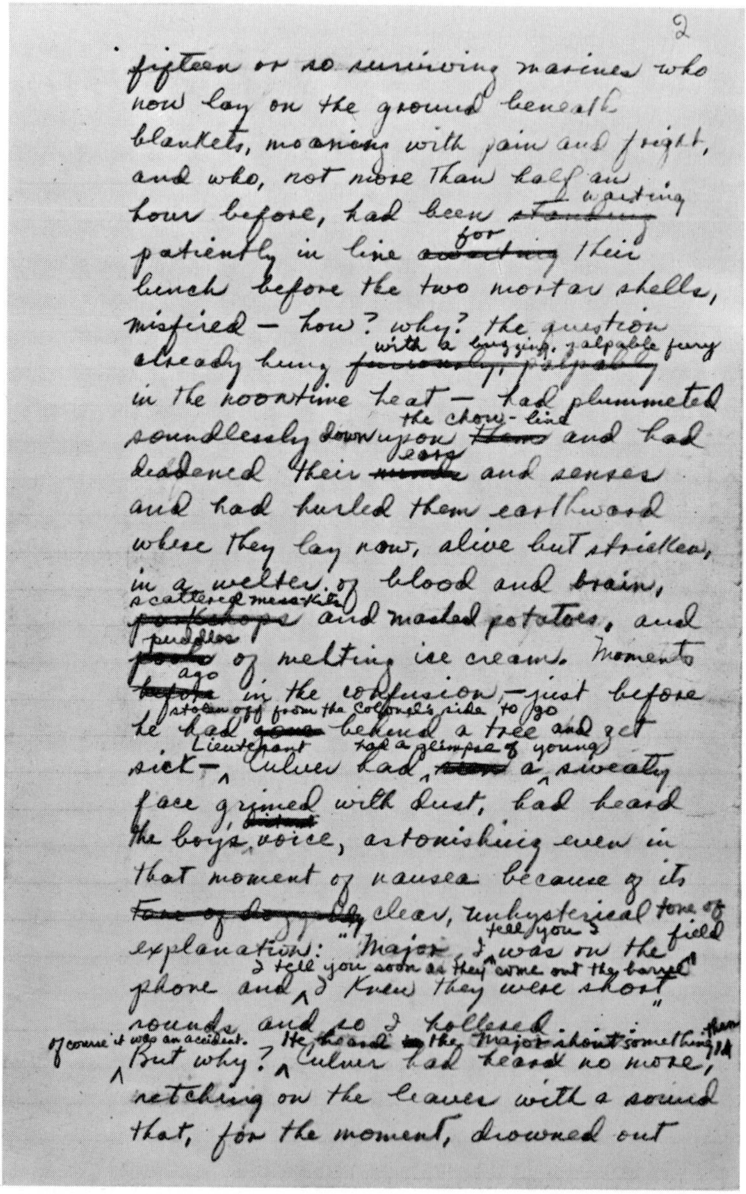

2

fifteen or so surviving marines who now lay on the ground beneath blankets, moaning with pain and fright, and who, not more than half an hour before, had been ~~standing~~ waiting patiently in line ~~awaiting~~ for their lunch before the two mortar shells, misfired — how? why? the question already hung ~~furiously, palpably~~ with a buzzing, palpable fury in the noontime heat — had plummeted soundlessly ~~down~~ upon ~~them~~ the chow-line and had deadened their ~~minds~~ ears and senses and had hurled them earthward where they lay now, alive but stricken, in a welter of blood and brain, ~~porkchops~~ scattered messkits and mashed potatoes, and ~~pools~~ puddles of melting ice cream. Moments ~~before~~ ago in the confusion — just before he had ~~gone~~ stolen off from the Colonel's side to go behind a tree and get sick — Lieutenant Culver had ~~seen~~ had a glimpse of a young sweaty face grimed with dust, had heard the boy's ~~[illegible]~~ voice, astonishing even in that moment of nausea because of its ~~tone of [illegible]~~ clear, unhysterical tone of explanation: "Major, I tell you I was on the field phone and I tell you soon as they come out the barrel I knew they were short rounds and so I hollered" Of course it was an accident. But why? He ~~heard~~ the Major shout something then Culver had heard no more, retching on the leaves with a sound that, for the moment, drowned out

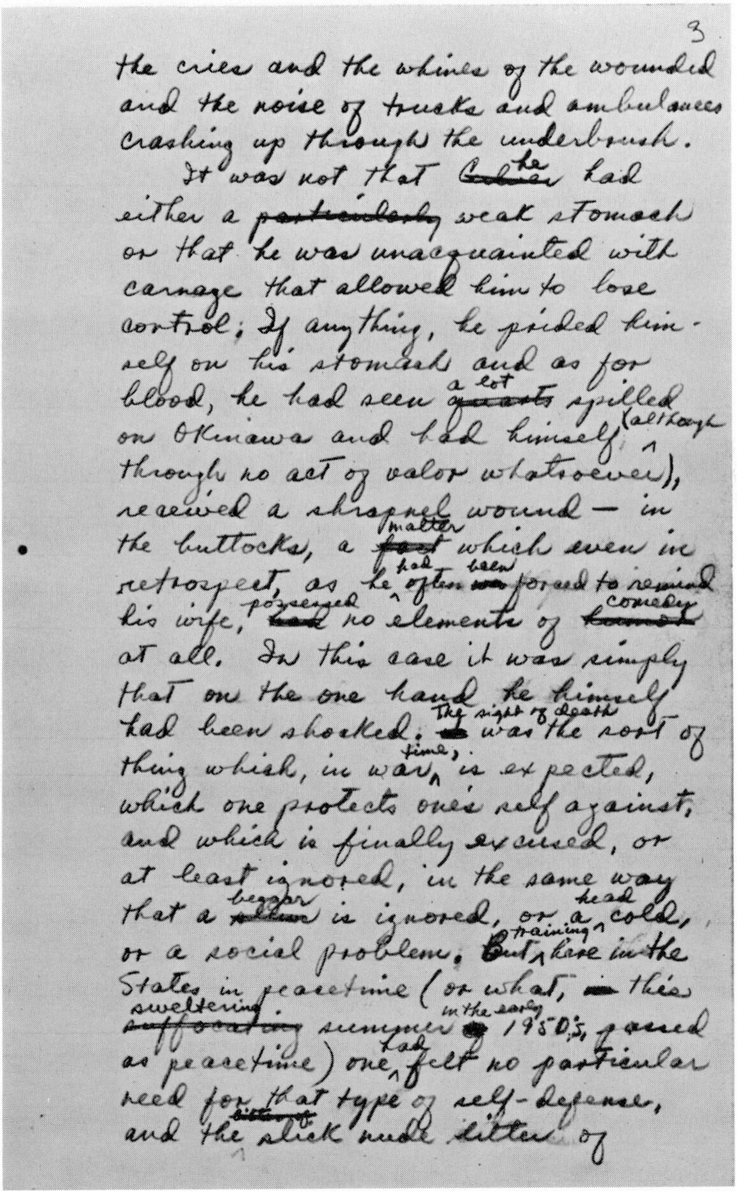
3

the cries and the whines of the wounded and the noise of trucks and ambulances crashing up through the underbrush.

It was not that ~~Culver~~ he had either a ~~particularly~~ weak stomach or that he was unacquainted with carnage that allowed him to lose control; If anything, he prided himself on his stomach and as for blood, he had seen ~~quarts~~ a lot spilled on Okinawa and had himself (although through no act of valor whatsoever), received a shrapnel wound — in the buttocks, a ~~fact~~ matter which even in retrospect, as he had often ~~so~~ been forced to remind his wife, ~~had~~ possessed no elements of ~~humor~~ comedy at all. In this case it was simply that on the one hand he himself had been shocked. ~~I~~ The sight of death was the sort of thing which, in war time, is expected, which one protects one's self against, and which is finally excused, or at least ignored, in the same way that a ~~whine~~ beggar is ignored, or a head cold, or a social problem. ~~But~~ training here in the States in peacetime (or what, ~~in~~ this ~~suffocating~~ sweltering summer ~~of~~ in the early 1950's, passed as peacetime) one had felt no particular need for that type of self-defense, and the sitting of slick nude litter of

4

intestine and shattered blue bones, among which forks and spoons peeked out like so many pathetic metal flowers, made a crazy, insulting impact at Culver's belly, like the blow of a fist. And on the other hand (and the ~~feeble~~ pulsing ache at his brow now as he vomited helplessly onto his shoes lent confirmation to what he'd been trying to deny to himself for five months): he was too old, he was no longer an eager kid just out of Quantico, with a knife between his teeth. He was almost thirty, he was old, and he was afraid.

Lieutenant Culver had been called back to ~~service~~ the marines early that spring. When, ~~early~~ one Saturday morning, his wife had tossed the brown envelope, containing his orders, onto the bed where he lay sleeping, he experienced an ~~almost~~ odd ~~dizziness~~ distress ~~announce shock~~ which ~~had~~ kept him wandering about, baffled and mumbling to himself, for days. Like most of his fellow reserves he had retained his commission after the last war— it was an insouciant gesture which he assumed would in some way benefit him in case of an all-out ~~war~~ conflict, say, thirty years hence, but one which made no provisions for such an

5

eventuality as a police action in Korea. It had all come much too soon, and Culver had felt weirdly as if he had fallen asleep in some barracks in 1945 and had awakened in 1951, to find that the intervening years of freedom, of growth, and of relative serenity had been only a glorious, if somewhat prolonged, dream. A flood of protest had welled up in him, for he had put the idea of war out of his mind entirely, and the brief six years since Okinawa had been the richest of his life. They had produced, among lesser things, a loving, tenderly passionate wife who had passed on to their little girl, now aged three, both some of her gentle nature and her wealth of butter-colored hair; a law degree, the fruits of which he had just begun to realize, even though still somewhat impecuniously, as one of the brightest juniors in a good New York law firm; a friendly beagle named ~~[illegible]~~ Howard, whom he took for hikes in ~~Central~~ Washington ~~Park; and~~ Square; a cat whom he deigned to call by name, and despised; and a record-player that was ~~unapproachably classical and played Bach, Haydn and Mozart and no Schoenberg or Brahms.~~

6

brand-new and irreproachably pre-
romantic, playing little else but
Haydn, Mozart, and Bach. ¶ Up until
the day that his orders came — the day
that he tried to forget and the one Betsy,
his wife, soon bitterly referred to as "the day the
roof fell in" — they had been living
in a roomy walk-up in the Village, and experiencing the prosaic contentment
that comes from eating properly, in-
dulging themselves with fair moderation ~~moderately~~ in the
pleasures of the city, and watching the
growth of a child. This is not to say
that they were either smug or dull.
They had a bright circle of friends,
mostly young lawyers and newspapermen
and doctors ~~publishers~~ and their wives, ~~and~~
There were parties and occasional
week-ends in the country, where everyone became frankly drunk. There were
the usual household skirmishes, too, but
these were infrequent and petered out
quickly. Both of them ~~They~~ were too well-adjusted
to allow petty domestic misdemeanors
to develop into anything horrible; ~~assume the aspect of enormities~~ they
were well-adjusted, and each of them
found it easy to admit, five years
after the honeymoon, that they were deeply in
love. Months later at camp, ensnared
futilely in the coils of some administrative ~~bureaucr-~~
~~atic~~ flypaper, Culver would find

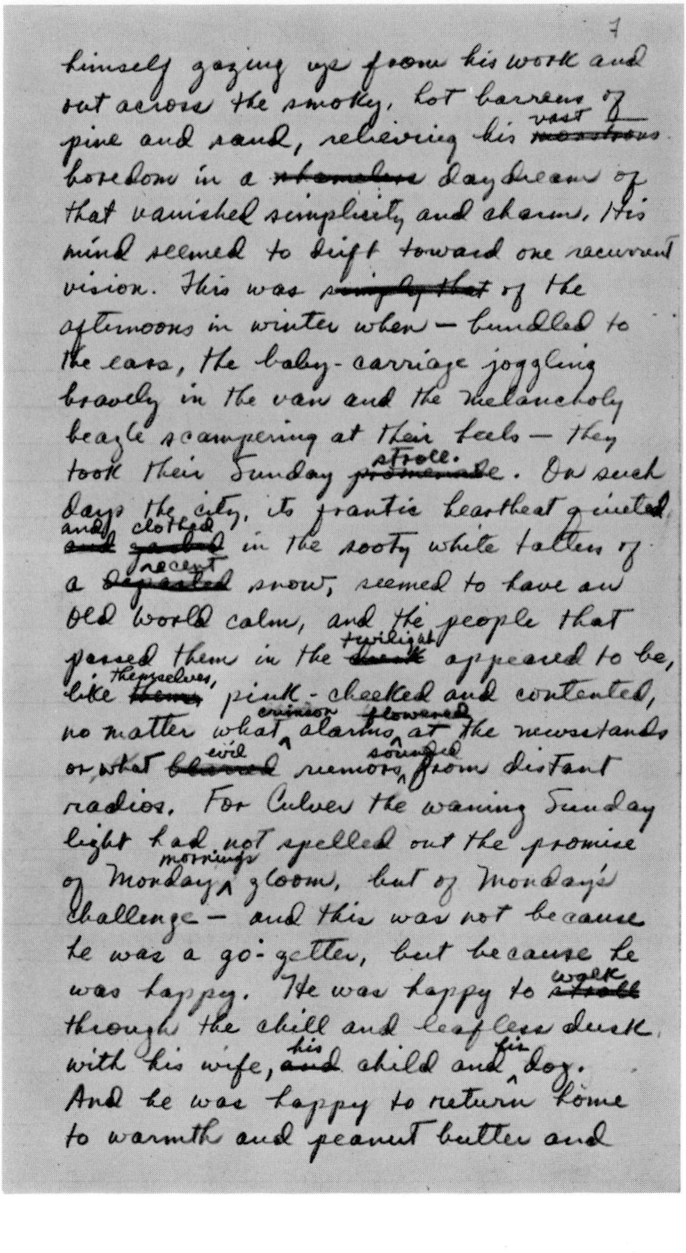
7

himself gazing up from his work and out across the smoky, hot barrens of pine and sand, relieving his vast ~~monstrous~~ boredom in a ~~[illegible]~~ daydream of that vanished simplicity and charm. His mind seemed to drift toward one recurrent vision. This was ~~simply that~~ of the afternoons in winter when — bundled to the ears, the baby-carriage joggling bravely in the van and the melancholy beagle scampering at their heels — they took their Sunday stroll ~~promenade~~. On such days the city, its frantic heartbeat quieted, and clothed ~~and [illegible]~~ in the sooty white tatters of a recent ~~departed~~ snow, seemed to have an Old World calm, and the people that passed them in the twilight ~~dusk~~ appeared to be, like themselves ~~them~~, pink-cheeked and contented, no matter what ominous alarms flowered at the newsstands or, what evil ~~[illegible]~~ rumors sounded from distant radios. For Culver the waning Sunday light had not spelled out the promise of Monday morning's gloom, but of Monday's challenge — and this was not because he was a go-getter, but because he was happy. He was happy to walk ~~stroll~~ through the chill and leafless dusk with his wife, his ~~and~~ child and fin dog. And he was happy to return home to warmth and peanut butter and

William Styron

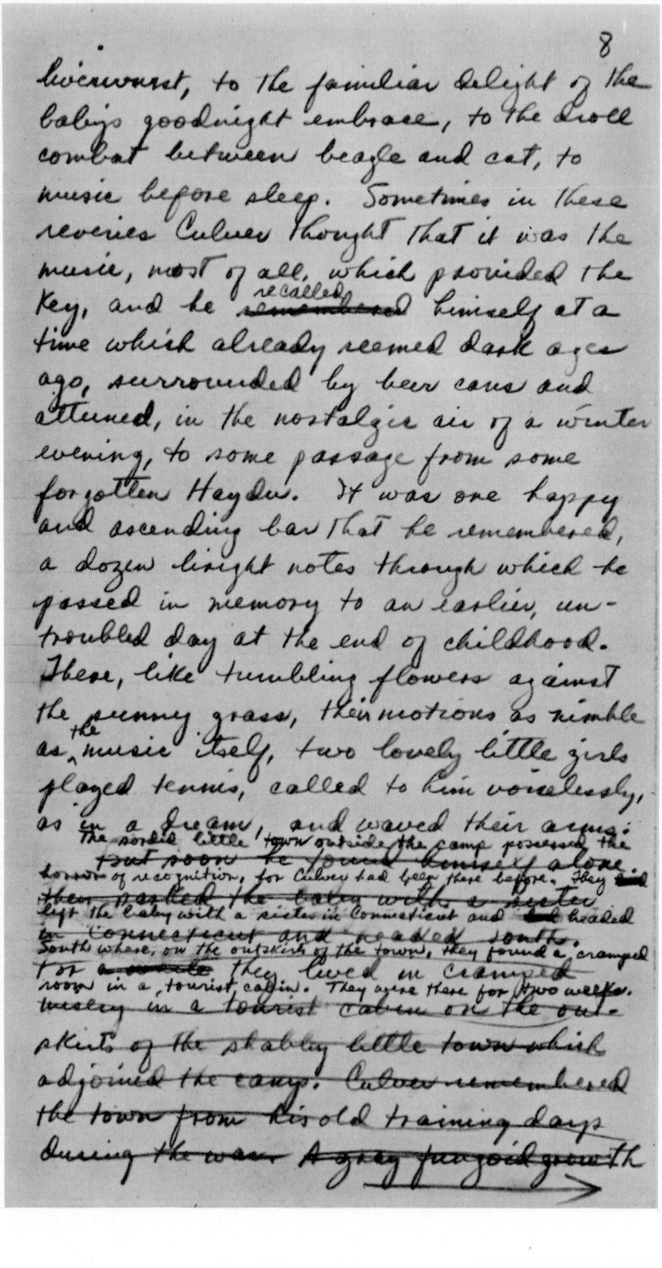

8

liverwurst, to the familiar delight of the baby's goodnight embrace, to the droll combat between beagle and cat, to music before sleep. Sometimes in these reveries Culver thought that it was the music, most of all, which provided the key, and he ~~remembered~~ recalled himself at a time which already seemed dark ages ago, surrounded by beer cans and attuned, in the nostalgic air of a winter evening, to some passage from some forgotten Haydn. It was one happy and ascending bar that he remembered, a dozen bright notes through which he passed in memory to an earlier, untroubled day at the end of childhood. There, like tumbling flowers against the sunny grass, their motions as nimble as the music itself, two lovely little girls played tennis, called to him voicelessly, as in a dream, and waved their arms.

The sordid little town outside the camp possessed the ~~That noon he found himself alone.~~ horror of recognition, for Culver had been there before. They ~~then parked the baby with a sister in Connecticut and headed south.~~ left the baby with a sister in Connecticut and headed South where, on the outskirts of the town, they found a cramped ~~For a~~ ~~They lived in cramped~~ room in a tourist cabin. They were there for two weeks. ~~living in a tourist cabin on the outskirts of the shabby little town which adjoined the camp. Culver remembered the town from his old training days during the war.~~ ~~A gray fungoid growth~~

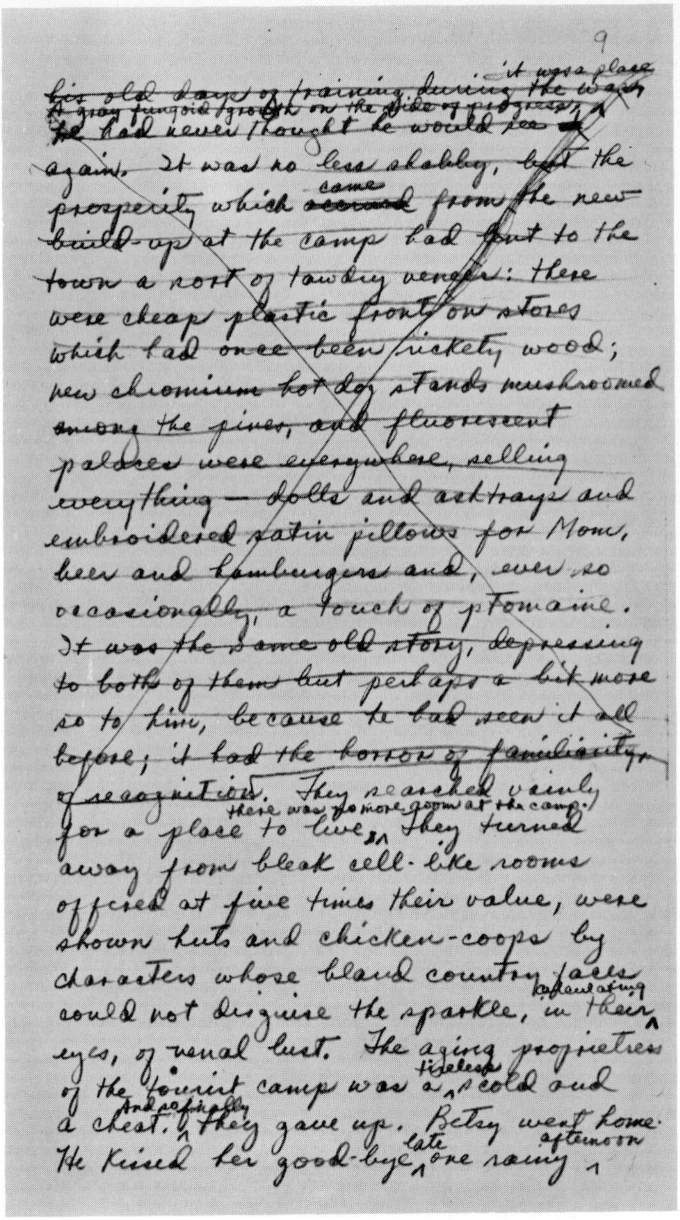
9

his old days of training during the war, it was a place
a gray fungoid growth on the side of progress,
he had never thought he would see
again. It was no less shabby, but the
prosperity which ~~seemed~~ came from the new
build-up at the camp had lent to the
town a sort of tawdry veneer: there
were cheap plastic fronts on stores
which had once been rickety wood;
new chromium hot dog stands mushroomed
among the pines, and fluorescent
palaces were everywhere, selling
everything — dolls and ashtrays and
embroidered satin pillows for Mom,
beer and hamburgers and, ever so
occasionally, a touch of ptomaine.
It was the same old story, depressing
to both of them but perhaps a bit more
so to him, because he had seen it all
before; it had the horror of familiarity,
of recognition. They searched vainly
for a place to live; there was no more room at the camp. They turned
away from bleak cell-like rooms
offered at five times their value, were
shown huts and chicken-coops by
characters whose bland country faces
could not disguise the sparkle, in their calculating
eyes, of venal lust. The aging proprietress
of the tourist camp was a tireless scold and
a cheat. And so finally they gave up. Betsy went home.
He kissed her good-bye late one rainy afternoon

10

in the bus station, surrounded by a horde of marines, and by cheap suitcases and fallen candy wrappers and the sound of fretful children – all of the unlovely mementoes, so nightmarishly familiar, of leavetaking and of anxiety. Of war. He felt her tears against his cheek. It had been an evil day, and the rain that streamed against the window, blurring a distant frieze of gaunt gray pines, had seemed to nag with both remembrance and foreboding — of tropic seas and stormswept distances and strange coasts.

~~[Space]~~ ~~(II)~~

II

William Styron

The Long March

ONE

One noon, in the blaze of a cloudless Carolina summer, what was left of eight dead boys lay strewn about the landscape, among the poison ivy and the pine needles and loblolly saplings. It was not so much as if they had departed this life but as if, sprayed from a hose, they were only shreds of bone, gut, and dangling tissue to which it would have been impossible ever to impute the quality of life, far less the capacity to relinquish it. Of course, though, these had really died quickly, no doubt before the faintest flicker of recognition, of wonder, apprehension, or terror had had time to register in their minds. But the shock, it occurred to Lieutenant Culver, who stood in the shady lee of an ambulance and watched the scene, must have been fantastic to those on the periphery of the explosion, those fifteen or so surviving marines who now lay on the ground beneath blankets, moaning with pain and fright, and who, not more than half an hour before, had been waiting patiently in line for their lunch before the two mortar shells, misfired—how? why? the question already hung with a buzzing, palpable fury in the noontime heat—had plummeted down upon the chow-line and had deadened their ears and senses and had hurled them earthward where they lay now, alive but stricken in a welter of blood and brain, scattered messkits and mashed potatoes, and puddles of melting ice cream. Moments ago in the confusion—just before he had stolen off from the Colonel's side to go behind a tree and get sick—Lieutenant Culver had had a glimpse of a young sweaty face grimed with dust, had heard the boy's voice, astonishing even in that moment of nausea because of its clear, unhysterical tone of explanation: "Major, I tell you I was on the field phone and I tell you as soon as they come out the tube I knew they were short rounds and so I hollered . . ." Of course it had been an accident. But why? He heard the Major shout something, then Culver had heard no more, retching on the leaves with a sound that, for the moment, drowned out the cries and whines of the wounded and the noise of trucks and ambulances crashing up through the underbrush.

It was not that he had a weak stomach or that he was unacquainted with carnage that allowed him to lose control. If anything, he prided himself on his stomach, and as for blood he had seen a lot spilled on Okinawa and had himself (although through no act of valor whatever) received a shrapnel wound—in the buttocks, a matter which even in retrospect, as he had often been forced to remind his wife, possessed no elements of comedy at all. In this case it was simply that on the one hand he himself had been shocked. The sight of death was the sort of thing which in wartime is expected, which one protects oneself against, and which is finally excused or at least ignored, in the same way that a beggar is ignored, or a head cold, or a social problem. But in training here in the States in peacetime (or what, this sweltering summer in the early 1950s, passed as peacetime) one had felt no particular need for that type of self-defense, and the slick nude litter of intestine and shattered blue bones, among which forks and spoons peeked out like so many pathetic metal flowers, made a crazy, insulting impact at Culver's belly, like the blow of a fist. And on the other hand (and the pulsing ache at his brow now as he vomited helplessly onto his shoes lent confirmation to what he'd been trying to deny to himself for months): he was too old, he was no longer an eager kid just out of Quantico with a knife between his teeth. He was almost thirty, he was old, and he was afraid.

Lieutenant Culver had been called back to the marines early that spring. When, one Saturday morning, his wife had thrown the brown envelope containing his orders onto the bed where he lay sleeping, he experienced an odd distress which kept him wandering about, baffled and mumbling to himself, for days. Like most of his fellow reserves he had retained his commission after the last war. It was an insouciant gesture which he had assumed would in some way benefit him in case of an all-out conflict, say, thirty years hence, but one which made no provisions for such an eventuality as a police action in Korea. It had all come much too soon and Culver had felt weirdly as if he had fallen asleep in some barracks in 1945 and had awakened in a half-dozen years or so to find that the intervening freedom, growth, and serenity had been only a glorious if somewhat prolonged dream. A flood of protest had welled up in him, for he had put the idea of war out of his mind entirely, and the brief years since Okinawa had been the richest of his life. They had produced, among lesser things, a loving, tenderly passionate wife who had passed on to their little girl both some of her gentle nature and her wealth of butter-colored hair; a law degree, the fruits of which he had just begun to realize, even though still somewhat impecuniously, as one of the brightest juniors in a good New York law firm; a friendly beagle named Howard whom he took for hikes in Washington Square; a cat, whom he did not deign to call by name, and despised; and a record-player that played Haydn, Mozart and Bach.

Up until the day that his orders came—the day that he tried to forget and the one that Betsy, his wife, soon bitterly referred to as "the day the roof fell in"—they had been living in a roomy walk-up in the Village and experiencing the prosaic contentment that comes from eating properly, indulging themselves with fair moderation in the pleasures of the city, and watching the growth of a child. This is not to say that they were either smug or dull. They had a bright circle of friends, mostly young lawyers and newspapermen and doctors and their wives. There were parties and occasional week ends in the country, where everyone became frankly drunk. There were the usual household skirmishes, too, but these were infrequent and petered out quickly. Both of them were too sensible to allow some domestic misdemeanor to develop into anything horrible; they were well adjusted and each of them found it easy to admit, long after the honeymoon, that they were deeply in love. Months later at camp, ensnared futilely in the coils of some administrative flypaper, Culver would find himself gazing up from his work and out across the smoky hot barrens of pine and sand, relieving his vast boredom in a daydream of that vanished simplicity and charm. His mind seemed to drift toward one recurrent vision. This was of the afternoons in winter when—bundled to the ears, the baby-carriage joggling bravely in the van and the melancholy beagle scampering at their heels—they took their Sunday stroll. On such days the city, its frantic heartbeat quieted and clothed in the sooty white tatters of a recent snow, seemed to have an Old World calm, and the people that passed them in the twilight appeared to be, like themselves, pink-cheeked and contented, no matter what crimson alarms flowered at the newsstands or what evil rumors sounded from distant radios. For Culver the waning Sunday light had not spelled out the promise of Monday morning's gloom but of Monday's challenge—and this was not because he was a go-getter but because he was happy. He was happy to walk through the chill and leafless dusk with his wife and his child and his dog. And he was happy to return home to warmth and peanut butter and liverwurst, to the familiar delight of the baby's good-night embrace, to the droll combat between beagle and cat, to music before sleep. Sometimes in these reveries Culver thought that it was the music, more than anything, which provided the key, and he recalled himself at a time which already seemed dark ages ago, surrounded by beer cans and attuned, in the nostalgic air of a winter evening, to some passage from some forgotten Haydn. It was one happy and ascending bar that he remembered, a dozen bright notes through which he passed in memory to an earlier, untroubled day at the end of childhood. There, like tumbling flowers against the sunny grass, their motions as nimble as the music itself, two lovely little girls played tennis, called to him voicelessly, as in a dream, and waved their arms.

The sordid little town outside the camp possessed the horror of recognition, for Culver had been there before. They left the baby with a sister and headed South where, on the outskirts of the town, they found a cramped room in a tourist cabin. They were there for two weeks. They searched vainly for a place to live, there was no more room at the camp. They turned away from bleak cell-like rooms offered at five times their value, were shown huts and chicken-coops by characters whose bland country faces could not hide the sparkle, in their calculating eyes, of venal lust. The aging proprietress of the tourist camp was a scold and a cheat. And so they finally gave up. Betsy went home. He kissed her good-by late one rainy afternoon in the bus station, surrounded by a horde of marines and by cheap suitcases and fallen candy wrappers and the sound of fretful children —all of the unlovely mementoes, so nightmarishly familiar, of leave-taking and of anxiety. Of war. He felt her tears against his cheek. It had been an evil day, and the rain that streamed against the windows, blurring a distant frieze of gaunt gray pines, had seemed to nag with both remembrance and foreboding—of tropic seas, storm-swept distances and strange coasts.